SHAPING THE WORLD

TWO HUNDRED YEARS OF THE
INSTITUTION OF CIVIL ENGINEERS

Printed in the UK on Arctic Volume. This paper has been
independently certified according to the standards of the
Forest Stewardship Council® (FSC)®.

A catalogue record of this publication is available from
the British Library.

ISBN: 978-1-911339-29-8

Printed by CPi Colour, London.

ICE 200 PROJECTS

————————

The projects in this book were nominated by the membership of the Institution of Civil Engineers from around the globe. A selection panel, led by former ICE President Gordon Masterton OBE, sought to find projects that represented the story of civil engineers and civil engineering over the past two hundred years, and of how engineering has transformed lives and shaped the world.

With more than 500 submissions made, the selection was exceptionally hard but hugely rewarding for the team. The impact engineers have had on the world has been immense and it is hoped that this book captures some of this. In a publication of this type there are always decisions to be made, and the Institution is hugely grateful to all those who proposed projects for inclusion. The fact that there were so many just goes to show the positive impact engineers have every day.

It would be almost impossible to feature every person and organisation who has contributed to each of the ICE 200 projects, and the Institution recognises the amazing work of all those involved in bringing them into being, even if they have not all be identified in the pages of this book.

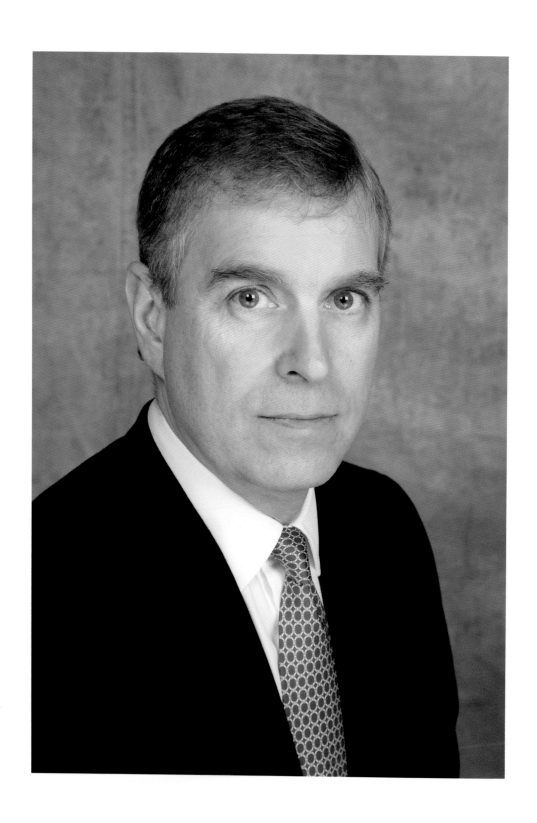

I am delighted to introduce this commemoration of the Institution's Bicentennial year. Throughout the year we have worked together to showcase to the public just how civil engineers have, and continue to, transform people's lives.

Civil engineers have, for centuries, been at the heart of social and economic progress - making the world a better place. And to celebrate the achievements of the past 200 years the Institution has selected 200 projects that so clearly illustrate the value of civil engineering to society.

The story begins on 2 January 1818 when a group of young engineers came together at the Kendal Coffee House on Fleet Street to found what would become the world's oldest professional engineering Institution.

ICE has grown into an organisation with more than 92,000 members throughout the world. In that time members of the ICE have built, designed and contributed to projects that have transformed countless lives for the better; and which shall safeguard the future for countless more. From the sewer systems designed and built by Joseph Bazalgette, which eradicated cholera from London, to the bridges built by QUEST Award winners in Rwanda connecting communities divided by rivers, from the world's first inter-city passenger railway connecting Liverpool and Manchester to the Halley VI Antarctic Research Station, it is civil engineers who transform lives.

Civil Engineers are at the cutting edge of solving the problems our world faces. Like their predecessors, they harness the inspiration of the best and most creative minds of our generation. Like Thomas Telford and Isambard Kingdom Brunel before us, we have the opportunity to make the world a hugely better place.

It is an honour to be the Patron of our Institution and I commend the work of our members in such an important year.

CONTENTS

CHAPTER THREE
SMART INFRASTRUCTURE

ICE200

ENGINEERING EXCELLENCE

APPENDICES

FOREWORD

Celebrations are an exciting time for any organisation, but recognising a bicentenary is particularly special. 2018 marked 200 years since a group of young engineers met at the Kendal Coffee House in Fleet Street and established what would become the world's oldest professional engineering body.

ICE 200 has been the perfect chance to celebrate the institution's longevity and to recognise the profession of civil engineering as well as, most importantly, the thousands of members who make this institution what it is.

We have put on an impressive programme of events across all corners of the world, from Pitch 200 events in Wales to the world's longest Lego Bridge in Hong Kong and Café 200 events in Qatar. We have used our bicentenary as an opportunity to remind the general public that civil engineers transform their lives for the better and safeguard the future for their families.

This book provides clear and powerful examples of the ways in which the work of civil engineers has improved the lives of millions. It illustrates how civil engineers have consistently used their skill and expertise to make a valuable impact on the world. You will read about water infrastructure projects in the Middle East, tunnel-boring machines that have helped to dig tunnels that connect communities throughout the world, and flood prevention schemes such as the Thames Barrier that keep people safe.

Civil engineers have often been described as "invisible superheroes", as they tackle real problems that affect people across the world daily. To illustrate this, we hosted the Invisible Superheroes exhibition at our headquarters in London, showcasing the extraordinary talent of some amazing engineers, from icons such as Joseph Bazalgette and Isambard Kingdom Brunel to current professionals Dr Anne Kemp and Dr Ellie Cosgrave.

It has been incredible to see how this campaign to help tell the story of our industry has resonated with people young and old, and I have no doubt that it has encouraged a new generation to see civil engineering as a creative, rewarding and highly enjoyable career.

Civil engineering will continue to benefit from developments in science, technology, media and the arts. But we have to make sure that young people know that their skills, whatever they may be, have a place in our profession. We must convince people that civil engineering is fast, modern and creative, embracing the very latest technologies and involving many disciplines. The ICE 200 programme has done just that.

I would like to thank all those who have contributed to making our 200th year such a success, in particular our members. Their hard work, expertise and enthusiasm in getting out and sharing what they love about civil engineering has made 2018 an important marker for the next 200 years in our journey.

_____

LORD ROBERT MAIR
PRESIDENT OF THE INSTITUTION OF CIVIL ENGINEERS

THE FIRST 200 YEARS

————————

Civil engineering has played a key role in how the world looks and operates today. Yet 200 years ago, the profession was very much still in its infancy. At a time when design and construction relied more upon hard labour and time-consuming methods than on sophisticated machinery and engineering innovation, eight young engineers met in a coffee shop in London to set up an organisation to promote the importance of engineering and further the learning of its members.

That organisation was the Institution of Civil Engineers, which celebrates its bicentenary this year. Looking back across 200 years of history, it can sometimes be difficult to imagine the motivations and desires of individuals acting more than two centuries ago. Happily, the long, unbroken history of the Institution allows us to understand our engineering forebears and to identify patterns in their thinking that could influence the way we approach the next 200 years.

Back in 1818, the world was very different. The UK's population was expanding at an alarming rate, which put untold pressure on cities and resources. A wave of new technologies was causing a stir in the scientific world, leading to an unprecedented sharing of ideas and enthusiasm for the potential power of engineering.

AN INSTITUTION IS BORN

The driving force behind the Institution was Henry Robinson Palmer, a 23-year-old civil engineer from East London who saw the need for a society that would share the rapidly developing knowledge of his profession. Just as a similar innovator would have done in the 21st century, he held his first meeting with a group of fellow engineers in a local coffee shop – Kendal's in Fleet Street. Thus began the story of the world's first engineering body.

As the Institution grew, it became a model for similar organisations all over the world. Its members have helped shape the development of the engineering profession on an international basis, leading the transformation of the world around us and safeguarding the future

> "A wave of new technologies was causing a stir in the scientific world, leading to an unprecedented enthusiasm for the potential power of civil engineering"

of millions of people for the past two centuries. This is an impressive feat in its own right, but even more so when one considers Henry Robinson Palmer's modest original resolutions:

- a society be formed, consisting of persons studying the profession of a civil engineer
- to prevent reserve in the junior members, the age of admission should be 20–35
- the society shall meet once a week for the purpose of mutual instruction in that knowledge requisite for the profession
- guidelines for debate would be entered in a book by the secretary for future discussion, books and invention would be reviewed
- people who do not study the profession as a means of subsistence but devote their leisure to such pursuits, may be admitted as honorary members
- members should be proposed by professional engineers and seconded by two more, all testifying to the reasons for their proposal
- members could be ejected if they were unqualified or careless about the interests of the Institution.

In 1820, the Institution received renewed impetus when Thomas Telford became its President. Telford was one of the leading civil engineers of the time and had influential political and society contacts. He knew numerous people within the engineering community and regularly introduced new members, as well as donating his personal book collection to form the Institution's library. Most importantly of all, Telford was successful in 1828 in obtaining the Royal Charter for the Institution, which allowed its members to enjoy official recognition and formal status as professionals.

DEVELOPMENT AND GROWTH OF THE PROFESSION

By the mid-19th century, a more mature Institution was beginning to drive the civil engineering agenda at the same time as the social and political significance of the railways was being felt throughout the country. The world's first intercity railway using steam locomotives was the Liverpool and Manchester Railway, built in 1830. The connection of these two economic powerhouses through a new emerging technology changed the world forever, and the Institution's members were firmly in the driving seat of that change.

Railways brought recognition to the membership and prestige to the Institution. Its president and leading members played a pivotal role in the development of the Great Exhibition of 1851, which showed the world the wonders of Britain's Industrial Revolution. Successful innovations were also being led by civil engineers within steamship construction, road transport and water supply.

Professional engineering examinations were introduced by ICE in 1897 to judge prospective candidates' engineering knowledge. In 1914, the concept of training under agreement was also introduced. Since then, the Institution's entrance qualifications have set standards that have been the envy of the world, with continued emphasis on both academic prowess and practical skills.

The two world wars of the 20th century saw the civil engineering profession come to the forefront of rebuilding Britain after each conflict. As the century unfolded, the development of new materials, such as reinforced and prestressed concrete and high-strength steel, coupled with more sophisticated machinery led to new thinking, innovative architectural styles and improved ways of working. By the late 1970s, computers were rising in prominence, allowing calculations of unprecedented speed and complexity to be made. Machines developed to tackle the harder tasks via automation reduced construction times and removed much of the heavier manual work from labourers.

As the Institution of Civil Engineers continues to go from strength to strength, it can be helpful to place its founding and development in the historical context of social upheaval, technological change and unprecedented innovation. The Institution is, and always has been, a deep well of information, inspiration and support that will go on helping civil engineers around the world to tackle their own specific challenges head on.

ICE TODAY

————————

In 1828, the Institution of Civil Engineers gained its Royal Charter from King George IV and, in so doing, officially declared its intention to "foster and promote the art and science of civil engineering". Two centuries later, it is doing just that, with more than 90,000 members worldwide, input into major engineering projects of world-changing significance and an undoubted influence on the global political stage.

2018 sees the celebration of 200 years since ICE was founded. In that time, the world has changed beyond recognition. It is a better, safer and cleaner place to live for a significant number of its inhabitants. Innovation is leading technology as humanity pushes the boundaries of knowledge ever further. Civil engineers are at the forefront of such advancements; the profession leading the way in, quite literally, making the impossible possible.

Today, ICE is a centre for excellence around the world. It is the gatekeeper of professional standards and a guardian of its core values of integrity, trust, ethical behaviour, quality and professionalism. Its members have been described as "invisible superheroes", taking on the problems faced by people the world over. In the UK alone over the past 40 years, ICE members have taken leading roles in the development of such innovations as the Thames Barrier (1984), the Channel Tunnel (1994), the Øresund Crossing (2000), the Queen Elizabeth Olympic Park (2012), the Queensferry Crossing (2017) and Crossrail (2018).

A DIVERSE MEMBERSHIP

Just as engineering ambition knows no limitations, so the membership of ICE has widened to reflect society. Prior to the 20th century women's role in civil engineering was limited to office support – a tradition established in the 18th century by John Smeaton's daughters. From the 1920s, as the effects of female emancipation were felt across society, women aspired to become professional engineers. Dorothy Buchanan, an engineer on the iconic Sydney Harbour Bridge, became the first female qualified member in 1927 (having been a student since 1923). Mary Fergusson became the first female Fellow in 1957 – she was already the first partner in a consultancy, Blyth and Blyth. In 2008, Jean Venables became its first female President. Today, just over 11,000 women are members of ICE, so there is still some way to go to achieve full equality of numbers between the genders. ICE has thrown its support behind encouraging young women to join the profession through providing STEM (science, technology, engineering, maths) ambassadors, visiting schools, holding exhibitions and generally working to change attitudes towards the presence of women in engineering.

"The membership of ICE has widened. ICE has thrown its support behind encouraging young women to join the profession, working to change attitudes towards the presence of women in engineering"

ICE has had an international membership since its early days and one of its first overseas members was Ardaseer Cursetjee, the Parsi shipbuilder from Mumbai. There are currently members in more than 150 countries, with the largest numbers in Hong Kong, India and Australia. ICE has offices in Hong Kong, Dubai and Malaysia that work closely with its headquarters in London. Just like their forebears, today's members benefit enormously from their links to ICE and recognise the importance of making connections with fellow engineers from around the world.

"I joined ICE because I wanted international professional recognition," says Ishmael Paul Otoo from Ghana. "Being a graduate member gives me the opportunity to be mentored so I can qualify as a qualified member of ICE (MICE). It also gives me a sense of belonging to a community of engineers across the world." Hisanao Kajiura CEng MICE from Japan agrees. "Being an ICE member has been invaluable in my job because it proves I have the competence to manage international projects successfully," he says.

KNOWLEDGE IS POWER

It could be said that the secret to ICE's longevity of influence lies behind its eagerness to share knowledge. Such openness has enabled its members to enjoy a powerful influence on how the world is shaped and challenges in society are tackled. ICE members have been instrumental in projects that open up the world by improving transport links; safeguard public health through sanitation and water supply; and protect the future of international communities through renewable energy, flooding prevention and the development of smart cities and smart infrastructure.

One area of knowledge-sharing of which ICE is particularly proud is its resource library. The function has auspicious beginnings, stemming from the donation, 198 years ago, of Thomas Telford's books and papers. Today, ICE's library is the largest collection of civil engineering resources in the world. Much of it has been digitised and made available to members online, while work is nearing completion on an improved catalogue system to increase its accessibility more than ever before.

Linked to this desire to share information and further its positive influence, ICE has established an authoritative body of expertise across the full breadth of civil engineering knowledge domains through its committees, expert panels and specialist registers. These bodies curate and disseminate the knowledge required by members and are the source of knowledge for the ICE's external affairs and public voice activities. The ICE's Reservoirs Committee is delegated by UK Statute to maintain the panels of appropriately qualified civil engineers to inspect and supervise reservoirs, a weighty responsibility in the interests of public safety. Other registers in ground engineering, health and safety, security and conservation engineering also require registrants to demonstrate and maintain the highest peer-reviewed standards of competence.

ICE has also developed relationships with a number of associated specialist interest societies, or membership bodies in order to have the widest possible network in which knowledge is shared and a community created. Several commercial divisions have also been established to oversee such functions as publishing, training and recruitment. ICE has been a publisher since the formation of Learned Society Publishing in 1936 and now provides a vast digital resource with its virtual library. A dedicated team looks after the stunning ICE headquarters at One Great George Street, working on conference venue hire, member facilities and overall maintenance. Finally, the "NEC" (New Engineering Contract) division manages ICE's formalised system for drafting documents on civil engineering and construction projects, as well as obtaining tenders and awarding contracts.

FROM STRATEGY TO SUPPORT
The core purpose of ICE has remained unchanged since its founders laid down its original resolutions in 1818. Namely, to support and advise the profession and promote the sharing of knowledge to benefit the wider society and advance scientific development. The Institution does this through a variety of actions, from public strategy to individual support.

ICE plays an active and enthusiastic role in policy and public affairs. The policy team works to monitor the political landscape and liaise with MPs, civil servants and special advisors within national, devolved and local government. This team fosters strong links with the worlds of business, academia, think tanks and finance to ensure that ICE members' voices are represented at the highest level of national and international political and commercial decision-making.

The ICE Benevolent Fund has also been in existence since 1864 to assist members experiencing financial hardship and to provide services such as counselling, practical help, well-being advice and support for members' families.

SOCIETAL BENEFIT THROUGH STANDARDS
ICE has established, through its Learned Society, some industry-changing initiatives that have become significant contributors to how the UK and the world operate. In 1901, Sir John Wolfe Barry set in motion the Council of the ICE to form a committee of six to address the issue of standardising various kinds of iron and steel sections. This Engineering Standards Committee was so successful that in 1903 the first British Standard on steel sections was published. It became the British Standards Association in 1918 and in 1931 the British Standards Institution.

In 2000, an ICE research project led to the establishment of CEEQUAL – the evidence-based sustainability assessment, rating and awards scheme for civil engineering, infrastructure, landscaping and public realm projects. In 2003, it became an independently operated scheme (with ICE retaining a standing position as chair of the board), providing a framework for teams to promote, influence, deliver and ultimately celebrate the achievement of high environmental and social performance on their projects. It was the first of its kind in the world and remains the leading international infrastructure rating scheme, operating in Europe, the Middle East and the Far East.

"The core purpose of ICE has remained unchanged. Namely, to support and advise the profession and promote the sharing of knowledge to benefit the wider society and advance scientific development"

THE FUTURE OF ICE

————

There are challenges across the world that must be overcome. The global population is increasing exponentially, while resources are becoming stretched and fossil fuels are providing less and less of a long-term solution to our energy needs. It is time to think sustainably to ensure that life goes on as we know it, and civil engineers are at the forefront of this huge responsibility.

The challenges engineers face today are very different from those experienced even 20 years ago. As the 20th century drew to a close, the focus was still very much on building roads, improving water-treatment facilities and strengthening power networks in order to solve problems of overcrowding and undercapacity. Now, priorities have shifted towards thinking on a more global scale, looking towards more sustainable projects and smarter use of evolving technologies to offer longer-term solutions to challenges in both local communities and the wider world.

Tomorrow's world is arguably already upon us, as the planning, design, engineering, construction and ongoing use of modern infrastructure is a long-term programme. ICE's vision has always prioritised innovation and adaptability, urging members to share knowledge, contribute to global society and be seen as an independent voice and reliable source of advice. And already entrusted by society to create a sustainable world and enhanced quality of life, ICE members are now embarking on a future of serving competently, collaboratively and ethically against the backdrop of the digital age.

BUILDING A SUSTAINABLE WORLD

In the midst of all this development, however, is the big question of sustainability. We face massive issues, including climate change, CO_2, water shortages, energy needs and population growth. The United Nations' Sustainable Development Goals address issues like these, providing a sturdy framework for civil engineers to turn their aspirations into reality.

The UN predicts that there will be two billion more people in the world by 2050, which will create a 70 per cent increase in demand for food. Eighty per cent of us will be living in cities by then, consuming mainly bought-in food. Water demand will rise, too, as will the need for renewable energy. One in five people worldwide still lacks reliable access to modern electricity, and the pressure on fossil fuel to provide this will grow as reserves diminish.

Three billion people still use wood, coal, charcoal or animal waste for cooking and heating. The UN wants to reduce the carbon intensity of fossil-fuel use and increase awareness of green living. A focus on renewable energy sources will help developing countries build resilient infrastructure, promote sustainable industrialisation and ensure their population's access to adequate roads, communication technologies, sanitation, electrical power and water.

Civil engineers are paramount in these developments. Technological advances are revolutionising this crucial work, and the increased use of eco-friendly building materials is also informing how civil engineering adapts to global needs.

"Already entrusted by society to create a sustainable world and enhanced quality of life, ICE members are now embarking on a future of serving competently and ethically in the digital age"

SMARTER THINKING

Engineering evolves, often building on ideas that have come before. Every so often, however, a new way of thinking emerges, as is happening right now with the rise of smart cities and smart infrastructure. As more of us shift to an urban lifestyle, cities need to be able to support a growing population. They have shifted in purpose, from being mainly trade hubs to becoming complex amalgams of places used for different goals that require a degree of synergy between them for the city to thrive.

Thanks to research carried out by ICE members, the technology behind smart cities is growing ever more sophisticated. High-tech materials such as graphene are being heralded as a major turning point in construction. The durable, elastic structure of graphene gives it incredible flexibility and energy-conducting properties, making it a highly versatile component used in projects ranging from electronics to road building.

Yet the growth of smart cities must be overseen alongside carbon management and efforts to counteract the problems caused by climate change, such as the effect of sea-level rises on coastal communities. This is just as important to sustainability as infrastructure resilience, future-proof design and smart technology.

Smart cities are already thriving thanks to technological developments that would have seemed unfathomable even a decade ago. Robotics and artificial intelligence are increasing

"How today's civil engineers act will impact massively upon generations to come. No small responsibility. However, it is one that ICE members are embracing with relish"

in sophistication, and we are starting to see such innovations come to life as carbon-breathing batteries, biometric materials, space-based solar-energy projects and worldwide Wi-Fi. Similarly, 21st-century technology is impacting hugely on civil-engineering methods. ICE members are seeing massive leaps forward in digital planning and modelling techniques, virtual-reality capabilities, 3D printing and BIM (building information modelling).

ENGINEERING THE FUTURE

It is therefore clear that society is changing rapidly and that a number of key issues must be addressed today. How the civil engineers of today act will impact massively upon generations to come. No small responsibility. However, it is one that ICE members are embracing with relish.

ICE resources allocated for future research into technology, physics and political trends are enabling detailed analysis of infrastructure and engineering systems and how they could evolve in the future. This work is offering valuable insights into what could theoretically be possible one day in terms of urban living, travel, health, defence and energy provision.

ICE is investing in attracting and retaining talented engineers, while supporting initiatives to engage with skilled people from all backgrounds, both within and outside the engineering sector. New areas being approached for collaborative working include the military and technology sectors. This is done in a bid to share knowledge and promote understanding – just like ICE's founders set out to do in 1818.

Together, these brilliant minds are working to turn future possibilities into reality – for example, the Hyperloop, which would enable trains to travel at speeds comparable to commercial jet airliners. Space travel is firmly on the agenda, too, with all parties realising the enormous potential of reaching out to the stars to sustain our way of living here on Earth.

As ICE enters its third century, the potential for future success is huge. Despite its many achievements over the last 200 years, it is entirely possible that the best is yet to come.

CHAPTER ONE

CONNECTED COMMUNITIES

Every time we take a journey, whether going to work, visiting friends and family, or to explore new places, civil engineers helped build the roads, railways, bridges, tunnels and airports that get us there. Communities thrive most when they are connected. The past 200 years have seen greater connectivity than ever before. The first steamships opened up new trade routes, while railway engineers widened the horizons of the public en masse through the freedom and thrill of train travel. Cities have been shaped by their networks of roads and bridges, and populations served by the underground trains running beneath their feet.

ICE 200
CANADIAN PACIFIC RAILWAY
UNITING THE CANADIAN NATION, EAST TO WEST

—————

LOCATION NORTHERN ONTARIO TO BRITISH COLUMBIA, CANADA
CONSTRUCTION DATES 1881–86

ON 1 JULY 1867, four of the British colonies of eastern Canada – Ontario, Quebec, Nova Scotia and New Brunswick – joined together to form the Dominion of Canada. The colony of British Columbia joined the confederation in 1871, on the condition that a railway linking east with west be provided.

Surveying started in 1872 under the direction of Sandford Fleming, and involved more than 500 surveyors and assistants, working in largely virgin territory. A northerly route was selected across the prairies and through the Rockies over the Yellowhead Pass and down the Fraser Valley to Port Moody on the west coast, near present-day Vancouver.

Government looked to private enterprise for the construction and in 1880 a syndicate primarily comprising Scottish-Canadian businessmen submitted to the government a proposal to finish the railway by 1891. Following approval from the Canadian parliament, the Canadian Pacific Railway (CPR) was incorporated on 16 February 1881, with government subsidising construction with $25 million in cash, to be paid in stages, and by the granting of 10 million hectares of prairie land.

The overall distance linking the existing railhead in northern Ontario to Port Moody was some 2,900 km and construction was carried out in three sections. The first from North Bay to Winnipeg, the second from Winnipeg across the prairies into the Continental Divide and the third from the West Coast to the Selkirk Mountains.

In June 1880 (Sir) Collingwood Schreiber replaced Fleming as Chief Engineer, and oversaw the completion of the railway on behalf of the Canadian government.

By the end of 1881 progress was slow, with only 260 km of track laid, and so the CPR appointed an American, Cornelius van Horne, as general manager. Described as "the ablest railroad general in the world", van Horne promised 800 km of line in 1882, a commitment that most people considered an impossibility. Despite major flooding of the Red River in 1882 delaying the start of construction from Winnipeg, nearly 700 km of main line plus some 90 km of sidings were completed by the end of 1882. The section across the prairies involved moving 10 million cubic metres of earth with a workforce of over 5,000 men and 1,700 horse teams. Progress averaged 5 km a day, with a record of 10.2 km being laid in one 15-hour shift.

In British Columbia, the route followed the Fraser River Canyon and 13 tunnels, as well as a number of trestles and bridges, had to be built in one 30 km section. A cantilevered bridge crossed the Fraser at Cisco Flats with the steel being fabricated in sections in England and shipped to Port Moody around Cape Horn. Owing to labour costs and shortages, 15,000 contract workers from China were employed at low wages and lived in sub-standard conditions

Bridges had to be built in advance of track-laying and these were generally constructed from timber cut from local forests and processed in portable sawmills. These bridges would be replaced at a later date with steel or masonry structures.

On 7 November 1885, the final spike was driven at Craigellachie in the Eagle Pass in British Columbia, thus uniting Canada with a "ribbon of steel". Construction had been completed five years ahead of schedule and the first through train left Montreal on 28 June 1886, arriving in Port Moody six days later. Politically and economically, Canada had become united as a nation.

UK MOTORWAY NETWORK

HOW POST-WAR BRITAIN EMBRACED AND DEVELOPED THE "MOTOR ROAD"

―――――

LOCATION THROUGHOUT THE UK
DATES 1958–

THE BRITISH MOTORWAY age began in the late 1950s and since then motorway travel has become embedded in our everyday lives – whether as commuters, holiday makers or as recipients of the goods transported every day in lorries from ports and freight terminals. As with other parts of our infrastructure, like water mains and sewers, motorways are so embedded in our lives that most people forget this vital contribution of engineers to their daily lives until something goes wrong and congestion becomes intolerable.

The idea for a vehicle only special road was suggested more than a century ago in the early days of the motor car. In 1906 John Montagu placed a private member's bill before Parliament for the construction of a dual-carriageway "motor road" from London to Brighton. The route was designed by the engineers Douglas Fox and Partners and would have been similar to a modern motorway, limited to use by motor vehicles. Montagu was forced to withdraw the bill in the face of strong opposition from the railway lobby. Forty years later, the UK's post-war roads were becoming increasingly congested.

The Special Roads Act of 1949 gave powers to plan the UK's first motorways. Some engineers, impressed by motorways they had seen in the US and Germany, were keen to get started. One such was James Drake, County Surveyor of Lancashire, who led the team that designed the Preston Bypass, opened in 1958 as the UK's first motorway, later to be part of the M6. It was the start of a planned programme of motorways.

EXPANDING THE NETWORK

Opened in November 1959, the M1 was the UK's next major motorway. Designed by Owen Williams with standardised bridges for rapid construction, it was built by John Laing Construction in just 19 months. It covered 110 miles of carriageway with 183 bridges, 200 bridges and culverts. Other early English motorways included the M2, M5, M6 and M50, almost all built in shorter sections that were subsequently linked together, as was the M4 which provided direct connections between the expanding English network and South Wales.

In Scotland the first motorway was the Harthill bypass, opened in 1964, a four-mile length of the M8 planned between Glasgow and Edinburgh. Further extensions of the M8 would eventually include the Kingston Bridge, the major motorway crossing of the River Clyde, and the Charing Cross Inner Ring Road which transformed the centre of Glasgow, and the M8 St James Interchange at Glasgow Airport – the UK's first "design and construct" motorway on the route to the Erskine Bridge. Scotland's north-south artery, the M74, joins the M6 at the border. A smaller motorway network exists in Northern Ireland.

Connections between motorways created complex design challenges. In 1972 the Gravelly Hill interchange of the M6, the M1 and the M5 opened – nicknamed "Spaghetti Junction" – elevating 13.5 miles of motorway to accommodate two railway lines, three canals and two rivers. The M8/M73 Baillieston Interchange outside Glasgow (pictured overleaf) carries four levels of traffic.

The motorways required a major bridge-building programme. Three great suspension bridges were built – the Forth, the Severn and the Humber – as were cable-stayed bridges at Dartford, the Second Severn Crossing and the Queensferry Crossing over the Forth. More than 9,000 bridges have been built in all.

Postwar Britain saw the development of "New Towns" such as Stevenage and Harlow, close to motorways and with an easy commute to and from London. New towns were built around Glasgow and elsewhere, and major housing developments are often located in towns and cities with good motorway connections.

Another driving factor behind the UK's motorway network is to serve the economy and increase productivity. Since the 1970s and 1980s motorway junctions have provided the ideal location for economic development through the evolution of "out-of-town" retail centres, business parks and distribution hubs. Although most motorways provide long-distance, inter-urban links characterised by widely-spaced junctions with service areas at intervals, proposals for "urban motorways" were developed in several major cities. The M8 across Glasgow is the most complete example, but the potential impacts on communities were often so great that the original plans were only partially implemented (such as the A167(M) in Newcastle-upon-Tyne) or totally abandoned.

The M25 is the prime example of a third type, the "orbital motorway". Sir Patrick Abercrombie developed a scheme to provide five orbital roads as concentric rings around London in the 1940s to minimise through traffic. Short lengths of motorway were built over the following decades, but these gradually evolved into a single route linking the original "arterial motorways" heading off to all compass points.

SMARTER MOTORWAYS

Highways England and Transport Scotland have ambitious plans for future improvements to their networks. In England the "smart motorways" programme is a development of a "managed motorway" trial on the M42 part of the "Birmingham Box". Smart motorways use technology and data to improve performance and dispense with the need for hard shoulders. They feature CCTV cameras and variable message signs to regulate speed, automatically closing lanes in the event of an incident. By smoothing traffic flow, smart motorways aim to reduce congestion, improve safety and reliability and enable drivers to make smarter, informed travel choices. The Scottish equivalent is termed "Intelligent Transport System".

Tolls have been used to help fund some of the major estuary crossings, but various proposals for "road user charging" to help manage demand have yet to materialise. The potential impact of other new technologies such as autonomous cars, convoys of "platooning" lorries and wireless charging of moving electric vehicles also offer new challenges. While these may provide many benefits – such as reducing human error, maximising carriageway capacity and improved accessibility for those unable to drive – there is currently no clear understanding of the impact that such technologies may have on the future of motorways.

MILLAU VIADUCT
THE WORLD'S HIGHEST ROAD CROSSING

LOCATION MILLAU, FRANCE
CONSTRUCTION DATES 2001–04

THE MILLAU VIADUCT is a multiple-span cable-stayed crossing of the River Tarn gorge near the town of Millau in the Massif Central of France. Before it was constructed, traffic had to descend into the Tarn valley and pass through the town centre, causing congestion during the holiday season. As the only north-south route in the region, Millau became synonymous with delay, obliging the French government to consider a drastic solution in the 1980s: the new A75 motorway covering a 330 km stretch between Clermont-Ferrand and Montpellier.

Due to the high costs, sensitive natural location and complicated engineering challenges, the French Ministry of Public Works launched an architectural and engineering competition for a high-level solution, attracting over 200 entries. It was won in 1996 by a design team led by French structural engineer Dr Michel Virlogeux (Honorary FICE, awarded the ICE Gold Medal in 2005 for his design of this structure) with English architect Sir Norman Foster. The design-build-finance-operate (DBFO) contract included a 75-year concession awarded to a consortium led by the Eiffage group, which will recoup its investment by charging tolls.

Each of the seven piers is founded on four reinforced concrete shafts sunk into the bedrock and capped by a concrete slab. Divided into twin forked sections below the deck, the piers were slip-formed. Steel gantries erected between them provided additional support during deck-launching. At the north and south plateaux, prefabricated steel-core boxes were welded together and painted to form the continuous deck, then launched from each abutment to meet between piers P2 and P3 high above the river.

Work on site began in 2001 and took 38 months to complete. The curved viaduct is 2.5 km long. At 343 metres tall, mast P2 is the highest bridge pylon in the world, while the twin two-lane motorway deck – with an average height of 200 metres above the valley floor – was the highest road crossing in the world when inaugurated by President Jacques Chirac on 14 December 2004. The project proved very successful and the iconic viaduct, which captured the public imagination and blends well into the landscape, has significantly reduced air pollution by eliminating traffic jams. The viaduct received the 2006 Outstanding Structure Award from the International Association for Bridge and Structural Engineering (IABSE).

ICE 200

ØRESUND
FIXED LINK

CONNECTING DENMARK AND SWEDEN

—————

LOCATION COPENHAGEN, DENMARK TO MALMO, SWEDEN
CONSTRUCTION DATES 1994–2000

THE ØRESUND CROSSING is one of the world's most ambitious engineering endeavours, linking Denmark and Sweden over a busy shipping channel between Copenhagen and Malmo. From west to east, the 16 km road and rail structure passes through the immersed 4 km Drogden tube tunnel, the 4 km man-made Peberholm island, and the 7.8 km Øresund Bridge. It carries road and rail – the E20 motorway with two lanes of traffic plus one emergency lane in each direction, and a twin-track standard gauge (1.435 metre) railway, where trains are capable of reaching speeds of up to 124 mph.

In August 1991, the Danish and Swedish parliaments ratified an agreement to establish the fixed link. An international design competition was won by ASO, an Arup-led team. Design-and-build contracts involved many other consultants. Environmental considerations were particularly important because the Baltic is the world's largest body of brackish water. Its unique marine ecosystem depends upon on the water flow through the sound from the North Sea, carrying salts and dissolved oxygen.

The tunnel added to the project cost, but it allowed shipping to use the channel without causing obstruction to aircraft using the nearby Copenhagen airport. It also lessened the chance of ice floes blocking the channel. Building it involved pouring almost 500,000 cubic metres of high-strength concrete in just 24 months.

The Øresund Bridge is a two-level mainly steel structure and is the longest combined road and rail bridge in Europe. All bridge sections have a two-level deck superstructure. Steel girder trusses support the reinforced concrete upper decks that carry the motorway. The lower deck carries the high-speed railway, with the tracks in a reinforced concrete trough on the approach bridges and a steel deck on the high bridge. Double-acting jacks were used to position the lower deck bridge elements on their bearings, and to support the upper deck.

The approach bridge piers and bridge caissons were prefabricated in dry docks at Malmo north harbour. The approach bridge decks were manufactured by Dragados in Cadiz, Spain, while the high bridge decks were made at Karlskrona shipyard, Sweden. The various components were transported from Malmo to the bridge site by the floating crane Svanen.

ICE 200

CHANNEL TUNNEL

THE WORLD'S LONGEST UNDERSEA RAILWAY

––––––––––

LOCATION FOLKESTONE, UK TO COQUELLES, PAS-DE-CALAIS, FRANCE
CONSTRUCTION DATES 1988–94

FOR TWO CENTURIES, engineers dreamed about a fixed-link connection between England and France. In 1802, a tunnel was proposed with illumination by oil lamps and a mid-Channel island to change horses. Concepts by Thomé de Gamond and William Low kept the project in the public mind and John Hawkshaw, engineer to the South Eastern Railway, lent it his support in the 1860s. With another ICE president James Brunless, he acted as engineer to the Channel Tunnel Company who got the political go ahead for their proposal in 1876. Work started in 1881 but was abandoned in 1882 due to opposition on grounds of national defence.

The idea was revived after the First World War, but financial and security issues prevented any progress until the 1950s. Serious site investigation began following an Anglo-French agreement in 1966. Tunnelling began on a publicly financed basis in 1974, but work was halted in 1975 by a UK government desperate to control public expenditure.

The proposal was revived following the election of the Thatcher government in 1979 which was happy for it proceed if no government money was involved – a flagship for private investment in infrastructure. Competing consortia suggested both tunnel and bridge crossings. A contract was signed in 1986 with Eurotunnel, a special-purpose company which subcontracted construction to Transmanche Link, a consortium of ten British and French contractors. Work finally started in June 1988.

The adopted alignment generally passed through a 25-metre to 30-metre-thick layer of chalk marl stratum. There are three interconnected tunnels; one for services and access and two to carry the main rail services north and south. On the French side, five tunnel-boring machines (TBMs) commenced tunnel drives towards the entrance portals and to mid-channel, from a new access shaft sunk at Sangatte. On the UK side, the 1975 workings

below Shakespeare Cliffs were opened up using the New Austrian Tunnelling Method (NATM) from a new shaft, from which six TBMs drove the three tunnels seaward and landward. The undersea service tunnels were driven a kilometre ahead of the main drives to confirm the chalk strata, adjusting final alignments, gradients and depths where necessary.

On the UK side, one crossover cavern was built ahead of the main running tunnels using access from the service tunnel and excavated using NATM. On the French side, small-diameter tunnels were driven from the service tunnel around the main drives after they had passed the crossover cavern. These small tunnels were then grouted up to form a complete waterproof curtain around the future cavern space before the ground between the running tunnels was excavated.

Entering a crossover cavern during the construction phase was often described as walking into an underground cathedral. After completion of their undersea drives, the three English TBMs were driven downwards and abandoned off line to allow the three French TBMs to break through and be dismantled. Two systems of tunnel lining were adopted, either bolted together cast-iron segments with neoprene joints in areas of poor permeability, or precast concrete rings. More cast-iron lining rings were used on the French side because of the poor geology.

The tunnels themselves were only part of this massive infrastructure scheme. Significant elements included track laying, ventilation systems, signalling, electrical power supply, fire safety installations, special trains (double and single deck closed rolling stock for light vehicles and coaches, open carriage trains for lorries), a new country park (Samphire Hoe) on 30 hectares of reclaimed land, plus terminals on each coast with connections to the high-speed rail networks. The Eurostar and Shuttle services were used by 21 million passengers in 2016.

ICE 200
LONDON UNDERGROUND

THE FIRST EVER UNDERGROUND RAILWAY

LOCATION LONDON, UK
DATES 1863–

THE METROPOLITAN RAILWAY opened the world's first stretch of an underground railway in January 1863, running 6 km between Paddington and Farringdon. Since then, various lines have been built and then extended to form an underground network that is more than 402 km in length, serving 270 stations – making it the world's third's largest metro system, after Shanghai and Beijing.

In the first half of the 19th century, London had grown greatly and the development of a commuting population arriving by train each day led to traffic congestion with carts, cabs and omnibuses filling the roads. By the early 1850s, there were seven railway termini located around the urban centre of London – London Bridge, Euston, Bishopsgate, Fenchurch Street, Waterloo, King's Cross and Paddington. The concept of an underground railway linking these stations with the City of London had first been proposed in the 1830s.

John Fowler designed the first section of the Metropolitan Railway (now part of the Circle, Hammersmith & City and Metropolitan lines) using the "cut-and-cover" technique. The tunnels followed the routes of the roads above and the tunnels were dug from above and then covered over. The success of the Metropolitan encouraged other companies and the Metropolitan District Railway built a line from Paddington to Mansion House, now part of the Circle Line.

For the first time, the City was linked by rail with the entertainment district of the West End, the parliament buildings of Westminster, and the affluent residential districts of Chelsea and Kensington.

Cut-and-cover techniques proved disruptive and expensive while steam locomotives in tunnels were dirty and unpleasant for passengers. The advent of electric traction and a revival of the idea of the tunnelling shield offered the possibility of a deep tube network. James Henry Greathead developed an improved method for tunnelling for the construction of the City & South London Railway (now part of the Northern line) between King William Street (now Monument/Bank station) and Stockwell in 1890. The circular cutting face of his "Greathead Shield" adapted and improved on the principles pioneered by Marc Brunel's tunnelling shield used on the Thames Tunnel.

These deep tube tunnels used a tunnelling shield to dig deep below the ground. This was the first of the true "Tube" railways, and this tunnelling shield has developed into today's tunnel-boring machines (TBMs).

While he was an engineer for the Metropolitan District Railway, Sir Benjamin Baker experimented with the gradient of the track in and out of stations to assist acceleration and braking, saving 21 lb of coal per mile. This was introduced in some of the early tube lines, particularly the Central Line.

In 1898 came a one-stop tube link between Waterloo and Bank (now the Waterloo & City Line), while 1900 saw the opening of what is now the Central Line, between stations at Bank and Shepherd's Bush. In 1905 the District & Circle Line was electrified. In 1906, a further line was opened between Finsbury Park and Hammersmith, now known as the Piccadilly Line, and in the same year came the modern-day Bakerloo Line, between Baker Street and Waterloo. In 1907, what is now the Charing Cross branch of the Northern Line opened, with two northern spurs going as far as Archway and Golders Green.

Just as the Tube's expansion was at its most prolific, with practically every line extending its services further and further out into the suburbs, the First World War hit, and development was slowed. The Tube would never recapture its feverish growth of the early 1900s, but the late '60s saw the launch of London's first new Tube line in 60 years with the opening of the Victoria Line.

The Jubilee Line from Baker Street to Charing Cross opened in 1979 and by 1999 had been extended through the Docklands to Stratford. A 3.2 km extension of the Northern Line to Battersea in south-west London is due for completion in 2020.

Crossrail's Elizabeth Line will connect to the underground network on its east–west route beneath London. The trains now regenerate power when braking, achieving 30 per cent more efficiency.

Transport for London (TfL) is currently considering a proposal to extend the Bakerloo Line to Lewisham via the Old Kent Road and New Cross Gate, which would involve building five new or upgraded stations. This would improve transport connections in south-east London and enable new homes to be built and jobs created. If the scheme goes ahead, construction could start in 2023 and the line open in 2028/29.

Over the past 150 years, many engineers have been involved in the construction and maintenance of the underground, continually developing new techniques and methods for expanding, renewing and maintaining the network. Each day, there are close to five million journeys on the London Underground. It allows millions of travellers to reach places that would otherwise be practically inaccessible to them, opening up options for employment and socialising. The network continues to grow and it is very difficult to imagine a London without its underground.

ICE 200
IRON BRIDGE
CONSERVING THE WORLD'S FIRST CAST IRON BRIDGE

LOCATION SHROPSHIRE, UK
CONSTRUCTION DATES 1777–79

"THE IRON BRIDGE in Shropshire is one of the wonders of the modern world," says Kate Mavor, Chief Executive of English Heritage. "An iconic symbol of the Industrial Revolution, it is arguably the most important bridge ever built and one of the most important sites in our care."

Spanning a gorge of the River Severn and using 385 tonnes of metal, this 30-metre structure was the world's first-ever bridge to be made from cast iron. It was the brainchild of Shrewsbury architect Thomas Farnolls Pritchard who, in 1773, suggested to the ironmaster John Wilkinson that cast iron could be used for bridges. Wilkinson galvanised the local businessmen to support the scheme and an Act of Parliament was granted in 1776.

Work on the masonry abutments began in 1777 and casting of the main ribs began in September 1778 at Bedlam Furnaces, 500 metres downstream of the bridge site. Following the death of Pritchard in December 1777, construction was overseen by Abraham Darby III, grandson of the pioneer of the innovative method of iron smelting that made the mass production of cast iron economically viable. The detailing

of the joints fell to Thomas Gregory, foreman patternmaker at the Coalbrookdale ironworks, who used the techniques he was familiar with – dovetails, wedges, mortise and tenons.

The bridge officially opened on 1 January 1781 and proved so successful that investors received their money back within 12 years. The Iron Bridge design was rarely followed. However, it created confidence in cast iron as a structural material and engineers continued to improve on the concept pioneered at Coalbrookdale.

The south abutment began to crack in 1784. It was replaced with two trestle timber land arches in 1803, then rebuilt in cast iron in 1824 which survives to this day. By 1934, it had been scheduled as an Ancient Monument and closed to vehicles. Major interventions were required in 1975 and 1980. It is now in the guardianship of English Heritage, which in 2018 is repairing and repainting the cast iron, repairing masonry in the abutments, piers and parapets and resurfacing the deck. The project is a prime example of conservation engineering at its best.

ICE 200
ALBERT DOCK
FROM GROUNDBREAKING PROJECT TO WORLD HERITAGE SITE

LOCATION LIVERPOOL, UK
CONSTRUCTION DATES 1842–46

ALBERT DOCK IN Liverpool is a complex of five warehouses around an enclosed dock built on the Mersey foreshore. Engineers Jesse Hartley and Philip Hardwick designed a system where ships could dock and unload high-value cargoes directly into secure warehousing.

Dock construction in the 1840s was complex and labour intensive. The massive granite river wall had to be started at the low tide mark; the ground behind was backfilled, with the granite and sandstone quay wall being built simultaneously.

Unlike earlier dock warehouses, these five-storey buildings used no structural woodwork. Instead, an ingenious combination of cast-iron columns, wrought-iron beams and brick arches distributed the loads safely through the structure. Brick internal walls and fire doors completed the fireproofing.

For several decades, Albert Dock remained successful but, by the early 1900s, its unsuitability for larger ships meant that it had become uncommercial. The dock and warehouses were listed by English Heritage in 1952 for their architectural and technological value. Since the site was renovated in the 1980s it has become a huge tourist attraction, housing the Maritime Museum and Tate Liverpool. Along with five other Liverpool sites it became a UNESCO World Heritage Site in 2004. It remains a tribute to Hartley's engineering, his workforce, and their contribution to the prosperity of Liverpool and Britain.

ICE 200
ST LAWRENCE SEAWAY
A MARINE SUPERHIGHWAY LINKING THE GREAT LAKES TO THE ATLANTIC

LOCATION MONTREAL TO LAKE ONTARIO, CANADA AND USA
CONSTRUCTION DATES 1954–59

THE ST LAWRENCE Seaway is one of the outstanding engineering feats of the 20th century, and an example of how two great countries have the foresight to see the benefits of sharing the cost of large-scale infrastructure to mutual advantage.

The St Lawrence Seaway is a system of locks, canals and channels that link the Great Lakes and the St Lawrence River with the Atlantic Ocean. The seaway opened in 1959 and incorporates the earlier Welland canal in Canada between Lakes Superior and Erie, which was deepened.

It was an enormous project costing 470 million Canadian dollars and employing a total of 22,000 workers. The total seaway is some 3,700 km long from Anticosti Island in Canada to the head of Lake Superior in the United States, but the 600 km section between Montreal and Lake Ontario was one of the most challenging engineering feats in history. Each of its seven locks holds the equivalent of 30 Olympic-size swimming pools, which means the seaway can handle huge vessels of up to 225.5 metres long and 23.8 metres wide.

The Great Lakes–St Lawrence Seaway navigation system is critical to the economies of Canada and the US. Every year this marine super-highway moves more than 160 million tons of raw materials, agricultural commodities and manufactured products. It serves more than 100 ports and commercial docks in the Ontario, Quebec and the Great Lakes area.

LIVERPOOL AND MANCHESTER RAILWAY

THE FIRST PASSENGER-PAYING CITY-TO-CITY RAILWAY

LOCATION LIVERPOOL TO MANCHESTER, UK
CONSTRUCTION DATES 1827–30

RECOGNISED IN 2016 as an International Historic Civil Engineering Landmark, the Liverpool and Manchester Railway (L&MR) managed to overcome significant engineering challenges to become the world's first passenger-paying railway between two cities. Not the least of these was the demonstration of the reliability of the steam locomotive for regular long-distance transport, and the triumph of George and Robert Stephenson's Rocket at the Rainhill trials. The opening of the line in September 1830 ushered in the railway age.

Aside from its association with the "father of the railways" George Stephenson and leading bridge and dock engineer Jesse Hartley, the project established the reputations of two other engineers – Robert Stephenson and Joseph Locke. Both became presidents of the ICE. Between them, they engineered more than 5,000 miles of railway across five continents. Their involvement in this pioneer railway established their reputations. The project attracted immediate global attention. While the railway was being built it was visited by French, German, Russian and US engineers, and the opening ceremony was attended by representatives of many governments.

The first scheme for a railway between the cities (in 1824) was from Liverpool's Princes Dock. Opposition from landowners and navigation interests caused it to be rejected by Parliament. The railway as authorised in 1826 started at Wapping on Liverpool's Dock Road and extended to Irwell Street in Salford. An Act of 1829 moved the eastern terminus to a site within Manchester. The length between termini was 31 miles. At the Liverpool end the terminus was complex in that a separate station was provided for passengers at Crown Street, in addition to the goods terminus at Wapping, with stationary steam engines moving wagons with ropes and pulleys along inclined planes from Edge Hill in Liverpool.

The total cost of the railway was £820,000, about twice the original estimate. Wapping Tunnel cost £45,000 and Jesse Hartley's Sankey Viaduct £46,000. Sixty-three other bridges were built for £100,000, including the spectacular Skew Bridge at Rainhill. The 4.75-mile crossing of Chat Moss, once thought impossible, was achieved for £28,000. Other major works included the spectacular cutting through Olive Mount, Liverpool, with almost vertical sandstone sides up to 70 feet high, and Hartley's two span stone skew arches over the River Irwell near the Manchester terminus.

Sir Robert Rawlinson, president of the Institution of Civil Engineers, described Hartley "as the greatest stonemason England or any other country has ever produced". The high aesthetic quality of the Irwell Bridge is testimony of this: its construction over a busy navigable waterway required considerable engineering skill. Next to it, over Water Street is the site of Stephenson's cast-iron beam bridge, leading into the world's oldest surviving railway terminus at Liverpool Road, Manchester, now part of the Museum of Science and Industry.

The L&MR was originally laid with T-shaped malleable cast-iron "fishbelly" rails, supported by stone blocks where the formation was firm and by oak sleepers on the 13 miles of embankments. Later in the 19th century much of the line was quadrupled, but now only from Lime Street to Edge Hill.

Network Rail has recently completed electrification of the route, while the new Ordsall Chord line (linking Manchester's Piccadilly, Oxford Road and Victoria stations) has seen adjustments made to the setting of the Irwell Bridge – testament that this route between two great cities is as important today as it was when it was built, continually contributing to the economy of the region.

FORTH BRIDGES

SCOTLAND'S TRIO OF WORLD-RENOWNED BRIDGES

LOCATION FIRTH OF FORTH, SCOTLAND, UK
DATES 1890, 1964, 2017

IN THREE CENTURIES, the Firth of Forth has challenged generations of engineers to provide effective transport connections between Fife, Edinburgh and beyond. Since September 2017, the estuary has had a unique place in the engineering world, showcasing three major bridges constructed in three centuries in three distinct styles.

THE FORTH BRIDGE

The first crossing of the three was the Forth Bridge, the great rail bridge. This spectacular triple-cantilever bridge opened in 1890 and quickly became a worldwide engineering icon. It was the first major steel bridge in Britain and the longest of its kind in the world, and is now a UNESCO World Heritage Site. It was designed by two of the greatest railway engineers of their age, Sir John Fowler and Sir Benjamin Baker, who both served terms as elected presidents of ICE.

The Forth Bridge still forms a significant element of the East Coast Main Line north of Edinburgh. The superstructure was built between 1882 and 1890 by Tancred, Arrol & Co, which also manufactured much of the plant and equipment used in the construction process. William Arrol took personal charge and many of his ingenious techniques are still used today. French contractor M. Coiseau intrepidly sank the six caisson foundations, his workers hand-digging inside chambers of compressed air.

In a 10-year restoration programme completed in 2012, the bridge was given a protective, three-layer coating as commonly used for offshore oil rigs.

This replaced its original paint system. The new treatment protects the steel structure from the harsh climate of Scotland's east coast; and with ongoing maintenance it should last 25 to 30 years. The restoration was undertaken by Balfour Beatty for bridge-owner and operator Network Rail and earned a Saltire Civil Engineering Award in 2012.

THE FORTH ROAD BRIDGE

Her Majesty the Queen declared the Forth Road Bridge open on 4 September 1964. At a height of over 50 metres above the Firth of Forth, it is 2.5 km in length, with a main span of 1,006 metres between its two towers. When it opened it was the fourth longest suspension bridge in the world and the longest outside the USA. Designers were Mott, Hay and Anderson and Freeman Fox and Partners and contractors Sir William Arrol & Co, Cleveland Bridge and Dorman Long in joint venture. The bridge deck was a steel truss, Freeman Fox's last before developing aerodynamic box-girder decks for the Severn and later bridges.

The road bridge became a critical part of the transport system, which in turn supported the Scottish economy. More than 70,000 vehicles a day – including 7,000 heavy goods vehicles – relied on it, as did 100,000 people, many of them for business or leisure.

The bridge has limited resilience to allow it to cope with high winds and traffic incidents and breakdowns: it has no hard shoulders and no wind shielding to protect high-sided vehicles. The structure has been working very hard in

recent times. Originally designed in the 1950s to carry about 11 million vehicles annually – with a lorry weight restriction of 22 tons – by 2016 the bridge carried 25 million vehicles annually, with a lorry weight limit of 44 tons. Repair and replacement of bridge components is an ongoing activity, not least because of the harsh environment in which they sit.

In December 2015, the importance of the road bridge to Scotland was brought into focus during a 21-day emergency closure following the failure of a truss end link. Engineers became the heroes of the hour, working in extreme conditions under intense public, political and media scrutiny to reopen the bridge as quickly and as safely as possible. The Forth Road Bridge emergency repair project won the first ICE People's Choice Award in 2016.

Since the opening of the Queensferry Crossing in August 2017, the Forth Road Bridge has taken on a new role as part of a managed two-bridge transport corridor. It provides resilience to the network and keeps in readiness to take on the full burden of traffic should the need arise.

THE QUEENSFERRY CROSSING

The Queensferry Crossing was opened to traffic on 30 August 2017 and was officially opened by Her Majesty the Queen on 4 September 2017 – the 53rd anniversary of the opening of the Forth Road Bridge. Its deck was constructed as three balanced cantilevers, while its two flanking towers stand on two massive concrete-filled caissons embedded deep in the riverbed. The centre tower is based on the equally solid of Beamer Rock. The bridge has the highest bridge towers in Britain

and is the longest three-towered, cable-stayed bridge in the world. For just a few weeks before the centre tower deck fan was connected to its neighbours north and south, its 644-metre balanced cantilever was the longest ever constructed in the world.

It progressed from a concept in 2007 to a fully functioning transport corridor in under 10 years. The client was Transport Scotland; client's advisor and exemplar design Jacobs/Arup; principal contractor Hochtief/Dragados/American Bridge/ Morrison Construction, the design a joint venture involving Ramboll/Sweco/Leonhardt, Andra and Partner. The crossing provides greater resilience through the addition of hard shoulders, wind shielding, and a 22 km corridor managed with an intelligent transportation system, all helping to deliver benefits to the Scottish economy.

It took more than 15,000 workers over 19 million hours to build, and generated huge excitement among local communities as it gradually emerged out of the water and then "spread its wings" to connect to the new approach roads. On the first weekend of September 2017, more than 50,000 people were given the once-in-a-lifetime opportunity to walk across it.

The Forth Bridges are a monument to the science and art of bridge engineering over three centuries, and a reminder of the vital part that civil engineers play in the development, design, construction and maintenance of bridges to keep them safe and functioning. Preventative maintenance is especially important for such critical arterial links in the nation's infrastructure.

RIVER SEVERN CROSSINGS

LINKING ENGLAND WITH WALES FOR MORE THAN 140 YEARS

LOCATION MONMOUTHSHIRE TO GLOUCESTERSHIRE, OVER THE RIVER SEVERN ESTUARY, UK
CONSTRUCTION DATES 1875–79 (RAILWAY BRIDGE); 1873–86 (RAILWAY TUNNEL); 1961–66 (SEVERN BRIDGE); 1992–96 (SECOND SEVERN CROSSING)

BEFORE THE CROSSINGS of the Victorian era, the lower Severn and its estuary presented a formidable barrier between England and Wales. The Severn has the second highest tidal range in the world, which keeps the river from silting up, but the river has a unique range of obstructions, shifting sands, dangerous tides and currents that give turbulent conditions as far upstream as Gloucester.

The Severn ferry crossings were important and well-established routes through the ages. Roman legions are said to have used the Old Passage route on their way between Caerleon and Silchester. Over the years many eminent civil engineers such as Isambard Kingdom Brunel and Charles Blacker Vignoles had contemplated crossing the estuary, either by bridge or tunnel, but most of these plans were rejected or fell by the wayside.

The first railway to cross river below Gloucester was the Severn Railway Bridge, half a mile above the entrance to Sharpness docks. Completed in 1879 and designed by George William Keeling and George Wells Owen, the 4,162-ft-long single-line viaduct consisted of 21 spans supported on huge cast-iron cylinders.

On the night of 25 October 1960 two barges carrying fuel crashed and knocked down pier 17 of the bridge, bringing down two spans. The ignited petrol vapour set the River Severn ablaze for almost a mile upstream and five of the crewmen perished. The bridge was never repaired and was removed in 1969. The Severn Railway Bridge was a story of foul weather, bad luck and bravery and a victim of 'impediment to navigation', the implications of which should have been taken more seriously.

THE FIRST TUNNEL

In 1869 three separate proposals to build a railway tunnel under the estuary were put forward. These were driven by the desire of the colliery owners to find an alternative route to send coal from South Wales to English markets. The cost of one scheme put forward by Charles Richardson was estimated at £730,000 as only one mile of new railway would be required on each side of the river to allow for a gradual fall to the level of the tunnel.

In 1873 work began on the tunnel with Richardson as chief engineer and John Hawkshaw as consulting engineer. It would be the longest railway tunnel under water in the world, and a classic example of the engineer's fight against adversity. On 17 October 1879, the same day the Severn Railway Bridge opened, a great inrush of water occurred, flooding the works. With only 138 yards left to excavate, the work was brought to a standstill and the GWR made Hawkshaw engineer-in-chief, with Richardson's role much diminished. Hawkshaw also brought in Thomas Andrew Walker as contractor.

It was not until the end of 1881 – after the most strenuous efforts of the engineers, contractors and divers – that the tunnel was pumped dry and work could continue. The construction of the four-mile-628-yard-long tunnel took almost 14 years at a cost of more than £2 million, two and a half times the original estimate. The tunnel was opened for passenger traffic on 1 December 1886 and it took around 3 minutes 40 seconds to travel through.

The 20th century brought the motor car and pressure to secure faster modes of crossing the Severn. The Old Passage ferry crossing was reopened in 1926, with a car ferry between

Aust and Beachley, which operated until 1966 when the Severn Bridge opened.

A SUSPENSION MASTERPIECE

When it opened on 8 September 1966, the Severn Bridge realised a long-sought crossing but also marked a revolution in bridge design. Described as "the most perfect suspension bridge in the world", it led the way in bridge design for the following 25 years. The key to this was the box-girder bridge deck design pioneered by Dr William (Bill) Brown and Michael Parsons under the direction of Gilbert Roberts. The substructure was designed by Mott, Hay & Anderson and built by John Howard; the superstructure by Freeman Fox & Partners and a consortium of Arrol, Cleveland Bridge and Dorman Long.

The deck is thinner, lighter and less costly and offers much less wind resistance than the conventional deep truss girders of suspension bridges built in the United States of America and elsewhere. Developed for the Severn Bridge, thin aerodynamic decks have been used on 90 per cent of the world's long-span bridges spanning over 1,000 metres since 1966. The main span is 987.6 metres, suspended between two towers, with two side spans of 304.8 metres each.

By the 1980s traffic on the Severn Bridge had increased threefold and a complex six-year strengthening and refurbishment scheme was devised by Flint & Neill to extend its life with minimal disruption. Hangers were replaced, box girders strengthened and loads relieved from the main towers by jacking

On 26 April 1992, work began on a second crossing. Unlike the earlier suspension bridge, the second bridge has a central cable stayed section known as Shoots Bridge. This section is over 1,044 metres long and, with the approach spans, has a total length of over 5 km.

Many of the bridge components were precast or prefabricated and brought to the site to be floated out on a barge at high tide and lifted to the bridge. The viaduct is founded on 35 precast concrete caissons 53 metres wide each weighing 1,600 tonnes. The central bridge has two caissons of 2,000 tonnes, one on either side of the deep shipping channel. The English viaduct crosses over the Severn Tunnel and therefore its caissons required careful siting.

The project director was Norman Haste, who had worked on the Humber Bridge in the 1970s. At the time of the opening of the Second Severn Crossing in 1996, *The Independent* newspaper referred to him as "the Brunel of our times". Haste drew inspiration from the work of the Severn railway tunnel contractor Thomas Andrew Walker and the American engineer Washington Roebling of Brooklyn Bridge fame. Opened in 1996, the crossing won that year's British Construction Industry Supreme Award and Concrete Society Overall Winner Award.

The Second Severn Crossing now carries more than 60,000 vehicles every day and is designed to withstand earthquake loading and ship impact. The bridge is designed to remain open to traffic with any one cable missing under full load and any two missing with reduced load.

ICE 200
DELHI METRO
A RAIL SYSTEM GIANT IN THE MAKING

___

LOCATION DELHI, INDIA
CONSTRUCTION DATES 1998–

THE DELHI METRO is the second-oldest metro in India after Kolkata. Construction began on 1 October 1998 and it is being built in four phases, with the third phase currently under construction. When phase four is finished in 2021, the system will include 455 km of track and will be larger than the London Underground.

Delhi Metro Railway Corporation (DMRC) learnt from the Kolkata and Hong Kong Metro systems, and the first phase of the project was completed in 2005, nearly three years ahead of schedule. During the construction of the second phase, which opened in 2011, 14 tunnel-boring machines were used to build 35 km of underground tunnel.

The metro has reduced road accidents, improved road-traffic conditions and stimulated economic development. It was certified by the United Nations as the world's first metro rail system to get "carbon credits" for reducing greenhouse gas emissions and helping to reduce pollution levels in the city. To this end, it features solar panels and facilities for collecting rainwater at stations, and for every tree cut down 10 have been planted.

Delhi Metro proves that mass transit systems can be built in congested cities and has inspired further development: India currently has 1,300 km of metro in 40 cities in the planning stage. DMRC is acting as consultant for many of these and has set up a state-of-the-art training institute.

ICE 200
HAMBANTOTA PORT
THE REDEVELOPMENT OF SRI LANKA'S SECOND-LARGEST PORT

___

LOCATION HAMBANTOTA, SRI LANKA
CONSTRUCTION DATES 2008–

SRI LANKA LIES on the main shipping route between East Asia and Europe, and the inland harbour of Hambantota has a long maritime and industrial history. Hambantota is on the island nation's south coast and is Sri Lanka's second-largest port: the largest, Colombo, on the west coast, concentrates on container transport and does not have facilities such as ship repair and refuelling.

A proposal to develop Hambantota as a services and industrial port was unveiled in 2002, but work did not start until 2008 when the first phase was initiated by the China Harbour Engineering Company Ltd. Completed in 2010, five months ahead of schedule, this phase included four ship berths, two breakwaters to protect the port facilities, and refuelling facilities.

The second phase included a larger basin and deep-water quays. To avoid having to transport and dispose of the excavated material, the engineers built an artificial island harbour entrance.

Once the third phase is completed, with shipbuilding and repair facilities, the port will cover as area of 4,000 acres and will be able to berth up to 33 ships. This will make it the largest port in South Asia. Throughout its development it will have provided employment – directly or indirectly – for around 50,000 people.

ICE 200

PONTCYSYLLTE AQUEDUCT

THE HIGHEST AQUEDUCT IN BRITAIN

LOCATION WALES, UK
CONSTRUCTION DATES 1795–1805

TRANSLATING AS "CONNECTING bridge" in Welsh, Pontcysyllte Aqueduct was constructed between 1795 and 1805 as part of the Ellesmere Canal. It is by far the longest (300 metres) and highest (38 metres) navigable aqueduct in Britain and, for most of its life, was the highest in the world. It was constructed to carry the Llangollen Canal across the River Dee valley to improve the transportation of goods from the industries of north-east Wales to the canal network leading south-east to the English Midlands. Thomas Telford was the engineer for the project with William Jessop as consulting engineer. James Varley and John Simpson were the contractors for the masonry work.

This was an ambitious and groundbreaking project. Previous aqueducts were mass masonry arch structures with the waterway contained by thick puddle clay lining to the stone walls and canal bed. They rarely reached more than 10 metres above the level of the river or road below. Original plans were to build such a masonry aqueduct across the river, which required several locks on both sides of the valley to allow boats to get down to, and up from, the aqueduct.

The water used by the locks would be lost into the river and the canal would rapidly run dry.

Telford's revised proposal resulted in a level canal without locks for many miles. It involved building 18 slender stone piers up to 38 metres above the river and 3.7 metres x 2.1 metres at the top that, to save weight and material, were hollow from about 21 metres. The canal was then carried in a trough made of cast iron plates from William Hazledine's Plas Kynaston foundry near the site. The trough is 3.7 metres wide and 1.7 metres deep, and carried over each 13.5-metre span between the piers and onto the abutments at either end by four cast iron arch ribs. The plates were bolted together with joints filled with Welsh flannel, white lead and iron filings.

Pontcysllte is a Grade I-listed building, and the key structure of UNESCO's Llangollen Canal World Heritage Site. A strategic element in this popular leisure waterway, it also carries more than 50 megalitres of water to supply much of Cheshire.

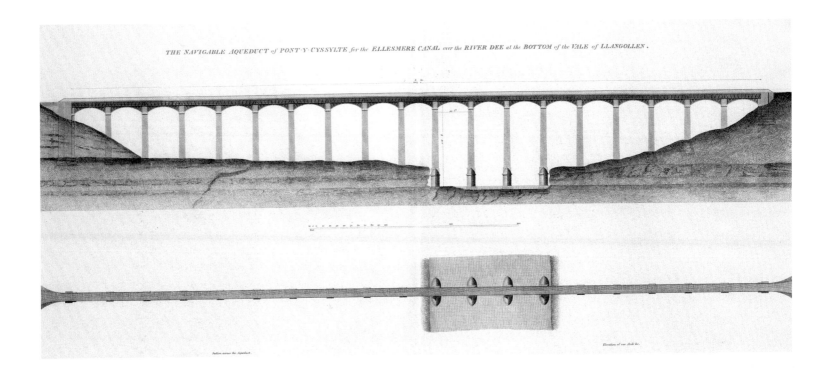

THE NAVIGABLE AQUEDUCT of PONT-Y-CYSSYLTE for the ELLESMERE CANAL over the RIVER DEE at the BOTTOM of the VALE of LLANGOLLEN.

MENAI CROSSINGS

THE WORLD'S LONGEST SUSPENSION BRIDGE AND TUBULAR RAILWAYS

LOCATION ISLE OF ANGLESEY AND MAINLAND WALES, UK
CONSTRUCTION DATES 1826 (BRIDGE); 1850 (RAILWAYS)

BEFORE THOMAS TELFORD'S Suspension Bridge opened in 1826, crossing the Menai Strait en route to Ireland was a slow and hazardous operation. The 1800 Act of Union increased travel between Dublin and London on what were poor and dangerous roads. In 1815 Telford was commissioned to bring the whole route up to acceptable condition. To cross the Menai Strait without interrupting navigation, Telford designed a suspension bridge, a form rarely used before then.

Building started on the two masonry towers and approach viaducts in July 1819, working towards the 100 feet (30 metres) above high water that the Admiralty required. For five years, 20,000 tons of limestone was quarried at Penmon, seven miles east of the bridge, and brought to the site in small sailing ships. Above road level, solid pyramids of around 16.2 metres high were constructed to carry the chains.

Iron founder William Hazledine developed the wrought iron chains that would support twin road decks across the 176-metre central span. The final arrangement was 16 chains in four sets of four (one above the other), two sets for each deck. The chain erection started from anchorage chambers and tunnels cut in rock beyond the approach viaducts to the top of the pyramids. The main span chains were raised one at a time with ropes, pulleys and 150 men turning winches.

For many years, Menai was the longest and highest suspension bridge in the world, but often suffered damage in the fierce storms affecting the strait. Eventually, from 1938 to 1940, the original chains and decks were replaced with four high-tensile steel chains and a single steel deck. Footways were added to the sides, retaining the original masonry structure.

By 1838 the Post was travelling by rail to Liverpool, which doubled the length of the sea crossing to Ireland. Pressure grew for a railway into North Wales, and various routes and ports were considered. The chosen proposal was Robert Stephenson's Chester and Holyhead Railway, which again involved crossing the Menai Strait.

Stephenson's Britannia Bridge consisted of two 461-metre-long, rectangular wrought iron tubes constructed to William Fairbairn's design. The tubes were supported 105 feet (32 metres) above high water on three masonry towers and two abutments, the central tower built on Britannia Rock in the middle of the strait. The two short 70-metre spans were constructed in situ on timber scaffolding. The longer 140-metre spans were fabricated on staging on the south bank of the strait, floated out on pontoons, fitted into the tower faces and raised, a few feet at a time, by chains fixed to steam jacks at the top of the tower. The ironwork was then completed through the towers, making the tubes continuous.

In May 1970, a fire destroyed the tarred, wooden protective roof over the tubes. The heat it generated weakened the tubes, rendering the bridge unusable. Lattice steel truss arches were constructed under the tubes. Rail services were restarted in 1972 through the eastern tube while the western tube was demolished and the permanent rail deck constructed for use in 1974. The eastern tube was demolished and subsequently a road deck was constructed above the railway, opening in July 1980.

Parts of the original bridges and other artefacts and context can be seen in the Menai Heritage Exhibition at the Thomas Telford Centre in Menai Bridge.

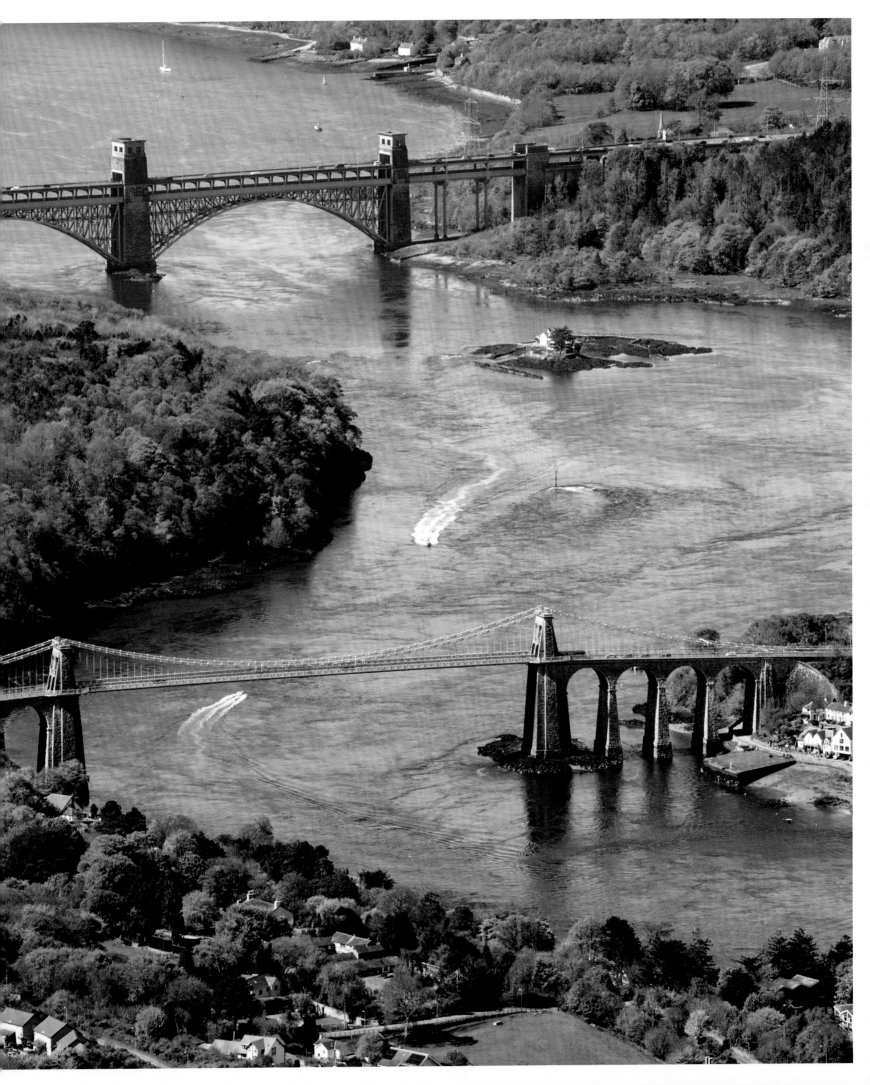

RIVER CONWY CROSSINGS

FOUR ESTUARY CROSSINGS, INCLUDING AN EARLY SUSPENSION BRIDGE

LOCATION CONWY, NORTH WALES, UK
CONSTRUCTION DATES 1826 (SUSPENSION BRIDGE);
1846–48 (TUBULAR RAILWAY BRIDGE); 1958 (ROAD BRIDGE);
1986–91 (CONWY TUNNEL)

BEFORE THOMAS TELFORD'S suspension bridge opened in July 1826, the only way of crossing the dangerous Conwy estuary was by means of rowed ferry boats. Telford set about improving the road from Chester to Bangor and, from 1822, he built a 615-metre-long rock-and-clay embankment between the eastern bank of the Conwy and a small rock island in the estuary. From that island to the western bank he constructed his 100-metre-long suspension bridge, a prototype for that at Menai.

The deck was supported on each side by four wrought-iron catenary chains. Each chain link was made up of five eyebars side by side, which were joined to the next five with six short plates and two three-inch pins. Telford used round castellated towers to support the chains, reflecting the shape of the 13th-century Conwy Castle that towered above the bridge and in which the western ends of the chains were anchored. Part of the castle had to be demolished during construction to secure the suspension cables.

The bridge carried main road traffic until 1958 and, although cables were added to strengthen it in the early 20th century and the deck was changed in 1896, the original Hazledine wrought-iron chains remain. The bridge is now owned by the National Trust and is open to visitors and for pedestrian use most of the year.

THE RAILWAY BRIDGE

In 1845, Robert Stephenson began work on the Chester to Holyhead Railway along the North Wales coast. He widened Telford's embankment on the upstream side and constructed his first tubular bridge to William Fairbairn's design alongside the suspension bridge. He used the latest shipbuilding technology to rivet together wrought-iron plates and angle irons, and two tubes were constructed on wooden staging on the western bank of the estuary. Each tube consisted of a large cell to carry the trains, strengthened with smaller cells above and below it. The tubes had a 122-metre span and were suspended 5.2 metres above high water. Their fabrication, subsequent floating out to the site and eventual raising up to the towers into position would test out the technology and procedures that would be used a year later in constructing Stephenson's much larger and higher four span Britannia tubular railway bridge over the Menai Strait.

The Tubular Bridge was the precursor of modern box-girder bridges, and Conwy is the only surviving example of the Stephenson/Fairbairn design. It still carries InterCity and regional train services along the North Wales coastline.

THE ROAD BRIDGE

By the 1950s, the single-lane, tolled and weight-limited suspension bridge was a major restriction to traffic using the A55 Chester to Bangor trunk road. In 1958, it was replaced downstream by a two-lane, 95-metre-span steel arch, designed by HW Fitzsimons and constructed by Sir William Arrol & Co. The project widened Telford's embankment to include amenity areas.

The original plan was to demolish Telford's bridge, widen the new bridge to four lanes and construct a dual carriageway road along the quay and around the north side of Conwy. This proposal met with strong opposition, as did a subsequent one for a new dual carriageway bridge immediately upstream of the railway bridge, with a road that passed through the south side of the ancient town.

CONWY TUNNEL

By the 1970s the A55 could not deal with the growth in traffic and, after the longest ever public inquiry into a road scheme, approval was given for a tunnel under the estuary as part of the A55 North Wales Expressway. Begun in 1986, Conwy Tunnel was the first immersed tube road tunnel in Britain. It was designed by Travers Morgan and Partners and the contractor was Costain Tarmac Joint Venture.

Six massive reinforced concrete units, each 118 metres long, 24.1 metres wide and 10.5 metres high, with openings for the carriageways and a central dividing wall, were made in a specially created casting basin on the western side of the estuary. Once complete, the ends of the units were temporarily sealed and the bank of the estuary was breached, flooding the basin. The units, each weighing 30,000 tons, were floated out into position. They were then sunk on to concrete pads which had been constructed in a trench dredged in the soft river bed. The trench lay between two previously built end portals: 120 metres long at the western end and 260 at the eastern end.

When all the waterproof joints were completed, a 1,090-metre-long continuous tunnel was built. The space under the units was pumped full of sand, the trench was filled in, the tunnel was backfilled and covered with a protective layer of rock. It was opened by Her Majesty the Queen in October 1991 and immediately relieved Conwy of its heavy trunk-road traffic. Material excavated for the casting basin and the trench was transferred to the eastern side of the estuary upstream of the bridges to form what is now a major RSPB wildlife reserve. The flooded casting basin was converted into a popular marina and an assortment of related businesses was developed on the adjacent site.

All four structures crossing the Conwy estuary were significant projects in their time and represent the development of civil engineering and infrastructure provision over the past 200 years. Each of them greatly improved the accessibility and safety of travel, while making positive contributions to both the natural and the built environment.

CAPE TO CAIRO RAILWAY

LINKING A CONTINENT WITH THE VICTORIA FALLS BRIDGE

LOCATION FROM EGYPT TO SOUTH AFRICA

CONSTRUCTION DATES FROM 1870s (RAILWAY); 1903–05 (VICTORIA FALLS BRIDGE)

THE PHRASE "CAPE to Cairo" was first used in 1874 by the *Daily Telegraph* editor Edwin Arnold to describe a part railway and part river route between the Congo and Sudan. The idea was taken up by various businessmen such as Cecil Rhodes, a mining magnate, who financed the railway from the Cape into the interior – with his friend Sir Charles Metcalfe of Douglas Fox and Partners responsible for much of the engineering. "My railway," said Rhodes, "would be the backbone and spinal cord to direct, consolidate, and give life to the numerous systems of side railways which will connect the vast central road with the seas on either hand."

The plan was not only to link the north and south of the continent but also to open up the interior by building railways branching off to the coastal ports. Cairo was already linked to Alexandria and Suez by railways built by Robert Stephenson in the 1850s, while in the south several lines ran out of Cape Town but were restricted by the mountains.

The Cape to Cairo route was never completed as a railway – the section between Wadi Haifa and Aswan was covered by a ferry service through Lake Nasser. No railway was built through part of South Sudan. However, much of the rest of the line was completed in sections and with upgrades, creating today's infrastructure links from the interior to the coast.

The highlight of the line is the Victoria Falls Bridge, which spans the Zambezi River on the border between Zimbabwe and Zambia. It gives a view of the falls, which are the largest in the world and are a UNESCO World Heritage Site. The bridge is a steel parabolic arch span designed by George Andrew Hobson of Sir Douglas Fox and Partners, assisted by Ralph Freeman, an assistant in the company at the time.

The bridge has a 198-metre span and is 128 metres above the river. It was built by the Cleveland Bridge and Engineering Company of Darlington, England and at the time of its opening in 1905 it was the highest bridge in the world.

The bridge components were made in Britain and shipped to Beira in Mozambique from where they were transported by rail to the site. The engineers were then faced with the challenge of transporting material to the other side of the river. They fired a rocket pulling a thin cable across the gorge and then pulled progressively thicker and stronger ropes and cables across. The final cable consisted of 19 steel wires surrounding a hemp core. It had a circumference of 8½ inches and weighed five tons. An electric conveyor was attached to the cable allowing materials to be transported across. The bridge could then be built out from both sides of the gorge.

The Victoria Falls Bridge was designed so that all parts were accessible with no parts that might trap water from the spray. The silver-grey paint was chosen so that any rust would be visible. In 1930, the bridge deck was raised and widened to carry a road and a pedestrian crossing. There has been no regular passenger service over the bridge since the 1970s.

The American Society of Civil Engineers listed the Victoria Falls Bridge as an historic civil engineering landmark. "It embodies the best abilities of the engineer to enhance the beauty of nature rather than detract from it." Although Rhodes' Cape to Cairo vision was never fully realised, the various railways along the route have indeed provided the backbone for today's African railway system.

DARTFORD CROSSING

BRITAIN'S BUSIEST ESTUARIAL CROSSING

_____

LOCATION RIVER THAMES, UK

CONSTRUCTION DATES 1959–63 (WESTERN TUNNEL);
1974–80 (EASTERN TUNNEL); 1988–91 (BRIDGE)

THE STORY OF crossing the River Thames between Essex and Kent can be traced all the way back to an active ferry service that ran between Gravesend in Kent and Tilbury in 1086. This small boat was able to operate from any low-lying part of the riverbank. But once larger vessels were needed to accommodate growing passenger numbers, crossing the Thames became a complicated business: anyone wishing to get to the other side had to hire a waterman's boat to get from the shore to the larger vessels.

In 1834 a pier catering for all sizes of vessel was finally built. Passenger traffic doubled in the pier's first year of operation; and, over the next four years, around a million people crossed the river using this service. From 1954 to 1965, use of the pier was restricted to the ferries. The opening of the western Dartford Tunnel saw such a steep decline in ferry usage that they stopped running soon after.

A tunnel to cross the Thames between Kent and Essex was first proposed in the late 18th century but abandoned for reasons of cost. The first serious attempt was begun in the 1930s, but stalled during the Second World War, not resuming until the late 1950s. Mott Hay and Anderson, engineering consultants, specified a tunnelling shield similar to that used on the London Underground. The first tunnel opened in November 1963 at a cost of £13 million. Tunnellers had to work in compressed air at pressures exceeding normal atmospheric pressure, to control the inflow of water and geological material.

Commuters had to wait 17 years for the opening of the second Dartford Tunnel (east) in 1980, again with Mott Hay and Anderson as engineers, and with a construction cost of £45 million. The twin tunnels became linked to the M25 in 1986, although the crossing itself remains the A282.

Rapidly increasing traffic flows prompted the launch of a competition for a privately financed bridge in 1988. A Trafalgar House consortium was successful with an £86 million bid for a cable-stayed bridge. Two pairs of steel cable towers rise 84 metres above the deck, supported on 53-metre-high concrete piers. These in turn are founded on two huge reinforced concrete caissons, constructed in the Netherlands and towed across the North Sea and sunk into position. Fifty six pairs of steel cables fan out from the top of the masts to support the deck. It is almost 3 km long and rises to 60 metres above the river. The 450-metre main span was the longest cable-stayed span in Europe when it was opened by Her Majesty the Queen in 1991, when it became the Queen Elizabeth II Bridge.

Around 160,000 vehicles a day now use the combined crossing. It had always been tolled and, since November 2014, an electronic charging system has operated. The success of all three elements of the Dartford Crossing are testament to the engineering professionalism of those involved. Both the tunnels and the bridge create a vital fixed link across the Thames that stimulates regional and international trade and economic activity.

However, constraints on the M25 make it difficult to provide further capacity at Dartford, so a new Lower Thames Crossing is proposed downstream to the east of Tilbury.

PENANG BRIDGE AND SECOND PENANG BRIDGE

MALAYSIA'S BIGGEST EVER CIVIL ENGINEERING PROJECTS

LOCATION PENANG STRAIT, MALAYSIA
CONSTRUCTION DATES 1982–85 (PENANG BRIDGE);
2008–13 (SECOND PENANG BRIDGE)

THE 13.5-KM-LONG first Penang Bridge opened to public on 14 September 1985. Designed by Howard, Needles, Tammen & Bergendoff, it established a physical link between Penang Island and the mainland of Malaysia, and contributed to a rapid growth in the island's tourism and industry sector.

By 2007, the bridge was becoming highly congested, with 23 million vehicles crossing each year, leading to demand for a second bridge. Totalling 24 km, with 17 km of that length over water, the Sultan Abdul Halim Muadzam Shah Bridge (or Penang Second Bridge) is one of the longest bridges in Southeast Asia. Many engineering companies were involved, including China Harbour Engineering, AECOM, UEM, MMSB and RB Perunding.

The bridge was constructed on soft clay, requiring special measures to avoid excessive settlement. The bored piles that support the main bridge piers are over 120 metres long penetrating the underlying rock to some considerable depth to support the towers holding the cable stays; over 5,000 driven piles were used to support the approach viaducts and embankments. The bridge also used high-damping rubber bearings for seismic isolation to minimise the risk of earthquake damage.

"The project pioneered numerous innovations in design and construction," said Dr Robin Sham of AECOM. "The natural hazards in that region and the extreme difficulty of construction in a hostile marine environment spurred our problem-solving creativity."

Penang Second Bridge adopted a number of green building technologies, such as generating kinetic electricity when cars drive over humps near to the toll plaza and a vertical wind turbine located nearby. A rainwater harvesting system was implemented and waste water is recycled for landscape irrigation. The bridge was nominated as "Green World Ambassador 2014" by the Green Organisation in 2013. The Penang Second Bridge has also won the International Star Award for Quality in Geneva in 2014 and ICE's Brunel Medal Award in 2015.

The bridges are the two largest civil engineering projects that the Malaysian government has undertaken. The first bridge cost 800 million Malaysian Ringgit, excluding the cost of land acquisition. The second cost 4.5 billion Malaysian Ringgit, funded through a public/private partnership. It opened in 2014 and was estimated to have increased the traffic to and from Penang by 25 per cent.

ICE 200
KWUN TONG LINE EXTENSION

EXTENDING ONE OF HONG KONG'S BUSIEST MTR LINES

LOCATION HONG KONG
CONSTRUCTION DATES 2011–16

THE KWUN TONG line is one of 11 on Hong Kong's MTR (Mass Transit Railway) network. The first section opened in October 1979 and ran from Kwun Tong station to Shek Kip Mei station. Within a year it had been extended twice to the south, first to Tsim Sha Tsui, and then to Central Station and Tsim Sha Tsui, crossing Victoria Harbour through Hong Kong's first underwater rail tunnel. The Jordan to Central Station section was taken over to become part of the Tsuen Wan line in 1982. Numerous other extensions were added to the line until the MTR Corporation decided to build a 2.6 km extension to serve people living in the southern Kowloon peninsular.

Meinhardt Infrastructure and Environmental Ltd (MIEL) was commissioned to undertake the environmental impact assessment for the project. The report was submitted in April 2010 and approved in June 2010. Work on the Kwun Tong extension started in 2011. Arup was appointed by the MTR Corporation as the lead consultant for this multidisciplinary commission, including full architectural input.

The Kwun Tong extension runs from Yau Ma Tei to a new Whampoa station, via Ho Man Tin. There will also be an interchange with the Shatin to Central Link (SCL) at Ho Man Tin station. The stations, along with their entrances, were particularly challenging for engineers due to their location, topography and ground conditions. These included soft ground and rock excavation, as well as man-made obstacles such as dockyard walls and existing foundations. Tunnelling, using the drill-and-blast method, was through mixed ground that was dominated by the need for rock excavation. Constructing Ho Man Tin station, for instance, involved the excavation of 690,000 sq metres of material.

The extended subway line significantly improves the transportation efficiency for the people living in densely populated Ho Man Tin and Wham Poa areas. This means of transportation provides a safe and convenient link for the people commuting in and out of these districts, who previously relied on public buses for commuting. The electric-powered railway is also environmentally preferred to the existing vehicular-based transport, particularly in regard to long-term air and noise pollution emissions. Ho Man Tin Station, in particular, will serve as an interchange station that strategically links the outer parts of Hong Kong to Central business district. It is currently the deepest subway station in operation.

HONG KONG MASS TRANSIT RAILWAY

ONE OF THE MOST RELIABLE TRANSPORT SYSTEMS IN THE WORLD

LOCATION HONG KONG
CONSTRUCTION DATES 1975–

DURING THE 1960s, the government of Hong Kong saw a need to accommodate increasing road traffic as Hong Kong's economy continued to grow strongly. A rapid transit rail system was recommended. This idea was new to the Hong Kong public. There was negative response from the public who claimed that only dead people will go underground and the current tram system was adequate.

The British consultants Freeman, Fox, Wilbur Smith & Associates started the initial study in 1966 and carried out subsequent updates with the new population prediction during the years. The final report was issued in 1970. On 7 May 1975, the Legislative Council passed legislation setting up the government-owned Mass Transit Railway Corporation (MTRC) and started the construction of the first phase later that year.

This 15.6 km stretch of the Mass Transit Railway (MTR) was completed in 1980 and included 15 stations from Charter Station to Kwun Tong Station. In 1985 the Hong Kong government awarded a franchise to a private consortium to build and operate a combined road and rail immersed tube tunnel under the harbour, providing an MTR link between Quarry Bay on the

Island Line and an extension to the Kwun Tong Line in Kowloon. Opened in August 1989, this second rail crossing of the harbour completed a circular MTR connection, putting the MTR network up to 41.5 km and 40 stations.

The network has since been extended to, in 2018, 91 stations. Following the merger of the Kowloon-Canton Railway Corporation and MTR in 2007, it now includes 221 km of rail with 155 stations, including 89 railway stations. It is well integrated into Hong Kong's wider public transport system of buses, ferries and light rail, and the MTR has links to Hong Kong International Airport, the AsiaWorld-Expo international exhibition centre and Hong Kong's Disneyland Resort.

It is one of the most reliable and profitable transport systems in the world. It has the world's highest "farebox recovery ratio" for a metro system of 187 per cent – a reference to the fraction of operating expenses that are met by fares paid by passengers (by contrast, the London Underground is at around 107 per cent, while many US networks are lower than 20 per cent). It has served as a model for other urban transit systems around the world, in particular China and Southeast Asian countries.

ICE 200
KOLKATA EAST-WEST METRO
KEEPING AN ANTICIPATED MILLION COMMUTERS ON TRACK

LOCATION KOLKATA, INDIA
CONSTRUCTION DATES 2009–

KOLKATA, PREVIOUSLY KNOWN as Calcutta, is one of the largest metropolises in India, with a total population of more than 14 million. Sometimes called "second city of the British Empire", it was founded more than 300 years ago and suffers from overpopulation and acute traffic congestion.

In the early 1920s, Bengal-born British engineer Sir Harley Hugh Dalrymple-Hay was asked to report on a system of tube railways for the city. A survey was carried out by a team of French engineers in the 1950s but nothing further happened until the Metropolitan Transport Project (MTP) was set up in 1969. Assisted by Soviet and East German engineers, MTP prepared a plan to provide five metro lines.

Work on the first of these did not start until 1972 but, helped by Indian engineers such as Paryhajit Part and Elattuvalapil Sreehharan, India's first metro opened in 1984. It was 3.4 km long and ran north to south on the five stations from Esplanade to Bhowanipur (now Netaji Bhavan). In 1995, the total length of 16.5 km was completed and started functioning on 17 stations between Dum Dum and Tollygunge.

The East-West Metro will be Kolkata's second metro line, running 17 km from Salt Lake to Howrah under the River Hooghly. Around 65 per cent of the railway is underground, while the rest runs on elevated viaducts. The line's 520-metre-long tunnel, which runs 13 metres below the river bed, is the first transport tunnel under a river in India and presented the greatest challenge.

This line will connect the two huge railway terminals of Howrah and Sealdah (both constructed in the 19th century) to cater for the huge demand of suburban passengers. It will also connect the iconic central business district of Kolkata and pass near the Writers' Building, Dalhousie Square and Esplanade, as well as the upcoming white industry and IT hub of Salt Lake.

Construction began in 2009 and the first part of the line is set to open in 2018 with the rest of the line opening in sections in 2019 and 2020. This project is being designed by a variety of international companies including AECOM, EGIS Rail and Jacobs. It is anticipated that 1 million commuters will use the line daily by 2035.

ICE 200
SYDNEY METRO
THE BIGGEST URBAN RAIL INVESTMENT IN AUSTRALIAN HISTORY

LOCATION SYDNEY, AUSTRALIA
CONSTRUCTION DATES 2010–

SYDNEY METRO, AUSTRALIA'S biggest public transport project, will transform the city when it opens in 2019. The new-generation railway will have the capacity to move more than 40,000 people an hour, almost twice as many as a typical suburban railway line. The programme will cost more than 20 billion Australian dollars and introduce many firsts, including the country's first fully automated railway.

Services will start with a train every four minutes during peak times on the city's north-west line, which alone cost 8.3 billion Australian dollars. Sydney Metro Northwest will have eight new metro stations and five upgraded existing ones. There will be 4,000 new commuter car spaces. It will also deliver twin 15 km rail tunnels (the country's longest), a 4 km elevated skytrain viaduct and the first cable-stayed railway bridge ever built on a curve in Australia.

The system will eventually extend through the Sydney central business district and beyond, including new metro rail tunnels deep under Sydney Harbour. By 2024, it will total 66 km of track, with 31 stations in all. Its ultimate capacity will be a train every two minutes in each direction beneath the city centre.

The Sydney Metro West line is in its early planning stages. It will deliver an underground link between the Sydney and Parramatta city centres in the later 2020s, doubling rail capacity between these two key regions.

ICE 200
NEW ZEALAND'S BROADBAND UPDATE
HOW THE ISLAND NATION GOT CONNECTED

LOCATION NEW ZEALAND
PROJECT DATES 2008–

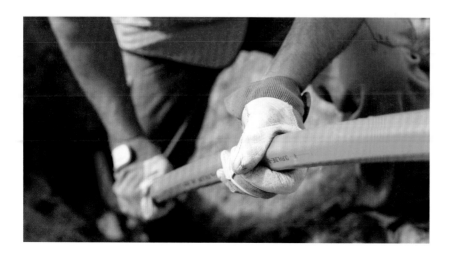

NOWADAYS MOST PEOPLE take fast internet for granted. But, in New Zealand in 2008, the rate of connection was slow and, in some places, nonexistent. At the time, the government was trying to focus its policies on delivering a stronger economy and higher wages. It recognised that if the country was to compete internationally it would require broadband to increase internet reliability and to enable video-conferencing and fast, cost-effective Cloud services.

However, providing the infrastructure was only half the battle. Potential customers would need to be encouraged to invest in adopting the upgraded service, which would probably mean updating their equipment. This was unlikely to happen without government subsidy.

The government allocated 2 billion New Zealand dollars and set up two programmes: Ultra-Fast Broadband (UFB) and the Rural Broadband Initiative (RBI). UFB is aimed at the fast broadband of towns and cities via fibre-optic cables. RBI is aimed at smaller towns and rural communities where cable was not the most economical solution. Since the government does not own or operate any telecommunication networks, it worked with several commercial companies.

Internet speeds have improved from a low in 2007 of nearly 2,000 kbps to an all-time high in 2017 of over 1,400 kbps. The aim is for 99 per cent of the population in 390 cities and towns to have access to broadband by 2025 via fibre-optic cables, with the remainder having wireless access, and to roll out improved rural broadband and a Mobile Black Spot Fund.

ICE 200
ADELAIDE–DARWIN RAILWAY
A TRANSCONTINENTAL RAILWAY 160 YEARS IN THE MAKING

LOCATION ADELAIDE TO DARWIN, AUSTRALIA
CONSTRUCTION DATES 1878–2004

NOBODY SHOULD UNDERESTIMATE the engineering difficulties of bridging 3,000 km north to south through the inhospitable interior of Australia. But, with this titanic construction, even these challenges were perhaps exceeded by the political and financial difficulties that needed to be overcome.

The first suggestion of a transcontinental line between Adelaide and the tropical north was made in 1858 by Melbourne businessman J Robertson. In 1876, the South Australian government authorised a railway from Port Augusta north to Farina. Seven years later the Australian government approved the 225 km Palmerston (now Darwin) and Pine Creek Railway to start the Northern Line, intended to join with the line being constructed from the southern coast. Both projects were led by South Australia's Chief Engineer Henry Coathupe Mais.

However, by 1891 the Southern Line had only reached Oodnadatta, 1,107 km from Adelaide. This remained the end of the line until 1929 when the line was extended to Alice Springs, opening up central Australia and replacing camel trains and horses to move people and freight.

It was not until the late 1970s that political will to complete the full line regained momentum. Finally, in 1997, the AustralAsia Railway Corporation was set up to call for tenders to complete the railway, including the final 1,420 km section from Alice Springs to Darwin. Work began in 2001 with a ceremony using the nickel-plated shovel originally used in 1878. The line was completed in October 2003 and the first freight train ran on 17 January 2004, and the first passenger train on 1 February 2004. The opening of the line was a milestone in the political, economic and social history of Australia. The railway realised the ambitions of the South Australian and Northern Territory governments and led to a boom in bulk mineral transport.

The AustralAsia Railway Project is far more than the sum of its engineering part: 1,420 km of steel rail, the new Elizabeth River Bridge south of Darwin, the restored 1918 Fergusson Bridge, numerous culverts built for tropical storms, and desert stretches built to withstand melting heat. Its completion and successful operation are the realisation of the 19th-century dream of a railway to link northern and southern shores, build a flourishing trade route with Asia and overcome the isolation of Australia's most sparsely settled lands. The railway has also encouraged tourism with the iconic Ghan passenger service – "a coast-to-coast expedition through the fiery red centre".

CROSSRAIL

CREATING A BETTER-CONNECTED CAPITAL

———————

LOCATION READING AND HEATHROW TO SHENFIELD AND ABBEY WOOD, UK
CONSTRUCTION DATES 2008–18

CROSSRAIL IS BUILDING a new railway for London and the South East. The project to introduce full-size trains on an underground route through the centre of the city, integrated with existing railways in the east and west, will provide the largest increase in central London's train capacity ever delivered by a single engineering project. It is a vital part of the United Kingdom's plan to deal with population growth in London. The resulting Elizabeth Line will increase choice, reduce journey times and transform travel in the capital. And that is only part of the story.

The building of the Elizabeth Line has been a significant engineering challenge. The project has involved boring 42 km of tunnels under Central London and building 10 major new stations, most of which connect with existing London Underground stations. It has meant incorporating new tracks and railway systems with existing infrastructure and the seamless integration of three different signalling systems to deliver a world-class, high-frequency service to 200 million passengers a year.

Following years of consideration, the journey really started in 2001. A team of engineers, planners, environment professionals, communicators and operations experts were brought together to develop and consult on an optimum route for the railway. A bill was delivered to Parliament in February 2005 and the Crossrail Act received Royal Assent in July 2008. Sponsored by the Department for Transport and Transport for London, Crossrail Limited was formed to manage the procurement, design and construction of the railway and its smooth handover into operations.

The new tunnels took three years to complete. Eight 1,000-tonne tunnel-boring machines worked beneath London, using over 200,000 concrete segments to form the 6.2-metre-diameter tunnels. The route was woven through a tangle of existing underground lines and utilities, giving machines less than half a metre of clearance from operational railways in places. Intensive ground monitoring and compensation grouting protected the historic buildings of London throughout. A further 14 km of station concourses, underground caverns and shafts were created using sprayed concrete lining, creating some of the largest excavated spaces ever built. Tunnelling works were completed in 2015 when work to complete station areas and fit out the new railway commenced. By mid-2017, a total of 51 km of new track was installed, the new rail depot was built and the first of the new fleet of trains commenced services on the eastern part of the route.

Design of the new railway looks to the future. The accessible stations are far larger than previous "tube" stations, often featuring two ticket halls for convenient access. Platforms are 200 metres long and there is passive provision for even more space, to allow trains to be extended at a later date. Locally sensitive station designs extend into public realm schemes that integrate new buildings into the landscape. Land around stations is being used by developers to increase homes, offices and retail facilities for the benefit of local communities. However, this new railway which will transform travel in London, is far from being the only achievement of the project.

"Everyone involved in Crossrail can be justifiably proud of the railway we leave behind," says Sir Terry Morgan CBE, who took over the role of Chairman of Crossrail in June 2009. "Yet our greatest achievements will be our contribution to the industry and to the skills of hundreds of apprentices who have started their careers with Crossrail."

Developing skills and knowledge in the industry has been the cornerstone of Crossrail since its inception. Crossrail built TUCA, the Tunnelling and Underground Construction Academy, in Ilford. It has trained over 18,000 people to work safely in tunnels and handed over the facility to Transport for London, for operational training thereafter. During construction, Crossrail and its supply chain employed over 700 apprentices, bringing new people into the industry and giving them the key skills to further their careers. Training mandated for lorry drivers accessing Crossrail work sites resulted in 10,000 safer drivers on the United Kingdom's roads. The Young Crossrail programme worked with 150 schools along the route, and engaged 44,000 children, parents and teachers to promote engineering as a career of choice.

Innovation has been a driving force. Collaborative work with Tier 1 contractors produced over 1,000 new ideas, 400 published innovations and 40 innovations implemented on the project. This work ultimately formed the basis of the new infrastructure industry innovation platform (i3P) that future projects can use as a springboard to develop their own projects with access to cross industry learning.

"Creating a collaborative culture helped us drive innovation generating new ideas and efficiencies for the project," says Andrew Wolstenholme, chief executive officer of Crossrail (2011–1018). "More than that, it has left a lasting legacy as a long-term driver of innovation in the industry."

There have been wider benefits too. The excavated material from underground tunnelling works has contributed to the creation of new wildlife reserves across the UK, including Wallasea Island in Essex. Light, aerodynamic rolling stock with LED lighting and efficient systems have reduced power requirements for the operational railway, helping reduce its carbon footprint.

An intensive archaeological programme delivered more than 10,000 finds to the Museum of London Archaeological Archive, including human remains with the first DNA identification of the plague, providing a resource for academics for years to come. The Crossrail Art Foundation charity will enhance new central stations with installations from internationally renowned artists, funded by commercial partners.

Crossrail has sought to share its experiences and publish its learnings throughout its lifecycle, culminating in the dedicated Learning Legacy website, which launched in 2016 (learninglegacy. crossrail.co.uk). In the spirit of sharing good practice for the wider industry, over 500 papers and resources are available covering engineering disciplines, governance, procurement, project management, health and safety, and stakeholder management.

The challenges facing engineering have never been greater, nor more exciting. When the Elizabeth Line opens, it will represent a huge leap forward for transport in London – and another step on the ladder of progress for engineering in the UK.

ICE 200

TRENT & MERSEY CANAL
THE WATERWAY THAT BROUGHT PROSPERITY TO ENGLAND

LOCATION FROM DERWENT MOUTH, LEICESTERSHIRE TO BRIDGEWATER CANAL, CHESHIRE, UK
CONSTRUCTION DATES 1766–77

TODAY, THE TRENT & Mersey Canal appears to be a quiet, green, corridor meandering across the Midlands, dotted with slowly cruising leisure craft. But, in its heyday, much of its 150-km length was choked with narrowboats carrying clay, pottery, lime, flint, iron, coal, timber, limestone and food. Entrepreneurs quickly took space along its banks and developed major industries, knowing that transportation of goods would be cheap and reliable.

It was the first of the major inland waterways and an important facilitator of the Industrial Revolution. The engineer, James Brindley, saw it as a key link in his "Grand Cross" to unite the whole of England. The project was initiated in 1765 at a meeting of the Company of Proprietors of the Navigation from the Trent to the Mersey.

In general, the canal follows the contour of the land, rising by locks singly and in groups to the summit level. Tunnels were used where unavoidable, for example at the summit, where more locks would have taken the canal above potential water supplies. The first sod was cut by Josiah Wedgewood – whose pottery at Etruria would make good use of the canal – in July 1766. It was completed in 1777.

Within a few years traffic exceeded all expectations and improvements had to be made. The Harecastle Tunnel, 2.6-km-long with no passing places, was a bottleneck, so Thomas Telford was commissioned to design a second tunnel with a towpath, completed in 1827. Telford also made other improvements, including straightening some sections and duplicating locks. Where the canal meets the River Weaver there is a 15 metre level difference. The innovative Anderton Boat Lift was built in 1875 and operated until 1983, after converting from hydraulic to electric operation in 1908.

As canals transitioned slowly from being wasting assets in the 1950s and '60s into valuable heritage assets that had a role in the regeneration of inner cities, the appetite for maintenance had a resurgence. During the 1980s much of the Harecastle Tunnel was rebuilt after being affected by mining subsidence, and Preston Brook tunnel was repaired after a collapse. The Anderton Boat Lift was restored, adopting hydraulic oil operation, and re-opened to boat traffic in 2002. The venerable Trent and Mersey, in use for over 240 years, cared for by civil engineers, remains a valued and vibrant national asset.

STOCKTON AND DARLINGTON RAILWAY

THE FIRST EVER STEAM-POWERED PUBLIC RAILWAY

_____

LOCATION COUNTY DURHAM, UK
CONSTRUCTION DATES 1821–25

IN APRIL 1821, engineer George Stephenson and Nicholas Wood, the manager of Killingworth Colliery, travelled from Newcastle upon Tyne to Darlington to meet a Quaker businessman called Edward Pease. Pease had just received parliamentary authorisation for an ambitious horse-drawn railway project, to transport coal from south-west Durham to the shipping port of Stockton. Stephenson quickly convinced Pease that "a horse on an iron road would draw 10 tons for one ton on a common road" and that a locomotive was "worth 50 horses".

The directors of the Stockton and Darlington Railway Company engaged Stephenson to build the world's first locomotive-hauled freight and passenger railway. His 19-year-old son Robert Stephenson, who was to go on to be one of the most influential engineers of the 19th century, assisted him with the survey work. Track-laying began in 1822.

The railway opened on 27 September 1825, when *Locomotion No.1*, a passenger coach called *Experiment* and 21 coal wagons – some fitted with seats – set off, carrying more than 500 people. They travelled just under nine miles in two hours. It clearly demonstrated the potential for locomotive passenger services soon to be realised on the Liverpool and Manchester line.

The movement of coal to ships in this area of the North East quickly became a lucrative business and the Stockton and Darlington Railway was soon expanded to a new port created at Middlesbrough, west into Weardale and east to Redcar.

TEESPORT NUMBER ONE QUAY RECONSTRUCTION PROJECT

THE DEEPENING OF BRITAIN'S THIRD BIGGEST PORT

_____

LOCATION MIDDLESBROUGH, UK
PROJECT DATES 2016–17

TEESPORT COMPRISES THE ancient fishing port of Hartlepool, much enlarged with the coming of the railways, and Middlesbrough's port, developed in the 1840s, with its link to the Stockton and Darlington Railway. Owner operator PD Ports recently completed the £50 million reconstruction of Number One Quay, an essential part of Teesport's infrastructure.

Completed over three phases, the project posed numerous challenges for engineers Royal Haskoning DHV RPS and contractors McLaughlin and Harvey, including the demolition of the existing concrete quay deck without disrupting business. The quay has been designed to withstand the loads imposed by all manner of equipment including some of the heaviest cranes for handling offshore cargo. The berth pocket alongside it was dredged to provide a depth of 14.5 metres below lowest astronomical tide. This makes Teesport one of the deepest general cargo berths in Britain.

"The completion of the quay is another example of our commitment to the future," says Jerry Hopkinson, Chief Operating Officer at PD Ports. "It is an important addition to our wider plans at Teesport and has a pivotal role in driving government plans to rebalance trade through the Northern Powerhouse. We are pleased to have secured funding through the Regional Growth Fund to help deliver this project, for which our application was supported by Tees Valley Combined Authority."

TYNE BRIDGES

SEVEN ICONIC BRIDGES ACROSS
THE TYNE GORGE

———————

LOCATION BETWEEN GATESHEAD
AND NEWCASTLE, UK
CONSTRUCTION DATES 1849–

IN TOTAL THERE are 26 bridges across the River Tyne, as well as two two-lane road tunnels and a pedestrian tunnel connecting Jarrow with North Shields. The seven big bridges over the Tyne between Newcastle and Gateshead form a living history of 170 years of bridge design and construction on a grand scale.

The longest-standing of these dates back to 1849, when Robert Stephenson's High-Level Bridge was officially opened by Queen Victoria, thus completing a rail link between the English and Scottish capital cities. The coming of the railway age and trade generated by the Industrial Revolution had increased the need for high-level crossings of the river (although the bridge also carries road traffic on a lower deck). Negotiating the steep banks down to and up from the low-level bridge was a time-consuming and often expensive operation, which frequently involved the use of extra horses.

This wasn't the first bridge connecting Newcastle and Gateshead. The Roman Emperor Hadrian had commissioned the Pons Aelius Bridge in 120 AD, and another bridge was destroyed in the great Tyne flood of 1771 and replaced with Robert Mylne's elegant Georgian masonry arch. However, this bridge was too low for river traffic and was restricting opportunities for local factories – particularly the armaments and battleships being manufactured upriver at the Elswick factory of Victorian industrialist and civil engineer William Armstrong. That's why, in 1862, Armstrong masterminded a project to replace the old Georgian bridge with a

hydraulically operated swing bridge, a project that was assisted by the Tyne Improvement Commission's engineer, John Francis Ure.

Essentially, what Armstrong did was to use one of the huge rotating gun mountings, which had been developed for his warships. However, instead of placing a gun on the mechanism, he placed the bridge. When river traffic needs to pass, the spanning section of the bridge remains parallel to the river but swivels 90 degrees around an island built in the centre of the Tyne, allowing space for ships of any height to pass on either side.

CROSSING HIGH

In 1871, the first high-level road-only crossing opened at Redheugh. The engineer was Thomas Bouch, who had successfully designed a number of bridges and railways in the north east of England before his notorious failure of the first Tay Bridge in Scotland which destroyed his career and reputation. Bouche's Tyne bridge was replaced in 1900 by another, built by Sir William Arrol and Company. However, by the later part of the 20th century, increased road traffic necessitated a new road bridge. In May 1983, Princess Diana opened the rather elegant pre-stressed concrete Redheugh Bridge, designed by Mott, Hay and Anderson.

Trains crossing Stephenson's High Level Bridge had the rather tedious task of reversing into Newcastle Central Station, as they had to leave the station in the same direction they entered. By the end of the 19th century the North Eastern Railway Company's Chief Engineer, Charles Augustus Harrison, designed a bridge that eliminated this problem in addition to providing much needed extra capacity. The King Edward VII Bridge was opened by the King, accompanied by Queen Alexandra, on 10 July 1906.

Royal patronage continued when King George V opened the Tyne Bridge on 10 October 1928 and it became the major road crossing of the River Tyne, carrying 50,000 vehicles per day by 2018. One of the designers of the bridge, who worked for the engineering firm Dorman Long, was Dorothy Donaldson Buchanan, who was the first female member of the Institution of Civil Engineers when she was admitted in 1927. The Tyne Bridge – which was designed and built at the same time and by the same company as the similar Sydney Harbour Bridge – became an iconic symbol of Tyneside. It is the centrepiece of the Great North Run, the world's largest half marathon: each year, scenes of 54,000 runners crossing the bridge on their way to South Shields are broadcast around the world.

MODERN DEVELOPMENTS

By the 1970s, road traffic congestion on Tyneside was a major hindrance to the local economy, which is why a major urban light rail scheme, the Tyne and Wear Metro, was developed to help relieve the situation. Trains travel in tunnels in both Newcastle and Gateshead, emerging to cross the river on the Queen Elizabeth II Metro Bridge, designed by WA Fairhurst & Partners, which was opened in November 1981.

In the latter part of the 20th century the decline of the traditional industries operating on the quaysides of Newcastle and Gateshead gave the opportunity to redevelop the area for residential and cultural use. The Gateshead Millennium Bridge, a spectacular tilt bridge for cyclists and pedestrians, designed by engineers Gifford and architects Wilkinson Eyre, was a key element in the redevelopment of the area with the result that the quayside is a major tourist destination. The bridge was the first low-level crossing to be built since the Swing Bridge in the 19th century but, rather than turn across the river, parallel to the water, this bridge tilts around 45 degrees to allow shipping traffic to pass underneath, leading to its nickname, "the Blinking Eye Bridge".

The superstructure of the Gateshead Millennium Bridge was fabricated in a shipyard six miles downstream and carried upriver, in November 2000, by Asian Hercules II, one of the world's largest floating cranes. When the contractor's civil engineer and agent was asked how on earth could his career top that moment he responded that he knew exactly where he was headed next: to build a sewage disposal works in Yorkshire. It is entirely probable, in its own way, that this scheme will have an impact on people's lives as much as the iconic Gateshead Millennium Bridge.

MANCHESTER SHIP CANAL

THE LONGEST RIVER NAVIGATION CANAL IN THE WORLD

LOCATION EASTHAM, CHESHIRE TO SALFORD, GREATER MANCHESTER, UK
CONSTRUCTION DATES 1887–93

AMID THE DETERIORATING economic climate of the 1870s, dues charged by the Port of Liverpool and railway charges from there to Manchester were regarded by Manchester's business community as excessive. It was often cheaper to import goods from Hull, on the opposite side of the country, than from Liverpool.

A ship canal was therefore proposed to give ocean-going vessels direct access from the Irish Sea to Manchester. The North West was suffering from the effects of the Long Depression, and investing in the development of the ship canal was an imaginative economic decision, which promised to boost competition and create jobs.

Thomas Walker was appointed as contractor and Edward Leader Williams as chief engineer. Williams's plan was to dredge a channel between a set of retaining walls and build a series of locks and sluices to lift incoming vessels up to Manchester. This formed the basis of a bill that was submitted to Parliament following a public campaign in 1882. But owing to stiff opposition from Liverpool and several railway companies, the canal's development only got the go-ahead in 1885 after some modifications to the original plan.

The ship canal took six years to complete at a cost of just over £15 million. It is still the longest river navigation canal (36 miles) and remains the world's eighth-longest ship canal, only slightly shorter than the Panama Canal in Central America. More than 53 million cubic metres of material were excavated; about half as much as was removed during the building of the Suez Canal. An average of 12,000 workers – peaking at 17,000 – were employed during construction.

The canal opened in January 1894. It enabled the Port of Manchester to become Britain's third busiest port despite the city being inland. Changes to shipping methods and the growth of containerisation during the 1970s and 1980s meant that many ships were now too big to use the canal and traffic declined. This resulted in the closure of the terminal docks at Salford.

Canal traffic dropped from 18.5 million tons of freight each year at its peak in 1955 to about 7.7 million tons in 2000, with the Port of Manchester now handling 7-8 million tons of cargo a year. There are plans to expand and redevelop the canal, and its operators are committed to growth in shipping.

ICE 200
QUEENSWAY TUNNEL
ONCE THE WORLD'S LONGEST UNDERWATER ROAD TUNNEL

LOCATION LIVERPOOL TO BIRKENHEAD, UK
CONSTRUCTION DATES 1925–34

CONSTRUCTION OF THE Queensway Tunnel and ventilation stations began in 1925. The tunnel was intended to connect the port of Liverpool to the south and west. It took 1,700 men to complete the £8 million project over a nine-year period, during which 17 of them were killed. When King George V opened it in July 1934, it was the longest underwater road tunnel in the world: a title it held for 14 years. It is a renowned historic structure, and won the ICE 2017 North West Heritage award. The Queensway Tunnel and Ventilation Stations are Grade II listed.

Sir Basil Mott designed and supervised the tunnel's construction with the help of engineer John Brodie. The art deco entrances, tollbooths and ventilation exteriors were designed by the architect Herbert James Rowse – who is often wrongly credited with the whole project – and decorated by artist Edmund Thompson. David Brown – of the DB series of Aston Martin cars that have featured in several James Bond movies – made the engine that powers the George's Dock Ventilation Station.

The standards of engineering precision on the project were second to none. The tunnel was built from each side of the river at Birkenhead and Liverpool, and when the bores met in the middle they were only 25mm out. More than 1.2 million tons of rock, gravel and clay were excavated, some of it used to build the foundations of Otterspool Promenade.

The tunnel entrance off Rendel Street near Birkenhead's docks was closed in 1965 after transport bosses decided the junction was causing too much congestion. It is still used for maintenance, access and as a film location. It has appeared in several films, including *Harry Potter and the Deathly Hallows Part 1* and *Fast & Furious 6*.

The Queensway Tunnel has hugely benefited the economic development of Merseyside, and an estimated 35,000 vehicles use it each day. By the 1960s it had so exceeded expectations that traffic congestion became a problem and a second, Kingsway Tunnel, was built in 1971. As part of a community engagement programme, Merseytravel regularly supports Queensway Tunnel tours for the general public, which provides an insight into the construction, operational and maintenance of the Queensway Tunnel and ventilation stations.

MANCHESTER AIRPORT

THE GLOBAL GATEWAY TO THE NORTH

LOCATION MANCHESTER, UK
DATES FROM 1938

MANCHESTER AIRPORT CELEBRATES its 80th birthday in 2018. It opened in June 1938 as the city's second municipal airport, after Barton Aerodrome, and was originally named Ringway Airport. It became an RAF base during World War Two, serving as an aircraft production and modification centre and the main training base for airborne forces, before reverting back to civilian use in 1946. Since then it has grown to become Britain's third busiest airport and one of the top 20 busiest airports in Europe. It has three terminals and is the only UK airport other than Heathrow to have runways over 10,0000 ft. Today, the airport handles more than 200,000 flights a year and 28 million passengers.

As the global gateway for the north it is at the heart of the British government's much-vaunted "Northern Powerhouse", connecting the region with key economic centres around the world. In the last few years, routes to China, Hong Kong, India and the United States have all opened up. It is also one the biggest sources of employment in the north west with more than 23,000 people working across the site. To increase capacity, Manchester Airport's £1 billion transformation programme was announced in June 2015. In one of the north west's largest ever construction projects, the airport will double the size of Terminal Two, due to the available land around it and the ability to phase the development while keeping the airfield operational. This was foreseen when the terminal was opened in 1993 and it was designed to be expanded easily. The project will introduce two new security halls, self-service check-in facilities, as well as up to 50 new retail, food and beverage outlets.

Progress on the project has been quick. Since the start in July 2017, a new 650-seat temporary gate lounge has been built, the western half of the terminal has been demolished and a new pier and link have already been built. By summer 2019 passengers will be using the new pier and link to the existing terminal, while the full terminal extension is scheduled to open in 2020. The entire construction site covers a massive 115,860 square metres and has brought a number of jobs to the region. The main contractor is Laing O'Rourke and, throughout the duration of the project, it is intended to employ around 150 apprentices.

ANTRIM COAST ROAD

A ROUTE TO PROSPERITY

LOCATION COUNTY ANTRIM, NORTHERN IRELAND, UK
CONSTRUCTION DATES 1832–42

IN THE EARLY 1800s, the Commissioners of Public Works in Ireland described the Glens of Antrim as being "a barren waste, cut off from any reasonable communication by the badness of roads over mountains and slopes varying from 1 in 6 to 1 in 12". They conceived the idea of building the Antrim Coast Road to open up the Glens of Antrim and the coastal area, to give better access for the military and to provide work to the unemployed.

The Commissioners' civil engineer, William Bald, rose to the challenge and completed the 40 km route between 1832 and 1842. Born in Burntisland in Fife in 1789, he was a civil engineer and surveyor who came to Ireland aged 20 to complete the trigonometrical survey of County Mayo.

Previous plans had been to build the road some distance inland, but this would have meant steep gradients, with the road having to traverse the valleys of the Glens, as their rivers flowed from the Antrim Plateau to the sea. Bald, however, had the vision of building the road along the foot of the high cliffs, some of which were more than 100 metres in height. His plan meant a level grade, ideal for the horse-drawn vehicles of the day.

Bald's ingenious method of blasting the cliff face to form the road foundation meant that little material had to be imported or hauled away. In his report, Bald wrote: "30,000 cubic yards of rock have been hurled down on the shore almost entirely by blasting, which has been executed by care and judgement. This has been greatly assisted by the use of Beckford's Patent Safety Fuse, an invention of the greatest certainty and economy which reduces, in a great degree, the chance of those accidents to which the operation of the miners has been particularly liable."

The Antrim Coast Road was a superb achievement of its day. It connected a large and isolated area with the rest of the island and changed the lives of the people of the Glens forever. Today, William Bald's legacy is one of the most famous tourist routes in the world.

BELFAST CROSS-HARBOUR BRIDGES

CONNECTING THE CITY TO A BRIGHT FUTURE

LOCATION BELFAST, NORTHERN IRELAND, UK
CONSTRUCTION DATES 1991–94

IN THE EARLY 1960s, to help alleviate Belfast's traffic problems, an elevated road circling Belfast was proposed and designed. The subsequent 30 years of political turmoil put paid to most of the scheme and only a short length of dual carriageway (the Westlink) was built in the 1980s between the M1 and M2 motorways. By the 1980s, the existing Queen's and Albert Bridges were unable to cope with increasing traffic so, in 1989, elements of the 1960s ring-road scheme – which crossed the River Lagan in central Belfast – were resurrected. Construction started in 1991.

The elevated road comprised dual carriageways of two to four lanes, running 790 metres in total. It linked the M2 to the north and the Westlink/M1 to the south with the A2 to the east. A parallel rail bridge – at 1,490 metres, the longest bridge in Ireland – links up the two previously separate rail systems. Both bridges cross the River Lagan just upstream of Belfast's harbour area.

The project was awarded as a design-and-build contract to a joint venture consisting of two local companies: Graham Construction and Farrans Construction. Together they came up with a precast concrete bridge design that had the approval of the Royal Fine Art Commission.

Due to the soft ground conditions, the bridge was supported on piled foundations, using concrete piles on land and, in the river, tubular steel piles driven 36 metres to the underlying sandstone inside steel sheet pile cofferdams. Pilecaps and reinforced concrete piers were then cast on top of the piles.

At the outset of the project, a dedicated factory was built in Belfast Harbour to precast the 1,058 concrete units needed, each typically 4 metres long. These varied between 2.2 and 5 metres in depth and 45 and 98 tonnes in weight. They were "match-cast", with each segment cast against the previous one. This ensured a perfect fit when the segments arrived at the site, and controlled the geometry once installed. Each deck segment was then transported to the site, via lorry for the land section and via barge for the river, and lifted into position using cranes.

Each segment was offered up to the previous one, the ends coated with an epoxy glue and the two segments stressed to each other using high-tensile bars. The deck was constructed using the balanced cantilever method whereby one segment was erected on one side of each pier, followed by another on the other side to keep the deck in balance during construction. Once the deck segments were installed, they were stressed together using steel tendons.

While the bridge was undoubtedly an engineering triumph, it was equally a project that had a huge social impact. "Little did I appreciate at the time, but this was a project where civil engineers, in a single project, were to bring about huge improvements to the infrastructure of Northern Ireland," says Philip Brown, Graham Construction's Engineering Director, who had only recently qualified as a civil engineer when he started work on the project in 1993. "It linked up the road network, greatly reducing traffic congestion and the resultant pollution in Belfast. It also integrated the previously separate rail systems, making a huge difference to passengers using the network."

Completed towards the end of "the Troubles", the bridges were formally opened by Her Majesty the Queen in March 1995 and have since acted as a catalyst for economic development.

TAY CROSSINGS

SPANNING A RIVER, AND THE ERAS

LOCATION FIRTH OF TAY, BETWEEN DUNDEE AND WORMIT, FIFE, SCOTLAND, UK
CONSTRUCTION DATES 1871–78; 1882–87; 1963–66

FOR RAILWAYS COMPETING to open up the east coast of Scotland, the Firth of Tay was a major obstacle. From 1854 there had been plans to replace the train ferry with a bridge but work did not begin until 1871. Thomas Bouch, engineer to the Edinburgh-based North British Railway, designed the Tay Bridge, a single-track iron-lattice design. Originally it was to have brick piers but the design had to be changed when the bedrock was found to be deeper than initially thought. The brick piers were replaced with lighter cast-iron columns and the number reduced, resulting in longer spans.

The first Tay Bridge opened on 31 May 1878 and within a year it had transformed the fortune of the railway, with passenger numbers between Dundee and Fife doubling. However, on 28 December 1879, just 19 months after opening, the bridge failed during a terrible storm. The middle 13 girders collapsed, taking with it a train, which was crossing at the time, and killing all 75 passengers. An enquiry into the failure blamed the bridge's design, its construction supervision and its maintenance, all part of Bouch's remit. His reputation was destroyed. Within a year he was dead.

William Henry Barlow was invited to report on the best way to rebuild the bridge and, on his recommendations, the foundations and high girders would be much more substantial. The bridge would be built just 18 metres upstream from the first bridge and slightly lower – 23.5 metres instead of 26.8 metres – although some of the original girders were reused in the replacement bridge.

The new bridge took just five years to build. The engineers were William Henry Barlow and his son Crawford; the contractor was William Arrol. It consisted of 85 pairs of piers and,

at over 3 km long, was the longest bridge in Britain. Unlike the first bridge, it carried a double railway track (only one track is used today). The bridge was opened on 20 June 1887 and is still in use today. It was refurbished and strengthened in 2003, the work winning the Saltire Civil Engineering Award.

The first road bridge crossing the Tay at Dundee was not built until the 1960s. The longest road bridge in Europe when built, the 2.25 km Tay Road Bridge gracefully spans the estuary of the River Tay between Dundee and Fife and is still one of Europe's longest. Costing £4.8 million and built between 1963 and 1966, it was designed by William A Fairhurst, with Duncan Logan (Contractors) Ltd of Muir of Ord as the main contractor.

The main structure comprises 42 spans, the majority 55 metres in length, increasing to 76.3 metres at the four navigation channels, before reducing to 24.4 metres at the Dundee end. Concrete piers in the river support twin parabolic concrete columns varying between 5.5 and 30.5 metres high as the bridge rises towards Fife. Twin columns support twin hollow steel box girders 3.65 metres wide and 3 metres deep and support a 300-mm-thick composite concrete slab carrying the roadway. The columns are elegant in form and function. The bridge was built as a deliberate optical illusion. Span distances decrease towards Dundee, tricking the eye to see them as equally spaced.

Opened by Queen Elizabeth the Queen Mother on 18 August 1966, the bridge brought some sadness. The much loved "Fifies", a ferry shuttle service across the Tay, stopped that day. The Fifie captains all became toll operators on the new crossing. Tolls were abolished in 2008 and the bridge carries about 26,000 vehicles daily.

BORDERS RAILWAY

CONNECTING THE SCOTTISH CAPITAL WITH THE BORDERS

LOCATION EDINBURGH–MIDLOTHIAN–SCOTTISH BORDERS, SCOTLAND, UK
CONSTRUCTION DATES 2012–15

THE BORDERS RAILWAY, connecting Edinburgh with Midlothian and the Scottish Borders in the south east of Scotland, is the longest domestic railway to have been reinstated after its removal during the UK's "Beeching" cuts in the 1960s. Opened by Her Majesty the Queen in 2015, on the day she became Britain's longest-reigning monarch, the line is breathing new life into the entire region.

A survey carried out for Transport Scotland found that, since it opened, over 65 per cent of tourist users said that the rail line was a factor in their decision to make their trip and that 23 per cent said they wouldn't have visited the area if it hadn't been for the new railway. In addition, more than 50 per cent of users stated that the railway had been a factor in their decision to move house and it informed the decision of over 80 per cent of those who changed job.

By making the area more connected, the line is also stimulating new and growing enterprises, creating jobs and making it easier for people to do business. This economic and social revitalisation is being driven by the Borders Railway Blueprint – a strategy supported by local organisations that is driving development along the route.

"The Borders Railway is much more than a transport project," says Danny Cusick of Scottish Enterprise, who leads the Borders Railway Blueprint. "It is an economic development opportunity for revitalising the entire region, stimulating the local economy."

Construction of the new railway involved extensive mining remediation. A million tonnes of earth was moved, 30 miles of new railway and 90,000 sleepers were laid, and seven rail stations and six station car parks were built.

Passengers can now travel from Edinburgh to Tweedbank in the heart of the Scottish Borders in less than an hour. The railway has opened up a new corridor of opportunity in both directions for living, working and investing in the area.

ICE 200
FALKIRK WHEEL
THE ONLY ROTATING BOAT LIFT IN THE WORLD

LOCATION FALKIRK, SCOTLAND, UK
CONSTRUCTION DATE 2002

"EVEN NOW, 15 years after it first started turning, the Falkirk Wheel never fails to amaze me," says Richard Millar, Director of Infrastructure at Scottish Canals. "It's an elegant, modern solution to an issue that has challenged engineers since ancient times – how to move boats uphill – and a beautiful fusion of art and engineering. It's nothing short of epic."

The largest waterway regeneration project ever undertaken in Britain, the £84.5 million Millennium Link scheme returned Scotland's 250-year-old Lowland canal network to a navigable state for the first time in almost four decades. It also saw the creation of the Falkirk Wheel, the world's only rotating boat lift.

Transforming the contaminated site of a former tar works, the Falkirk Wheel opened in 2002 and replaced a flight of 11 locks that once stepped the Union Canal down to the level of the Forth & Clyde, more than 100 feet below. Whereas weary travellers once had a day's heavy work opening and closing 44 lock gates to complete the journey between the two canals, the Falkirk Wheel allows vessels to transit between the two waterways in just a few minutes.

Now one of Scotland's busiest tourist attractions, the Falkirk Wheel attracts around 500,000 visitors from around the world each year to marvel at a working sculpture that combines modern engineering and technology with ancient principles set out by Archimedes more than 2,000 years ago. When one of the structure's gondolas is lowered, the opposite one rises, keeping the vast, 1,800 tonne boat lift in perfect balance as it carries canal barges 35 metres into the air in a matter of minutes. Incredibly, the structure uses just 1.5 kWh – the same power as it would take to boil eight domestic kettles – for each rotation.

With a unique design inspired by the ribcage of a whale and the vast propeller of a Clyde-built ship, It's no surprise the Falkirk Wheel has captured imaginations all over the world. It's a soaring steel symbol of the renaissance of Scotland's canals and proof that they are just as economically and culturally important today as they were when they were carved through the heart of the nation 250 years ago.

ICE 200
HONG KONG INTERNATIONAL AIRPORT
THE WORLD'S MOST EXPENSIVE AIRPORT PROJECT

LOCATION CHEK LAP KOK ISLAND, HONG KONG
CONSTRUCTION DATES 1991–98

FOR MORE THAN 70 years, aircraft coming in and out of Hong Kong had to do so through the Kai Tak International Airport, a notoriously difficult place for pilots to negotiate. It had a runway that jutted out into Victoria Harbour, surrounded by skyscrapers and rugged mountains, which required pilots to perform a low-altitude turning manoeuvre before banking sharply to the right for landing. Between 1947 and 1994, more than a dozen accidents took place at Kai Tak. But, rather than safety concerns, the reason for replacing it with an airport in another part of Hong Kong was insufficient capacity with limitations on further expansion.

Away from the congested city centre, Chek Lap Kok Island also has a more pilot-friendly runway, with flight paths routed over the South China Sea rather than populous urban areas, enabling the efficient round-the-clock operation of multiple runways. Construction work on the new Chek Lap Kok site began in 1991, and the new Hong Kong International Airport began operations on 6 July 1998 – an incredibly fast turnaround.

Hong Kong International Airport (HKIA) was built on a large artificial island formed by levelling Chek Lap Kok and Lam Chau islands and reclaiming 9.4 sq km of the adjacent seabed. Levelling Chek Lap Kok Island required the aid of 56,000 tonnes of explosives. The 12.5-sq-km airport site added nearly 1 per cent to Hong Kong's total surface area, connecting to the north side of Lantau Island near Tung Chung New Town – the first new town on an outlying island, which was also part of the 10-project programme spearheaded by the construction of the airport.

The detailed design for the airport terminal was awarded to a consortium led by Mott Connell (the Hong Kong office of UK consultant Mott MacDonald), with British Airports Authority as specialist designers for airport-related aspects, Foster and Partners as architects and Ove Arup as specialist structural designers for the roof. Many other firms contributed. Doug Oakervee, later to be a president of ICE, was Project Director for HKIA. The construction involved new roads and rail links to the airport, with associated bridges and tunnels, and major land reclamation projects both on Hong Kong Island and in Kowloon.

ICE 200
AUCKLAND HARBOUR BRIDGE
NEW ZEALAND'S COLOSSAL HARBOUR CROSSING

LOCATION AUCKLAND, NEW ZEALAND
CONSTRUCTION DATES 1956–59

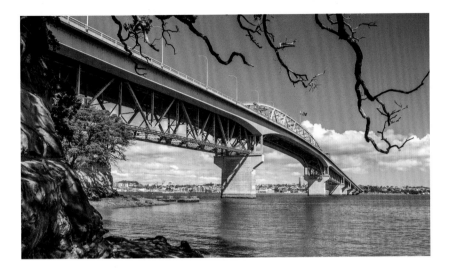

THE AUCKLAND BRIDGE, which crosses Waitemata Harbour, is the longest span bridge in New Zealand and is crucial in linking the central business district with the suburbs on the North Shore. The bridge was designed by Gilbert Roberts at Freeman Fox, and the steelwork was made in Britain by Cleveland Bridge Company and Dorman Long and Co.

Since opening, more than a billion cars have travelled across the bridge and its success can be seen by the transformation of the North Shore from its largely rural state in the 1950s to the urban sprawl of today. However, the bridge was built with no cycle, pedestrian or rail facility, and fewer lanes than recommended. As a result, clip-on extensions were added from 1966 to 1969, increasing the number of lanes from four to eight.

In the 1980s, the bridge became the first to have a movable concrete barrier installed, which improved safety and traffic flow. Special machines move the barriers four times a day, enabling the bridge to have five out of its eight lanes going in the direction of rush-hour traffic.

The bridge was recognised by the Institution of Professional Engineers New Zealand (IPENZ) as part of the "Engineering to 1990" project celebrating the country's 150th anniversary. In 2016, funding and planning permission were granted for the Sky Path walkway and cycle path to be added to the bridge.

ICE 200
BANGABANDHU BRIDGE
A MULTIPURPOSE BRIDGE UNITING BANGLADESH

LOCATION BHUAPUR TO SIRAJGANJ, BANGLADESH
CONSTRUCTION DATES 1994–98

THE JAMUNA RIVER is one of the largest in the Indian subcontinent and creates a natural barrier that divides Bangladesh into east and west. While the east benefited from gas, electricity and communications infrastructure, the agricultural areas in the west were left underdeveloped after Partition. The multipurpose Bangabandhu Bridge addressed this imbalance, carrying four lanes of traffic and a railway, as well as electricity pylons, telecommunication cables and a gas pipeline.

The Jamuna is a braided river, meaning it flows through a number of small channels separated by temporary islands of sediment, often changing shape across a wide area. The river needed to be "trained" using guide banks to reduce its width from 14 km to under 5 km. During the flood season, it is deep and fast-flowing, with typical seasonal variations in levels of 8 metres. Construction materials could therefore be transported from the coast 300 km away only during certain periods.

The bridge is built on unstable ground that is affected by earthquakes, so the design of the foundations – with more than 120 steel piles, each 80 metres long – was particularly important. The bridge deck consists of over 1,200 pre-stressed concrete segments. At 4.8 km long, the bridge was the largest project undertaken in Bangladesh at the time and the first major crossing of the Jamuna. It opened in June 1998, and traffic levels in the first year delivered an economic justification for its construction.

ICE 200
GATWICK AIRPORT
ONE OF THE WORLD'S BUSIEST AIRPORTS

LOCATION CRAWLEY, WEST SUSSEX, UK
CONSTRUCTION DATES 1933–

GATWICK HAS GROWN from humble beginnings to become a major international airport, the second busiest in the United Kingdom. Its growth has included a number of firsts. It was the first airport to have a circular terminal building with an integrated control tower and telescopic gangways providing covered access from the building to the aircraft. The "Beehive" was the idea of Morris Jackaman, who bought the airport in 1933 and obtained a public licence allowing commercial aircraft to use it. Opened in 1936, it is considered to be an important example of airport terminal design.

The Beehive comprises a reinforced concrete frame with brick infill walls, exposed concrete being a popular building material then. It was designed to keep departing and arriving passengers separate.

In 1952, the government selected Gatwick as London's second airport, behind Heathrow. It was redeveloped by Alfred McAlpine from 1956, with a new terminal (now South Terminal). When it reopened in 1958, it was the first airport in the world to combine road, rail and air transport. The Beehive was no longer used as a terminal, although it remains as offices. The Satellite Terminal, the second circular terminal in the UK after the Beehive, opened in 1983, followed by the larger North Terminal in 1988. A new control tower was built in 1984 and was the tallest in the UK at the time.

Although Gatwick actually has two runways, because of their positioning, only one can be used at a time, the other remaining spare in case the main runway needs to be closed. The main runway has been extended several times, as have the terminals. In 2014, Gatwick handled a record 906 aircraft movements in a day, with an aircraft movement every 63 seconds, the first time a commercial airport handled more than 900 movements from a single runway.

Today, Gatwick is used by 45 airlines flying to 228 destinations in 74 countries, carrying 45 million passengers annually on short- and long-haul services. It is also a major economic driver for the UK, contributing £5.3 billion to national gross domestic product and generating 85,000 jobs nationally, with around 24,000 on the wider airport campus alone. The airport has excellent public transport links, including the Gatwick Express.

Both Gatwick and Heathrow have put forward expansion plans to increase aircraft capacity in the South East. Gatwick's plans include a third runway.

ICE 200
HUMBER BRIDGE
FORMERLY THE WORLD'S LONGEST SPAN SUSPENSION BRIDGE

LOCATION HESSLE, YORKSHIRE TO BARTON-UPON-HUMBER, LINCOLNSHIRE, UK
CONSTRUCTION DATES 1972–81

THE PEOPLE OF Hull and Lincolnshire had campaigned for a bridge linking both sides of the Humber since the 19th century, but planning did not start until a bill was passed by Parliament in 1959. The viability of the Humber design benefited from the use of the aerodynamic profile of the box deck developed from the Severn Suspension Bridge. This was a saving in weight of about a third of the conventional truss system.

The Humber Bridge designers, Freeman Fox and Partners, chose concrete rather than steel towers. During construction, the 155-metre high Barton Tower swayed 947 mm from the vertical as the saddles were adjusted.

During the construction of the river foundations for the Barton Tower there was a major delay of about two years. Bore holes had been taken to establish the founding level, but unfortunately they missed a pocket of artesian water in the clay. One day the cutting edge of the concrete caissons pierced a pocket of artesian water, flooding the works higher than the river level. The insurgence of water destroyed the bentonite lubricant around the perimeter of the caissons and they were stuck in the river bed

material. To get them moving again 4,000 tonnes of steel kentledge had to be hired from the local steel mills at Scunthorpe and the designers had to change the configuration of the pier top.

For the superstructure of the bridge, the cables and deck were all manufactured in the UK. The deck was made up of 124 steel boxes weighing between 120 and 168 tonnes, delivered to a painting and assembly yard by train and lifted from the river or ground by two 20 tonne gantries that sat on the cables. One Friday evening, when the gantries were being moved up the cables, they slipped and fell, smashing into two previously erected boxes 100 metres below. This broke the temporary connections and these boxes were left dangling like gigantic butterfly wings. One steel erector was seriously injured on the catwalk but, by Monday, the hanging butterfly boxes had been rotated back into position and temporary connection reinstated.

Her Majesty the Queen opened the bridge on 17 July 1981 and, for 17 years, it was the longest spanning bridge in the world. It has since won many awards, and was listed Grade I by Historic England in 2017.

TAMAR CROSSINGS

LINKING DEVON AND CORNWALL FOR MORE THAN A CENTURY

LOCATION RIVER TAMAR, BETWEEN DEVON AND CORNWALL, UK
CONSTRUCTION DATES 1854–59 (ROYAL ALBERT BRIDGE); 1959–61 (TAMAR BRIDGE)

"WENT TO SALTASH – much too wide to be worth having a bridge." So wrote the 22-year-old Isambard Kingdom Brunel in 1828. Yet, 30 years later, he would bridge the wide, deep and tidal River Tamar at that very spot, to carry the westward extension of the railway network into Cornwall. Until that point, the only way of crossing the Tamar was by ferry.

Site work on what became Brunel's Royal Albert Bridge started in 1854 with construction of the midstream support pier. A 35-ft-diameter wrought-iron cylinder was sunk vertically so that its base rested on the bedrock and its top was just above water level. Within this was built a column of solid masonry, 96 ft high from its foundation in the bedrock. After the iron cylinder was removed, four 100-ft-high cast-iron pillars were built on top of the column to support one end of each main span high enough above high tide level for tall ships to pass underneath; solid masonry piers support the landward ends.

Each of the two main spans consists of an elliptical wrought-iron tube, forming an arch, with the ends tied by two tiers of wrought-iron suspension chains on each side; the inward pull of the suspension chains resists the outward thrust of the arch. Each span was built on shore, then floated out and jacked up to the top of the piers. Prince Albert officially opened the bridge on 3 May 1859. Brunel was too ill to attend, but he was later carried across lying in a cot on a railway wagon. He died on 15 September 1859. Network Rail now owns and maintains the bridge, which was significantly refurbished in 2015 to extend its life.

A century after the opening of the Royal Albert Bridge, work was underway on the Tamar suspension bridge, now a key link between Devon and Cornwall carrying the A38 trunk road. Until then, the only crossing at Saltash was by ferry,

which had been established before the 13th century. In 1832 civil engineer James Meadows Rendel, FRS, completed a "floating bridge" at Saltash, which consisted of fixed chains on the river bed along which a steam-powered ferry pulled itself across. Increasing demands on the ferry crossing led to a joint venture promoted by Plymouth City Council and Cornwall County Council. The Tamar Bridge Act for a self-financing toll bridge received Royal Assent in 1957. Designed by Mott, Hay and Anderson Consulting Engineers, the bridge was constructed in just over two years by the Cleveland Bridge and Engineering Company, opening to traffic in 1961.

Between 1998 and 2001 the bridge was strengthened to cope with modern traffic loading and widened by adding cantilevers to both sides of the main deck. The concrete deck was replaced by a lighter steel deck and supplementary cables were added to cope with loads during the modifications. These works required a new act of Parliament and were designed by Hyder Consulting Engineers. The bridge had to remain open to traffic throughout the construction by Cleveland Bridge UK Ltd. Strengthening and widening a suspension bridge while keeping it open to traffic – a feat achieved through the innovative use of compressed air to keep water out of the excavation – is thought to be a world first. In 2002, the project received the British Construction Industry Civil Engineering Award, the Institution of Structural Engineers Structural Achievement Award and the Institution of Civil Engineers' Historic Structure Award.

Ferries do still cross the Tamar. Three miles south of these two bridges the Torpoint ferries – three direct descendants of another of Rendel's floating bridges – remain a vital link between Devonport and Cornwall's Rame Peninsula.

CLIFTON SUSPENSION BRIDGE

AN ICONIC SUSPENSION BRIDGE SPANNING THE RIVER AVON

LOCATION CLIFTON, BRISTOL, UK
CONSTRUCTION DATES 1836–64

THE CLIFTON SUSPENSION Bridge has a chequered history. Its origins lie in the desire of an 18th-century Bristol wine merchant to span the Avon Gorge with a masonry bridge, for which he left a legacy. However, the distance was too great for traditional arched bridges in masonry or cast iron, and it was not until the development in the early 19th century of level deck suspension bridges – a form ideally suited to spanning exceptionally wide crossings – that such a venture began to seem feasible. This was confirmed by the completion of Telford's Menai Bridge in 1826 with its central span of 580 ft.

An enabling act was passed in May 1830 and Isambard Kingdom Brunel was employed as engineer in 1831, but money was always insufficient, and work did not begin until 1836. The project limped on until it was finally cancelled in 1853. Of Brunel's design, only its main chains, the Leigh Woods abutment and "two unsightly piers which deformed the landscape" were actually built.

Shortly after Brunel's death in 1859, Sir John Hawkshaw was engaged on the Charing Cross Railway Bridge, which entailed the demolition of Brunel's Hungerford suspension bridge, making available its wrought-iron chains. Hawkshaw and WH Barlow seized the opportunity to use them to complete the Clifton Bridge and form "a monument to their late friend Brunel, and at the same time removing a slur from the engineering talent of the country". They set up a private consortium to finance it.

Barlow and Hawkshaw's bridge differs in almost every respect from Brunel's. For instance, there are three chains, not two, and they do not come down to deck level as specified by Brunel. The masonry piers were to have been completely clad in decorative cast-iron plates,

concealing their basic construction. For reasons of economy, Barlow and Hawkshaw left the piers bare, designing instead handsome cast-iron caps in a vaguely Egyptian style as a nod to Brunel's original architectural features. Their caps make the bridge instantly recognisable.

What really makes the bridge their own is the deck design. Suspension bridges are a notoriously unstable form of structure and the early designers were preoccupied with the strength of wrought iron and the ability of the chains and hangers to support a platform and its moving loads. They took little account of the contribution of the deck to overall stability beyond sometimes providing, as Brunel did for his Clifton designs, inverted catenary chains to tie down and laterally restrain the light timber decks. However, a number were put out of use due to wind damage, including Montrose Bridge (1838) and Menai Bridge (1826 and 1839), leading to better understanding of the destructive impact of high winds. The decks of both these bridges were stiffened and made heavier, as prerequisites for resisting gust loads.

Barlow and Hawkshaw were thus able to draw on information unknown to Brunel in 1831. They also took advantage of the development of wrought-iron lattice and plate girders, standard features of railway bridges from the late 1840s, of which Hawkshaw had considerable experience. The deck comprises plate girders beneath the chains and substantial lattice parapet girders, interconnected by lattice cross-girders, providing much greater stiffness and resilience under turbulent winds than Brunel's bridge could ever have done. The Clifton Suspension Bridge was ceremonially opened in December 1864 and tolls are still collected from users, supporting regular maintenance.

ICE 200

YORK RAILWAY STATION

ONCE THE WORLD'S LARGEST RAILWAY STATION

LOCATION YORK, UK
CONSTRUCTION DATES 1874–77

YORK'S TRAIN SHED design makes it one of the most distinctive railway stations of the Victorian era. Its gigantic arch of iron ribs, sweeping round to follow the curve of the tracks, is a tremendous source of local pride. When it opened in June 1877 it was the world's largest station; but it was soon overtaken.

York's original terminus (1841) was trapped within medieval city walls, which admitted the railway through a graceful Gothic arch. But the cramped site precluded any major enlargement being undertaken to handle the city's increasing traffic. So the North Eastern Railway (NER) decided to build a passenger and goods station on a new bypass line just outside the city walls. The NER's chief engineer, Thomas Elliot Harrison, began planning the building in 1872 (and served as ICE president for two years during the station's construction). He and NER architect Thomas Prosser designed the train shed and offices.

York was and remains one of the busiest interchanges on the East Coast Main Line; yet Harrison used partial traffic closures on a few Sundays to manage the replacement of its key infrastructure. Three decades on, platform lengthening necessitated some elegant glazed canopies at the London end, which act as a visual foil to the original roof and demonstrate the lightness of touch that became possible as the century neared its end.

ICE 200

SCAMMONDEN DAM AND THE M62

THE FIRST MOTORWAY BUILT ON A DAM

LOCATION THE PENNINES FROM MANCHESTER TO LEEDS, UK
CONSTRUCTION DATES 1964–70

THE TRANS-PENNINE section of the M62 was a model of innovative road building. It made a significant improvement to the road network between Lancashire and Yorkshire and more than halved the journey time between Liverpool and Hull. The new stretch of road included Scammonden Bridge, which at the time was the world's longest single-span non-suspension bridge.

The terrain around the Pennines is some of the harshest in Britain, so it was essential that the new route be accessible whatever the weather. While the motorway was being planned, the Huddersfield water authority was considering a proposal for a dam and reservoir. It became clear a much larger dam could be built if it were sited on the route of the motorway, across the Dean Head Valley. So the village of Scammonden came to be flooded deliberately, with the M62 crossing the dam wall 63 metres above the original valley floor. It was the first reservoir embankment in the world to carry a motorway and required special legislation. It remains the only one of its kind in Britain.

The dam was a collaborative venture between the Ministry of Transport and Huddersfield Corporation Waterworks. Rofe, Kennard & Lapworth designed the reservoir, with Sir Alfred McAlpine & Son the main contractor. The project is a fine example of a multiple-use structure that solves two problems and makes both economically viable.

HUDDERSFIELD NARROW CANAL AND STANDEDGE TUNNEL

BRITAIN'S HIGHEST CANAL AND LONGEST CANAL TUNNEL

LOCATION STALYBRIDGE TO HUDDERSFIELD, UK
CONSTRUCTION DATES 1794–1811; REOPENED 2001

FOR 50 YEARS the Huddersfield Narrow Canal and Standedge Tunnel lay derelict. During that time it was often referred to as "the impossible restoration", a description that would be refuted when it reopened in 2001.

During the original build there were tremendous obstacles to overcome, even though the canal is only 32 km long. At its summit it is the highest navigable canal in Britain at 197 metres, meaning 74 locks had to be built. The toughest challenge was the Standedge Tunnel, which at nearly 5 km was the longest, deepest and highest canal tunnel in the country. Excavated by navvies using explosives, picks and shovels, the project was dangerous and there were problems with water seeping in and misalignment. As a result the canal took 17 years – instead of the anticipated five – to complete, almost bankrupting the canal company. When engineer Benjamin Outram resigned from the project in 1801, Thomas Telford took over to oversee its completion.

To save money the tunnel was built with no towpath. Horses were led over the top while barges were steered through it by "leggers" who propelled the boats by pushing their feet against the wall. As the tunnel was only two metres wide, boats could only pass each other at four passing points. This eventually led to a system whereby westbound and eastbound barges would take turns, using the tunnel for four hours each.

The Huddersfield Narrow Canal was designed for narrow boats, meaning cargo had to be transferred at each end. It proved useful until 1845, when the Huddersfield and Manchester Railway Company bought it as a means of moving waste from the construction of the railway that would signal its redundancy. After a slow decline, the canal closed in 1944.

In 1974 the Huddersfield Canal Society was formed with a view to reopening the canal. This was no mean feat as some sections had been filled in and even partly built on. Standedge Tunnel had been impassable for many years; 10,000 tons of silt and 3,000 tons of rock had to be removed. Some parts of the tunnel wall needed to be stabilised with rock bolts and some were lined with concrete. But with funding from various sources, the "impossible" restoration was achieved.

ICE 200

BANGKOK MASS TRANSIT SYSTEM

INCREASING PUBLIC TRANSPORT OPTIONS FOR 8 MILLION PEOPLE IN THE THAI CAPITAL

LOCATION BANGKOK, THAILAND
CONSTRUCTION DATES 1999–

BANGKOK HAS LONG suffered from the transport challenges that afflict many other big cities, particularly in Asia. Until 1999, Bangkok's commuters were reliant on just two public transport options. There were boat services, which still operate on the Chao Phraya river and on two canals, and buses which had replaced electric trams in 1968.

It was becoming clear that, by the end of the 1980s, this transport infrastructure was insufficient for a large and growing city of more than 8 million. To help address this challenge the Thai government's Ministry of Transport set up the Mass Rapid Transport Authority (MRTA) in 1992.

The first of the MRT (Mass Rapid Transport) lines was opened in July 2004. By 2018, the Blue Line (officially the Chaloem Ratchamongkhon Line) ran for 21 km across 19 stations, from Tao Poon Station in a southward arc along Ratchadaphisek Road. It terminated at Hua Lamphong, where it connects to the central railway station.

The Purple Line (officially the MRT Chalong Ratchadham Line) opened in August 2016, running for 23 km across 16 stations between Tao Poon (interchanging with the Blue Line) and Khlong Bang Phai.

The MRTA in 2018 is building several extensions, as well as four other lines – the Orange, Pink, Yellow and Brown lines. There is also a planned extension to the Blue Line, with two routes that will cross the Chao Phraya River. One line, running between Bang Sue, Bang Phlat and Tha Phra, is due to open in 2020, and two more – from Hua Lamphong to Lak Song, and from Lak Song to Phutthamonthon Sai 4 – are scheduled to open by 2019. A southern extension to the Purple Line is also due in 2023.

One of the biggest civil engineering challenges will be tunnelling under the Chao Phraya River, after which the line will surface and split, one section going along a viaduct further to the west and one section heading north.

A privately financed and operated elevated railway, BTS Skytrain, opened in 1999 and by 2018 was a 55 km elevated metro that runs across 25 stations.

In 2018, the MRT serves more than 410,000 passengers a day, and the Skytrain 698,009 giving a total metro patronage in Bangkok of 1.1 million passengers a day.

ICE 200
THIRD MAINLAND BRIDGE
FORMERLY THE LONGEST BRIDGE IN AFRICA

LOCATION LAGOS, NIGERIA
CONSTRUCTION DATES 1976–90

THE THIRD MAINLAND Bridge is one of three road bridges connecting the commercial district on Lagos Island to the mainland. At 11.8 km, it was the longest bridge in Africa until Cairo's 6th October Bridge opened in 1996.

During the 1970s the heavy traffic in Lagos – the population of which is now over 20 million – led to government directives limiting travel to alternate days for cars with odd- and even-numbered registration plates. The bridge was part of a motorway designed to ease transport both in the city and from the port.

The eight-lane bridge was built in two phases by Julius Berger Nigeria. The first, between Lagos Island and the Ebute Metta interchange, was constructed between 1976 and 1980. The second phase continued building northward to the coast at Oworosonki between 1988 and 1990. It was built as a series of 45-metre spans with reinforced and prestressed concrete deck sections on the piers and 42-metre-deep piled foundations.

The finished bridge was opened in 1980 by President Ibrahim Babangida. It succeeded in easing the traffic congestion but led to a housing boom, which has ironically resulted a very high volume of traffic on weekdays, when tailbacks often reach several kilometres. In 2016 the Lagos government agreed to begin construction on a 38 km fourth bridge to further relieve congestion and serve the rapidly growing industrial areas.

ICE 200
TRANSANDINE RAILWAY
ONCE THE SPEEDIEST UPHILL CLIMB IN SOUTH AMERICA

LOCATION ANDES, CHILE AND ARGENTINA
CONSTRUCTION DATES 1887–1910

THE CENTRAL TRANSANDINE Railway ran 148 km over the Andes between Chile and Argentina. Its hair-raising construction had to contend with steep inclines and narrow passages, mudslides and avalanches.

In 1874, the Clark brothers – Chilean entrepreneurs of British descent – won the concession to build the railway. After myriad financial and construction difficulties, work began in 1887. While there were higher railways in Peru and Bolivia, the Transandine's gradients to its 10,000-ft summit were steeper and called for a narrow gauge, rack-and-pinion railway for optimum traction.

The railway opened in sections between 1891 and 1910, by which time it was owned by the British Argentine Railway Company with Livesey and Henderson as consultants. It joined with four other railways to complete a 1,408 km rail link between ports on the Pacific and Atlantic oceans, at Buenos Aires and Valparaiso. The route involved two changes of train where the rail gauge differed. It was far from straightforward; but a journey that had taken 11 days by ship was reduced to 36 hours by train.

The railway was never a commercial success, however. Its trains were lightweight, held limited cargo and moved slowly with frequent derailments and delays. The Transandine was closed in 1984 and partly dismantled. Despite the Chilean and Argentine governments' talk of restoration, little progress has been made.

ICE 200
SZÉCHENYI CHAIN BRIDGE
THE BRIDGE THAT UNITED A CITY

LOCATION BUDAPEST, HUNGARY
CONSTRUCTION DATES 1840–49

IN 1832, THE Hungarian statesman and reformer Count István Széchenyi and a fellow aristocrat visited London to inspect British engineering and get ideas for a permanent bridge over the icebound Danube, connecting the towns of Buda and Pest both physically and symbolically. On examining Hammersmith Bridge, he remarked on "the astounding appearance of the structure". "The ideal and airy form in which it presents itself," his besotted report said, "tends to overwhelm the senses and to deprive man of his judgement."

The two counts arranged to meet its engineer, William Tierney Clark, who agreed to design a similar bridge over the Danube on a much larger scale (380 metres long). Tierney Clark's innovative designs suspended flat chains from neoclassical stone arches to support the carriage deck. One advantage to building such a suspension bridge over the Danube was that it only required two piers to be built in the riverbed: one 60 metres tall (towards Buda) and the other 55 metres tall (towards Pest).

The critical iron elements of the Danube Bridge (renamed the Széchenyi Chain Bridge in 1899) were manufactured in England and carried on barges to the site. British workmen and supervisors were engaged in all aspects of the construction, and some of them settled in Hungary. The biggest engineering challenge the project presented was building the piers in an icebound river. George Burge of Herne Bay was contracted to build gigantic cofferdams to keep the water at bay and to withstand the buffeting of ice sheets. In 1848, when the first chains were being raised, a link broke. Four hundred tons of iron crashed into the river, almost killing Count Széchenyi.

Opened in 1849, it was the first permanent bridge down the Danube since ancient times, having survived heavy bombardment during 1848's Hungarian Revolution, thanks partly to the ingenuity of Scottish superintendent engineer Adam Clark (no relation). The original piers and arches have since supported two rebuilds, in 1915 and again in 1949, after it was blown up during World War II.

Today, the enduring image of the bridge built with British expertise appears on every Hungarian passport. And each year, Hungary commemorates its favourite British designer with the Tierney Clark Award for Civil Engineering, presented by the Association of Hungarian Consulting Engineers and Architects (the Hungarian equivalent of ICE). In 2014, bronze plaques were erected in memory of William Tierney Clark on the actual bridge and in Hammersmith.

HARLAND AND WOLFF BUILDING DOCK
BELFAST'S GIANT DRY DOCK

LOCATION BELFAST, NORTHERN IRELAND, UK
CONSTRUCTION DATES 1968–70

IN AUGUST 1967 Messrs Harland and Wolff received an order for two 250,000 tonne supertankers. Boldly, the directors commissioned a feasibility study for a new building dock capable of building 1,000,000 tonne ships from consulting engineers Babtie, Shaw and Morton who recommended a dry dock 556 metres long, 93 metres wide and 11.6 metres deep, the largest in the world. By comparison, the Thompson, or Titanic Dock (in 1911 the world's largest), is 259 metres long, 39 metres wide and 10.7 metres deep. A dry dock enables a ship to be built in the dry and then floated out, or enables ships to be floated in for repairs or painting in a dry environment.

It was reasoned that the provision of a new large dry dock would secure the future of shipbuilding and repair in the port of Belfast, supporting a significant workforce and underpinning the economic viability of Northern Ireland.

In the new dock an intermediate gate was provided so that the next ship could be commenced at the head of the dock while the seaward end of the dock was flooded to release the preceding completed hull. Two main pumps can dewater the entire dock in an overnight shift of 12 hours.

When constructed an 840-tonne capacity travelling portal crane straddled the dock. It spans 140 metres and is 92 metres above the dock floor. Two 60-tonne capacity cranes service each side of the dock.

The project was fast-track designed by Babtie, and George Wimpey & Co was appointed contractor in February 1968. The first tanker was begun in the part-completed dock in spring 1969 and construction was sufficiently advanced to allow its float-out as planned in late 1969, a phenomenal achievement. A second portal crane was added soon afterwards. The two cranes which dominate the east Belfast skyline are known as Samson and Goliath.

Due to foreign competition shipbuilding is now uneconomic in Belfast but Harland and Wolff still use their Building Dock today to construct heavy structures for offshore wind farms and execute oil and gas projects from global clients. Whilst the two Harland and Wolff dry docks remain operational in the port of Belfast, others such as the Alexandra and Hamilton dry docks and the Titanic Quarter have become part of the city's burgeoning tourist industry.

SYDNEY HARBOUR BRIDGE

AN AUSSIE ICON AND THE WORLD'S TALLEST STEEL-ARCH BRIDGE

LOCATION SYDNEY, AUSTRALIA
CONSTRUCTION DATES 1923–32

AN INSTANTLY RECOGNISABLE national symbol, Sydney Harbour Bridge must be one of the most photographed bridges in the world. Nicknamed the coat hanger for its dramatic arch-shaped design, it carries road, rail, cyclists and pedestrians and – at 134 metres from top to water level – is the tallest steel-arch bridge on earth. With a span of 504 metres, it was the second longest-spanning arch bridge in the world when built. Its width of 48.8 metres made it the world's widest long-span bridge until overtaken by Vancouver's Port Mann Bridge in 2012.

Before the bridge was built, passengers travelled across the harbour by ferry, with an astonishing 75 ferries an hour carrying passengers between the north and south sides of the harbour. This could be a hazardous crossing, and a bridge was initially proposed in 1815. It was not until 1914 that Dr John Bradfield was appointed chief engineer of Sydney Harbour Bridge and Metropolitan Railway Construction. Bradfield favoured a cantilever bridge but work was cancelled due to the First World War. After the war, Bradfield travelled overseas and on his return put forward an arch bridge design based on New York's Hell Gate Bridge, the same bridge that inspired the Tyne Bridge linking Newcastle and Gateshead.

The Australian government invited tenders and received 26 designs from six companies. The winning design was an arch bridge by Dorman Long that would be cheaper and more sturdy than a cantilever or suspension bridge. Under the direction of Bradfield and the New South Wales Department of Public Works, the bridge was built by Dorman Long and Co Ltd of Middlesbrough, with Ralph Freeman (the English engineer who also designed the Victoria Falls Bridge in Zambia) and GC Imbault of Douglas

Fox & Partners as design consultants. ICE's first woman corporate member Dorothy Buchanan was also involved in Dorman Long's design office.

The bridge used 53,000 tonnes of steel, nearly all of it from Britain, and is held together by six million Australian-made hand-driven rivets. At each end of the arch stands a pair of 89-metre-high concrete pylons, faced with granite. These were not in the original design and do not affect the structure of the bridge, but they reassured the public of the strength of the bridge and complemented the design.

The opening on 19 March 1932 attracted nearly a million people but did not go without a hitch. Just as the New South Wales premier Jack Lang was about to cut the ribbon, Captain Francis de Groot – a member of a loyalist, ultra-conservative paramilitary organisation called the New Guard – arrived on horseback and slashed the ribbon with his sword. He believed that a member of the royal family should have opened the bridge.

The bridge cost 6.25 million Australian pounds, one of the most costly civil engineering projects at that time, and was not paid off in full until 1988. However, not only did it help to expand Sydney north of the harbour, but it also provided a lifeline to some 1,400 construction workers who worked on the bridge during the Great Depression, earning the project its nickname "the iron lung". Tragically, 16 of them were killed in accidents during construction.

Painting the bridge has become an endless task. Approximately 80,000 litres of paint are required for each coat, enough to cover an area equivalent to 60 soccer fields. Before the comedian Paul Hogan became famous as the star of *Crocodile Dundee*, he worked on the bridge as a rigger.

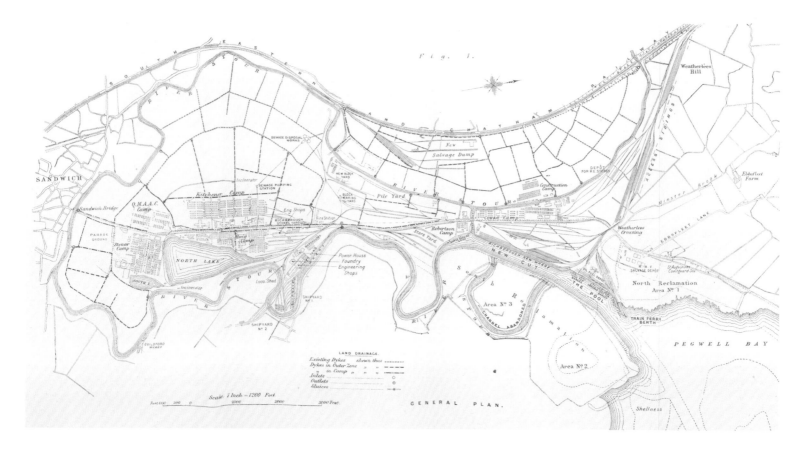

RICHBOROUGH PORT

A SECRET PORT BUILT TO SERVE IN THE FIRST WORLD WAR

LOCATION SANDWICH HAVEN, KENT, UK
CONSTRUCTION DATES 1916–19

IN ANCIENT TIMES, Sandwich Haven was the most significant port in England. Although 19th-century ships of 300 tons were able to anchor there, the site was not fully developed until the outbreak of the First World War.

When the French railway and seaports became overburdened, the British Army set out to create a secret barge service across the Channel using the French canals to reach forward battle areas. Since Dover was at capacity, Richborough Port at Sandwich Haven was chosen as the site from which to build and launch the required fleet.

Work began in June 1916 and the first barge entered service in September. The existing wharf had only 258 feet of river frontage, so plans were made to build a much larger wharf nearer the river mouth. These involved an innovative form of construction not previously used on large works: 40-foot steel sheet-piles in 15-inch-wide sections were driven into dry land and the channel was cut in front of it afterwards. By the Armistice, 24 slipways were in production and 230 barges were in service. The barges had carried 1.8 million tons of freight without

a single loss to enemy action. The workforce also built cranes, gun emplacements and railway wagons.

Richborough Port also pioneered the use of a train-ferry as a solution to the challenge of transporting very heavy loads such as tanks with a minimum of personnel. A berth was constructed using sheet-piles to form a U-shaped basin into which the ship's stern would fit exactly. Three 363-foot train-ferries were designed, built and in service by February 1918.

At the end of the war, tons of freight were returned to England using the train-ferry, but the service declined completely by 1922. The ships were sold and used for freight from Harwich to Zeebrugge until 1987. Richborough was used for military purposes again towards the end of the Second World War, when the Royal Engineers returned to make components for the Mulberry Harbours for D-Day.

Although the port was short-lived, it made a significant contribution to the war effort and demonstrated what civil engineers can achieve in a real emergency.

ICE 200
COLOMBO HARBOUR
ONE OF THE WORLD'S BUSIEST PORTS

LOCATION COLOMBO, SRI LANKA
CONSTRUCTION DATES 1873–85; 2011– (SOUTH CONTAINER TERMINAL)

COLOMBO HARBOUR IS one of the busiest ports in the world and has one of the largest artificial harbours. Due to its position on the Indian Ocean it has a long history as a military and trading base.

In the 19th century, Sir John Coode designed a 1.5km-long breakwater enclosing a 502-acre harbour. It was built between 1875 and 1885 using stone from a quarry at Mahara, 11 miles away. More than 100 tons of rubble were transported daily to Colombo by rail, and a Titan overhead crane placed almost a thousand masonry blocks, each weighing up to 31 tons, to create the breakwater.

By 1882, the advantages of a sheltered harbour were becoming apparent and P&O moved its Royal Mail steamships to Colombo from their southern base at Galle. Over the next six years, the value of shipping using Colombo Harbour increased by 60 per cent; and it continued to grow steadily during the 20th century.

After the country gained independence in 1948, the port was extended. Queen Elizabeth Quay opened in 1954, adding 16 berths and more sheds and warehouses. The Sri Lanka Ports Authority was formed in 1980 and

the harbour was modernised to handle containerised cargo. By 2000, five new container terminals had been built and the main channel deepened to 15 metres to allow larger vessels to use the port. But the government was already thinking in terms of future expansion.

By 2005, the port was again reaching capacity and the 12-metre-deep harbour was proving too shallow for larger ships. Deepening the harbour would require major dredging. If Sri Lanka was to remain a premier port in South Asia, a new terminal with deeper berths and the latest equipment would be required. That year, the construction of a new, 5km-long breakwater started, within which the terminals were to be developed.

In 2011, construction began on the new South Container Terminal, kick-starting an expansion project that will take 35 years to complete. The first phase includes a 1.2 km-long container quay with nine berths and a new breakwater of nearly 7 km. The harbour is 18 metres deep but designed to be deepened to 22 metres. The material removed by dredging has been used to reclaim land next to the terminal, and a planned second phase will add three more berths and a new terminal.

ICE 200

ICE PRESIDENT'S APPRENTICES/ FUTURE LEADERS

INJECTING YOUNG LIFE INTO THE INSTITUTION

———————

LOCATION LONDON, UK
ESTABLISHED 2005

ICE PRESIDENT'S APPRENTICES programme, now known as the President's Future Leaders, began in 2005. Initially, the inspiration for President Gordon Masterton was the BBC series *The Apprentice* – but with the emphasis on "you're hired" rather than "you're fired". He wanted to bring the perspective of young engineers to the institution, giving a small group of graduates a place at the heart of the profession. While Masterton mentored each of them, he maintains that they guided him in return. It has clearly worked. All of the presidents who have succeeded Masterton have, in turn, selected their own "apprentices" and set them challenges to help develop the institution.

"When we started the scheme, one of the great attractions to me was that it was a bit edgy, a bit radical, to have a group of young people placed so close to the president, with influence," says Masterton. "I liked the informality of it." Thirteen presidents so far – and 102 young engineers – have taken on a wide variety of challenges. There has been research for ICE State of the Nation reports and policy initiatives, promoting UN Sustainable Development Goals, creating an ethics toolkit and a toolkit for international development. There's been a review of innovation in the industry and more recent campaigns to promote digital engineering; the Create Sport Challenge for schools in the run up to the London Olympics; competitions to generate images and videos to celebrate civil engineering; and the Pitch 200 competition to encourage engineers to speak to the public in more interesting ways. And that's just the start.

"Thanks to the outstanding qualities of that first group of seven," says Masterton, "and how they responded to my challenges, and then to all the subsequent Apprentices and Future Leaders, value has been added to the institution in increasingly imaginative ways. They have exceeded my hopes and expectations, many times over."

Many apprentices continue to be actively involved with the institution after their first year – joining ICE panels or being elected to Council. One, Molly McKenzie, is now an ICE Regional Director. ICE looks forward to seeing one of them become a future president in due course. Most continue their engineering careers in a variety of ways: international development, research, contracting, consulting, in government or its agencies. Others branch out and apply their insights in new directions: for example, one now advises governments and industry on future skills needs; another turned his project into a new career by moving into human resources to improve diversity in the industry. And, to celebrate the fact that civil engineers change the world, Brittany Harris appears in the ICE200 "Invisible Superheroes" exhibition in 2018: ICE's very own Water Woman!

Today the scheme is a fantastic opportunity for up-and-coming engineers and technicians to boost their career by learning from industry leaders. It is open to enthusiastic, articulate and capable graduate and technician members who have the confidence to challenge the status quo. It typically involves 15 days out of the office, so each candidate needs their employer's full support when applying. In return, ICE helps to accelerate their development by offering experiences that normally come much later in life – if ever.

One President's Apprentice of 2013–14, Sakthy Selvakumaran, explains. "In my year, we worked on the theme of 'communications and engagement', helping to organise a video competition to inspire the next generation and setting up the Construkt Youth scheme to give hands-on employability training to disadvantaged young people," she says. "I'm still involved with ICE – helping with policy blogs, inspiring the next generation and understanding civil engineers' involvement in international development – and keep in regular touch with my apprentice group (including former President Geoff French). They form a great sounding board, support and encouragement, and a good excuse for a social occasion! The year was a unique learning experience, which has stayed with me long term."

Future Leaders see the president throughout their year, in a variety of different forums: stakeholder meetings, regional visits, project feedback sessions, mentoring sessions. They also engage with ICE divisions on projects and in workshops to gain a practical insight into public affairs, the creation and sharing of knowledge, and campaigns to inspire the public. The scheme lasts for a minimum of one year but with the option to continue working on ICE projects until becoming professionally qualified. They become part of the Presidents' Future Leaders alumni network from the moment they join – and therefore can draw on the experience and expertise of a network of similarly motivated engineers.

In ICE's 200th anniversary year, it is striking that the success of the scheme has parallels in the early years of the institution. The first association for civil engineers in Britain, the Society of Civil Engineers – today known as the Smeatonian Society – was established in 1771. It flourished as a select dining and networking group but did not provide a voice or even a seat for young engineers. Seeing a need to share ideas and experience, a group of younger engineers began to demand a better forum to aid their profession and the Institution of Civil Engineers was formed in 1818.

The fledgling institution struggled to attract new members until Thomas Telford, the leading civil engineer of the day, became its first president. ICE has not looked back since. It is a reminder that any healthy and vibrant membership body needs the vitality of youth as well as experience and connections. The President's Future Leaders scheme shows that that view remains at the heart of the institution in the 21st century.

PORT OF DOVER

THE CREATION OF EUROPE'S BUSIEST FERRY PORT

LOCATION DOVER, UK
DATES FROM 43 AD

THE PORT OF Dover has a 2,000-year history, dating from the earliest moorings on the banks of the River Dour, overlooked by the Roman Pharos. It was important enough to have been established as one of the five Cinque Ports, although the first recorded pier was not built until 1495.

Following the Napoleonic wars, pressure grew to create a "harbour of refuge" in East Kent to provide shelter from storms in the English Channel that caused hundreds of ships to be stranded or wrecked every year, and numerous eminent civil engineers devised a range of schemes. Meanwhile, 1844 saw the arrival of the South Eastern Railway in Dover which further boosted the established packet-boat services to France.

Work started on a western pier in 1847 under the supervision of James Walker as the first part of an Admiralty Harbour. Further stages were completed after his death, and the first trains used the pier in 1861. The Admiralty Pier was completed in 1875, and a second major pier was designed by Sir John Coode and built by the London firm of (Sir) John Jackson before opening by the Prince of Wales in 1902. The Admiralty Harbour scheme was finally completed in 1909 by construction of the

Eastern Pier, Southern Breakwater and Admiralty Pier extension, designed by Coode, Son & Matthews and constructed by S Pearson & Son. The main elements were Grade II listed in 2009.

Captain Stuart Townsend started a car ferry service in July 1928, with vehicles being loaded and unloaded by crane. A train-ferry dock was put into operation in 1936, and a roll-on/roll-off car ferry terminal was opened in the Eastern Docks in 1953. Hovercraft services began in 1968 before moving to a purpose-built hoverport beside the Prince of Wales Pier between 1978 and 2000. Jetfoil and Seacat services were also operated from the Western Docks for a time.

Following the closure of Dover Western Docks railway station in 1994, the Grade II-listed building was converted into a cruise terminal, and this successful new facility was later extended by conversion of the nearby former train-ferry dock. The original harbour now forms Dover Marina, and in 2018 the Dover Western Docks Revival Project commenced to regenerate the former hoverport area. Despite the Channel Tunnel opening in 1994, Dover remains Europe's busiest ferry port.

DUBAI DRY DOCKS

THE LARGEST DEEPWATER FACILITY IN THE MIDDLE EAST

LOCATION PORT RASHID, DUBAI, UAE
CONSTRUCTION DATE 1978

WITH THE MIDDLE East oil industry expanding rapidly in the 1970s, the late ruler of Dubai, His Highness Sheikh Rashid bin Said Al Maktoum, recognised an opportunity to build a dry dock that could support, clean and repair the enormous oil tankers in the region, and Dubai was an ideal location. There was little available ground near Port Rashid, so the Dubai Dry Docks were built out into the sea, with the dock walls created from 163 concrete caissons, each 31 metres long and weighing 3,500 tonnes. Allowances had to be made for the position of the caissons, which resulted in 39 slightly varying designs.

The caissons were filled with wet sand, which the engineers discovered was liable to settle if they suffered a shock. They therefore had to develop a method of compacting the sand, forcing out the water, without causing too much stress to the caisson. This was achieved by inserting and removing a vibrating hollow steel tube rod.

For flexibility, tall pedestal cranes were installed rather than the more usual straddling Goliath cranes. The width of the piers and location of the crane tracks were designed to allow each of the five cranes to serve two docks.

The engineers of the project were Sir William Halcrow and Partners and the contractors were a joint venture of Costain and Taylor Woodrow. More than 10,500 drawings were needed to design the Dubai Dry Docks complex, which cost £232 million.

The shipyard is the largest deepwater facility in the Middle East and handles on average 350 vessels in a year, most of them very large (or "ultra-large") crude carriers. Since it opened in 1978, the shipyard has repaired over 7,500 vessels and several of the world's largest dredgers are serviced every year. In the 1990s, it began building ships and converting tankers for offshore oil storage.

The dry dock facility is also being used currently to build a high-voltage direct current (HVDC) converter platform that will be used to transmit electricity from offshore wind farms in the North Sea to the mainland of Germany. This will be shipped and installed nearly 100 km off the German coast at a water depth of approximately 40 metres. By 2019, this renewable offshore resource should transmit around 900 megawatts of wind power – the approximate annual electricity consumption of a million German households.

ICE 200
RIDEAU CANAL
A TRIUMPH OF ADAPTIVE ENGINEERING

LOCATION ONTARIO, CANADA
CONSTRUCTION DATES 1826–32

IN 1826, A mammoth engineering project to build a canal through 200 km of Canadian wilderness was begun. The British government funded it in order to provide a safe military supply route from the Ottawa River to the British naval base in Kingston, Ontario. Lieutenant Colonel John By of the Royal Engineers was appointed superintending engineer. The Royal Engineers designed and oversaw the build, with civilian contractors carrying out the work.

John By was a visionary. Although steam-powered boats were only just coming into use, he proposed building a steamboat canal. He decided to construct a slack-water canal, building dams to drown rapids rather than excavating canal cuts around those rapids. Unlike an engineering project today, detailed information was scarce. Survey parties were still working out what to do at various locations in 1827. At Smiths Falls, one of the engineers observed that providing navigation through the area "seems rather a puzzler".

The work was done manually, with the aid of draft animals, using locally sourced stone and wood. Working conditions were challenging: disease was the main problem – including a temperate form of malaria – with many men, women and children dying during the project.

Building the Rideau Canal is a classic example of adaptive engineering. Almost every one of John By's original plans had to be changed in response to the conditions he encountered. All his dams were originally proposed as overflow dams, but By's experience in 1827, with spring flooding on the Rideau route, quickly convinced him that weirs would be needed to provide water control at every lock station.

The Jones Fall dam is a particularly fine example of a masonry arch dam of its time. Less successful was the dam at Hog's Back Falls. It was washed away three times during construction. The adaptive engineering solution in this case was to abandon the stone-arch idea and build a stone-filled timber crib dam in its place.

The canal opened in the spring of 1832 with 47 masonry locks and 52 dams providing a navigation way between Ottawa and Kingston, one that can still be travelled today. In 2007, the Rideau Canal was recognised as a UNESCO World Heritage Site, partly because most of its original structures had survived, but also because of the sheer scale of John By's slack-water design.

ICE 200
WATERLOO STATION
THE ORIGINS OF EUROPE'S BUSIEST STATION

LOCATION LONDON, UK
DATE 1848

LONDON WATERLOO IS Britain's largest and busiest station, with 250,000 people using it every day to commute between London, Surrey, and the south and south-west of England. Indeed, when combined with Waterloo East and Waterloo tube station, it is the busiest station complex in Europe.

It was opened in 1848 as Waterloo Bridge station, when London & South Western Railway engineer Joseph Locke extended the line from its original Nine Elms terminus to the southern end of Waterloo Bridge to be closer to central London. Growth in passenger numbers associated with new suburban lines and routes into Devon and Cornwall led to a somewhat haphazard station development in the second half of the 19th century.

The L&SWR consultant WR Galbraith seized the potential of the new electric tube technology to address the inconvenience of the station's location by providing underground connections to the City via the Waterloo and City Line (1898) and to the West End by the Bakerloo and what is now part of the Northern Line (1906). The main-line station was completely rebuilt although some parts of the brick arch undercroft survive. Under L&SWR engineer Gilbert Szlumper, it became arguably the

best designed London terminus by 1922 with a concourse nearly 800 feet long. The station was also the key embarkation point for thousands of British soldiers in the Great War and also got an impressive new entrance, the Victory Arch.

In 1993 Waterloo became the terminus for Eurostar services to mainland Europe. Engineer Anthony Hunt, in close collaboration with architect Nicholas Grimshaw, designed an elegant sweeping curved industrial roof. The section closed in 2007 when Eurostar moved to St Pancras station, leaving five platforms unused for many years. In 2015, the Wessex Capacity Alliance – with consultants from AECOM, Colas Rail, Skanska and Mott MacDonald – started a mammoth project to increase the capacity of the station by 30 per cent during peak hours, and these five international platforms will be put back into use.

The project has also lengthened and modified platforms 1 to 9: significant realignment and signalling work has been completed to allow longer ten-car trains to use the platforms. Once completed, the 24 platforms of Waterloo will have a total length of over 5 km.

DEVONPORT ROYAL DOCKYARD

THE FIRST STEPPED STONE DOCK IN EUROPE

LOCATION PLYMOUTH, UK
CONSTRUCTION DATES 1692–2017

DEVONPORT ROYAL DOCKYARD has been in existence for 325 years. During this time, it has experienced a process of almost continuous transformation as it has adapted to the changing requirements of the Royal Navy.

The dockyard was established in 1692. The arrival of William of Orange in Britain three years earlier had removed the Dutch naval threat in the east; but then the Admiralty moved its focus to confronting France and Spain in the west. It needed to set up a permanent base in the west and tasked Edmund Dummer, Surveyor of the Navy, with finding a site and developing a dockyard.

Dummer had previously travelled the Mediterranean and researched naval facilities in his role as a midshipman extraordinary. He brought this experience to bear in finding a location and chose an inlet on the Hamoaze, a stretch in the Tamar Estuary. He built a yard comprising a dry dock, storehouse, hemp house, rope house, rope-yard buildings and officers' houses. He hoped the layout would eliminate the "great abuses committed in their Majesties' yards". These included "the tedious and expensive practices of carrying all things afloat for expediting of ship works, and which are many times very remote from the places where materials are kept, and workmen resort".

The layout of the yard was not the only revolutionary aspect of the facility; the dock was the first stepped stone dock built in Europe. Previous docks had been built largely from timber, which resulted in high maintenance costs and severe fire risk. The stepped construction reduced the amount of shoring needed and gave better access to the hull for the shipwrights.

The development of steam engines in the 19th century again put Devonport at the forefront of innovation. The existing dockyard facilities had run out of space as the town had expanded and encroached upon it. A new facility, the Keyham Steam Yard, was constructed further up the river for building and maintaining steamships. The yard was centred around an integrated factory, the largest of its kind anywhere at the time.

Warship design developed rapidly in the late 19th century, culminating in the first battleships. Accommodating these large ships resulted in the largest civil engineering project carried out at Devonport: the construction of the Prince of Wales Basin, which enclosed 35 hectares of water with four large docks. The basin was built out into the river and required a cofferdam more than 2 km long to enclose the site.

Although this was the last expansion of the dockyard, changes in naval technology have seen continued transformation of the site. One of the large docks was widened from 1938 to 1940 to take new aircraft carriers; and in the 1970s three docks were enlarged and covered to accommodate modern frigates. From the 1970s onwards, Devonport has had an increasing emphasis on refitting nuclear submarines and is now the only British facility for this purpose. Two new submarine docks and nuclear workshops were constructed in the 1970s, followed by the conversion of a third dock and the addition of more nuclear workshops and stores between 1997 and 2002. These new facilities have all been designed to resist large earthquakes, the only ones in British maritime construction. The introduction of future classes of ships and submarines will see further transformation of these facilities.

ROSYTH NAVAL DOCKYARD

SERVING THE ROYAL NAVY SINCE THE FIRST WORLD WAR

LOCATION ROSYTH, SCOTLAND, UK
CONSTRUCTION DATES 1909–15

"ROSYTH IS UNIQUE as an example of a modern naval port brought to virtual completion under the stress of war," says a 1926 paper for ICE. The decision was made in 1903 to build a large Royal Dockyard on the Firth of Forth to support and repair warships based in Scapa Flow, protecting the entrance to the North Sea from the German navy. Civil engineers Easton, Gibb & Son began construction in 1909 and the dockyard was due to be completed in 1916.

Construction was complicated by the geology, including the rocky island of Dhu Craig, which needed a channel blasted through it. Also varying levels of sand covering the more stable boulder clay meant that the engineers had to sink 120 concrete monoliths or posts through the sand to support the dock walls above.

At the start of the First World War in 1914 the dockyard was two thirds complete but no part was ready to accept ships. The submarine dock was opened in September 1914 but the struggle to supply both labour and materials made conditions difficult. The government decided that, rather than complete the whole project, the emphasis should be

on making the graving docks and basin available for use as soon as possible. The dockyard officially opened a year later in 1915.

HM Rosyth was equipped with three graving or dry docks and was designed to repair rather than build ships. It played a major part in ship refurbishment during the war, with the first ship HMS *Zealandia* arriving in 1916. Other ships that docked at Rosyth include the battleship HMS *Dreadnought*.

For more than 80 years, the site continued to operate as an HM dockyard, being re-equipped to refit the Polaris nuclear submarines in the 1960s. It was the first Royal Navy dockyard to be privatised in 1997 when it was sold to Babcock International. Rosyth also played a central role in the assembly of the Queen Elizabeth Class Aircraft Carriers – the centrepiece of Britain's defence capability for the 21st century.

Rosyth has long been the largest facility used by the Royal Navy outside southern England and is still one of the UK's largest waterside manufacturing and repair facilities, employing 6,000 people at its height, including many civilian workers.

KING GEORGE V DOCK AND LONDON CITY AIRPORT

HOW ONE INNOVATIVE STRUCTURE WAS RECYCLED INTO ANOTHER

LOCATION EAST LONDON, UK
CONSTRUCTION DATES 1911–21; 1986–87

WITH THE FORMATION of the Port of London Authority in 1909, new works were planned by its engineer, Frederick Palmer. Detailed design for the King George V Dock at North Woolwich – the last of the three Royal Docks – began in 1911. The First World War delayed progress and the dock was not opened until July 1921. It consisted of a wet dock (11.6 metres deep and covering 64 acres), a dry dock, an Arrol steel lattice swing bridge operated by hydraulic power, a double-leaf bascule bridge, three miles of new road, 11 miles of new railway track, and access to the River Thames and the existing Albert Dock.

The construction called for the excavation of gravel formed by the river over millions of years. Contractor S Pearson & Son recycled this and used it for aggregate to make the concrete behind the dock walls. The dock's entrance lock was revolutionary: at 244 metres, long enough to accommodate the largest ocean-going ships of the day.

The Royal Docks became less economically viable with the growth of container cargo from the 1960s and closed to commercial traffic in 1981. But that same year, the London Docklands Development Corporation was created and discussed the idea for an airport with Mowlem Engineering. The plan was to build a 1,080-metre length runway on the central wharf between the King George V Dock and Albert Dock, something that would provide the basis for an airport that would become a convenient transport hub for the financial industry. Construction started in May 1986 and the first commercial flight took off in October 1987. By 2008, London City Airport was serving 3.3 million passengers a year.

Since the airport opened, civil engineers have added further infrastructure to support economic growth. The runway was lengthened to 1,508 metres in 1992. In 2005 the Docklands Light Railway airport extension brought links to the City and Canary Wharf. Work is continuing to extend the terminal, the airport apron and aircraft facilities including a new taxiway alongside the runway to avoid the need for aircraft to backtrack on the runway. This will enable a rise from 70,000 to 100,000 movements and a rise from the current 4.5 million passengers annually to six million by 2021.

HUMBER PORTS

THE MAKING OF ONE OF BRITAIN'S
BIGGEST PORTS

––––––––

LOCATION HUMBERSIDE, UK
CONSTRUCTION DATES 1778–

THE PORTS OF the Humber today consist of Hull, Goole, Grimsby and Immingham. Between them they handled more than 65 million tonnes of cargo in 2017, with more ship movements than ever before. Immingham is the UK's busiest port by volume, while Goole is the entrance to Yorkshire's navigable waterways.

The sea has played a vital part in Britain's trading history, and the coast around the Humber provides a perfect illustration. There is evidence of activity since the Romans fortified the area to protect their navigation routes to Eboracum, modern-day York. The earliest surviving records of navigation channels in the Estuary are found on charts of 1560 and the route then was as challenging as it is now. Its shallow banks, curving deep channel and fast-moving tides make this one of the most difficult locations to navigate a ship safely, let alone build a port.

Major port construction, based on North Sea trade, started in the 1770s with the building of Hull (Old) Dock, designed by John Grundy Jnr. The dock was built out of local brick, but the cement had to be waterproof. To achieve this, pozzolana (a material made from volcanic ash) was imported from Italy. Dock construction was not easy. Poor ground conditions led to early failures of the wall before the dock was fully opened. Deeper piles and thicker walls were added retrospectively. The dock was at the cutting edge of knowledge at the time, and the early engineers had to learn fast and change the design as they went along.

The dock was an immediate success, and further docks were built by ICE President James Walker in the early 19th century. A substantial railway network was later built to serve the growing port, and new docks followed. On the south bank of the estuary, Jonathan Pickernell and John Rennie designed a rival port at Grimsby around 1800. Poor management hampered its growth, but it became one of the leading fishing ports in the country with the advent of the railways in the late 1840s. A dock was designed by James Meadows Rendel, fitted with the latest hydraulic machinery, connected to the Manchester, Sheffield and Lincolnshire Railway. The need for further capacity led to the design of Immingham Docks by Sir John Wolfe Barry in the early 20th century.

The ports suffered decline following war damage and changes in trade patterns, compounded in Grimsby's case by changes in the fishing industry. However, since the 1970s things began to change, with increased trade with Europe. Volumes have steadily increased and large-scale investment in oil, gas, bulk transports and car movements has turned the area around.

The latest major investment at Hull, with Siemens, is worth £310 million and will create a new wind turbine factory at Alexandra Dock. In order to get the space for the factory, old docks had to be filled in. The shifting sands of the bay meant settlement in the port was as high as 20 per cent, almost impossible to build on. Deep concrete piles hold the buildings up now, harking back to the early days of Hull Dock when massive timber piles were hammered deep into the ground.

2017 saw over 32,000 movements on the estuary and this is set to grow. The challenge faced by engineers in developing the estuary for bigger ships and more ship movements will keep them busy for many generations.

ICE 200

KANSAI INTERNATIONAL AIRPORT

AN AIRPORT BUILT ON AN ARTIFICIAL ISLAND

LOCATION OSAKA BAY, JAPAN
CONSTRUCTION DATES 1987–94

ONE OF THE world's most advanced airports, Kansai International Airport is built on an artificial island south of Osaka, Japan. Although other man-made islands had been built in the bay, this was to be 5 km off the coast where the water was more than 18 metres deep.

The sea bed is on alluvial clay and as weight was added the clay would slowly shrink as the water was squeezed out. It was estimated that the seabed would sink 5.5 metres because of the weight of the island. If this was left to happen naturally it would have delayed the project, so nearly a million sand drains, or vertical columns of sand, were installed to accelerate the settlement by allowing the water in the clay to be squeezed out more rapidly.

Despite the sand drains, the clay had not completely consolidated or settled when building began. The settlement of the alluvial layer (from the Holocene era) was completed during the construction period. However, there is an older layer under this, from the Pleistocene era, which is deep and difficult to improve technically, and it was predicted that the settlement of this Pleistocene clay would continue. A jackup

system was designed to maintain the building's level as the deep clay layer consolidated. A floating mat foundation structure was used to compensate for any settlement of recently reclaimed land.

The impressive first terminal building, nearly 1.6 km long, was designed by Renzo Piano, with Ove Arup and Partners as structural engineers. The roof is curved to avoid blocking the view from the control. As curved elements often cost more, the roof was designed by rotating a flat shape: a two-dimensional reference curve was moved horizontally for the main terminal building and, for the wings, was rotated along a circle with a radius of 16.8 km to draw a toroidal curve, allowing the cladding and other components to be a constant shape throughout the length of the building.

Like all buildings in Japan's earthquake zone, Kansai was designed to meet strict safety standards, and survived earthquakes in 1995 and 2011. A second runway was added on a separate man-made island in 2007. A new terminal opened in 2012. In 2001, the American Society of Civil Engineers cited Kansai International Airport as one of ten structures awarded "Civil Engineering Monument of the Millennium".

BAHIA AND SAN FRANCISCO RAILWAY

BRITISH ENGINEERING NOUS IN BRAZIL

LOCATION BAHIA, BRAZIL
CONSTRUCTION DATES 1858–63

THE 75-MILE-LONG BAHIA and San Francisco Railway – one of the first railways to be built in Brazil – was the first stage of a 360-mile railway connecting the city of Salvador, Bahia with the river São Francisco in the interior of the country.

In 1853, the British engineer Charles Blacker Vignoles was approached by a Brazilian businessman about a railway, and in October 1854, CB Vignoles sent his son, Hutton Vignoles, on the three-week voyage from England to Bahia to investigate the best route and provide the necessary mapping. The design and specification was prepared in London by CB Vignoles as Chief Engineer to the BSFR company, and the £1.8 million concession was signed with the Brazilian government in May 1856.

The construction commenced in September 1858 and was completed in January 1863, with Hutton Vignoles operating as Resident Engineer in Bahia. The contract was undertaken by John Watson, a colleague of CB Vignoles, employing a core of experienced British and Italian workers supplemented by local labour. The necessary construction material was sent by steamer from England, and an English photographer, Ben R Mulock, recorded the works progress.

The remaining 283-mile section to the River São Francisco was constructed by Brazilian engineers between 1875 and 1896. The original BSFR remained under British management until 1901, when it was taken over by the Brazilian government.

PORT OF FELIXSTOWE

BRITAIN'S BUSIEST AND MOST ECO-FRIENDLY PORT

LOCATION FELIXSTOWE, SUFFOLK, UK
CONSTRUCTION DATES 1886 (OPENED); 1967–2009 (ADDITIONAL TERMINALS)

THE PORT OF Felixstowe is Britain's largest and busiest container port, dealing with 42 per cent of its containerised trade. Although a small dock was built in 1886, it was the building of the Landguard Container Terminal, the first in the UK, in 1967 that heralded the port's success. Two more container terminals were built in 1981, followed by further extension between 1986 and 2003 – collectively now called Trinity Terminal. The latest terminal, Felixstowe South, is on the Landguard site, where Costain built a 730-metre quay in 2008–09.

The port is ideally positioned for ships using the main European shipping lanes between Hamburg and Le Havre. It is also well connected by both road and rail, with Felixstowe South having one rail terminal and Trinity two. The rail terminals all link the dock to the West Coast Main Line at Nuneaton in Warwickshire via the Ipswich Chord, which opened in 2014.

Around 30 shipping lines operate from Felixstowe, delivering to and from 400 ports around the world. The port handles more than 4 million containers on approximately 3,000 ships each year. It provides some of the deepest water of any European port, enabling it to serve the largest container vessels. The sheer size of the Port of Felixstowe also ensures that it is environmentally friendly. The huge megaships handled and the cranes unloading on the quays mean the port contributes less than 1 per cent of the total carbon embedded in goods through the supply chain.

ICE 200

HEATHROW AIRPORT

EUROPE'S BUSIEST AIRPORT

LOCATION HARMONDSWORTH, LONDON, UK
CONSTRUCTION DATES 1930 (AS GREAT WEST AERODROME); 1955 (TERMINAL 2);
1961 (TERMINAL 3); 1969 (TERMINAL 1); 1986 (TERMINAL 4); 2016 (TERMINAL 2A)

LONDON'S HEATHROW AIRPORT has grown from a small airfield to become the second busiest airport in the world for international passenger traffic – surpassed only by Dubai International – and the busiest in Europe. In 2016, it handled a record 75.7 million passengers.

British aeronautical engineer Richard Fairey bought up plots of land near the hamlet of Heathrow from 1929, eventually acquiring 240 acres to build what became the Great West Aerodrome for assembling and testing his aircraft. Today it forms the south-eastern part of Heathrow Airport.

By 1943 the government had begun requisitioning land as a major RAF transport base for the Far East. The military began construction in May 1944 on the "Star of David" pattern of runways plus a control tower. The first civil aircraft to land at Heathrow was Lancastrian *Starlight* on 6 December 1945, a civilianised version of the Lancaster. It became a civil airport on 1 January 1946, when the same Lancastrian became the first aircraft to take off from the new civil airport on a proving flight to Buenos Aires. Heathrow became London Airport officially in March 1946, becoming London Heathrow Airport from 1961.

When the airport first opened to the public in 1946, the passenger terminals were ex-military marquees with no heating, and basic facilities. There were no pavements and passengers had to walk over wooden decking to reach their aircraft.

During its first year 63,000 passengers travelled through the airport. By 1951 the number had risen to 796,000, leading to the construction of permanent passenger buildings. Planning allowed for three central terminals and

a control tower of 122 feet. The first passenger terminal to be built was the Europa building (later renamed Terminal 2), opened in 1955 along with the Queens Building for administration, which had roof gardens and viewing terraces. The Oceanic Terminal (Terminal 3) opened in 1961 followed by Terminal 1 – the then largest passenger terminal in Europe – in 1969.

With the arrival in the 1970s of Concorde and wide-body jets such as the Boeing 747, passenger numbers took off dramatically, with 27 million passengers passing through in 1978, leading to the opening of Terminal 4 in 1986. Heathrow has continued to grow and expand its facilities accordingly.

By 2002 only the two-east-west runways of the original Star of David pattern remain in use, the rest consumed by terminals. Construction on Terminal 5 – the largest single-span structure in the United Kingdom – began in 2002 and was completed in 2008. The curved, steel-framed roof is the size of ten football pitches. Glass panels flood the building with natural light. It has 60 aircraft stands, more than 100 shops and restaurants, and capacity for 30 million passengers annually. It also has a 3,800-space multi-storey car park and a hotel.

A new 87-metre-high cable-stayed air traffic control tower was fabricated in steel off-site, erected on the south side, and moved across the airport into position overnight in 2004. Terminals 1 and 2 were replaced in 2014 by the larger Terminal 2A and on 25 October 2016, the House of Commons approved plans to build a third runway, subject to ongoing legal challenges. The earliest possible opening year for this would be 2025.

ICE 200
BOSPHORUS BRIDGES
THREE GIANT BRIDGES LINKING EUROPE WITH ASIA

LOCATION ISTANBUL, TURKEY
CONSTRUCTION DATES 1969–73; 1986–88; 2013–16

THE BOSPHORUS IS a long, narrow strait running approximately 32 km and connecting the Black Sea with the Sea of Marmara. For centuries the strait – which varies between about 700 metres and 3 km in width – was only passable by ferry. History records how, in 512 BC, the Persian ruler Darius the Great watched as 700,000 of his soldiers crossed from Asia to Europe on a temporary "pontoon bridge" of boats. But it was not until 1973 that a permanent crossing was completed.

In 1969 British structural engineer Bill Brown and Freeman Fox & Partners were awarded the contract to design the first Bosporus Bridge, with contractors Cleveland Bridge and Hochtief. Brown had previously worked on the Forth Road Bridge and the Severn Bridge , and elements from both crossings are evident here. The deck is similar to the Severn, while the cable-spinning techniques pioneered on the Forth Road Bridge were refined, pulling individual wires back and forth across the bridge to form the cables. With a main span of 1,074 metres, the suspension bridge was constructed in record time, taking 400 workers and 35 engineers just over three years to complete. It opened in July 1973 as Martyrs Bridge and was Europe's longest suspension bridge until the Humber opened in 1981. Around 60 million vehicles cross it each year.

The second crossing, also designed by Brown, was completed in 1988 as the Fatih Sultan Mehmet Bridge and lies around 4 km north of the first crossing. Just over 1.5 km long, it is a more conventionally constructed structure than the first bridge, with vertical hangers. The aerodynamic deck, 39 metres wide, hangs on double vertical steel cables. On weekday mornings, commuter traffic flows mostly westbound to the European side, so five of the eight lanes run westbound and only three eastbound. On weekday evenings this is reversed. Around 240,000 vehicles pass daily in both directions. The closure of the first bridge to all heavy vehicles in 1993 meant that the second crossing was now the sole route for commercial vehicles until the construction of the third bridge in 2016.

The third Bosphorus Bridge, the most northerly of the three, was designed by Michel Virlogeux, the French engineer responsible for the spectacular Millau Viaduct. Named the Yavuz Sultan Selim Bridge, it is a mixed suspension and cable-stay bridge of 1,400 metres that carries the new Northern Marmara Motorway. The deck is 59 metres wide and supports two railway tracks and eight highway lanes. It is hung up by two main cables and 88 stiffening cables. The two towers, located onshore, are formed by two legs of 320 metres height. These legs are founded on shafts of 20 metres diameter. On each side, a reinforced concrete anchor block (40 x 50 x 30 metres) sustains the two main cables. The total volume of the foundation is more than a billion cubic metres.

The crossings – three bridges and now two tunnels – have had an astonishing effect on the city and people of Istanbul, linking the two sides of the strait, easing transport problems and fostering closer working relationships between east and west. Istanbul's population has increased from under two million in the early 1970s to around 17 million today. The crossings have been described as a catalyst for the socio-economic development of Turkey. As Dr Bill Brown said on the occasion of his first crossing: "A bridge not only to link both parts of Istanbul but a bridge to link people and nations as well."

PORT OF BUENOS AIRES

THE UPGRADING OF ARGENTINA'S BIGGEST PORT

LOCATION BUENOS AIRES, ARGENTINA
CONSTRUCTION DATES 1870–

TODAY, BUENOS AIRES is a thriving port, but when the original port was founded back in the 16th century, the natural harbour was prone to silting. Ships had to moor offshore and transfer goods in shallow vessels. In the 1870s a new harbour named Catalinas Norte was built closer to the city – the first harbour in Argentina to be created by reclaiming land.

In the 1880s plans were proposed for a series of four impounded or wet docks, which hold water, allowing vessels to remain afloat at low tide. Designed by Sir John Hawkshaw and Thomas Andrew Walker, the first opened in 1890, followed by the south basin a year later. The near collapse of the financial backer Barings Bank in 1890 delayed the works and the whole project was not completed until 1897, when it was named Puerto Madero. However, as early as 1907, it was struggling to cope with larger ships.

In 1911, Sir Brodie Haldane Henderson designed the Southern Dock, mainly for the booming refrigerated meat trade. It included the "Anglo" Frigorifico freezing plant, one of the largest meat-packing factories in the world. At the same time, work began on the Puerto Nuevo (New Port) north of the Hawkshaw docks. Work was delayed during the war and it was finally opened in 1925 having taken 15 years to build. The works included the northern breakwater and six new basins making Buenos Aires the largest port not only in Latin America, but also in the entire southern hemisphere.

These new ports sounded the end of Puerto Madero, which fell into disuse. However, over the past 20 years it has undergone a massive regeneration and is now a thriving waterfront area. Old warehouses have been converted into commercial, residential and retail properties among new parks, with the docks kept as reflecting ponds.

A new cruise terminal, the largest in South America, opened in 2000, bringing tourists to the heart of the city. The terminal building has an area of three acres spread over two floors, and in its first summer, it received 135 passenger ships carrying more than 350,000 visitors. Buenos Aires has retained its historic docks, but has also risen to embrace modern developments.

ICE 200

TSING MA BRIDGE

THE WORLD'S LONGEST ROAD AND RAIL SUSPENSION BRIDGE

LOCATION TSING YI TO LANTAU ISLAND, HONG KONG
CONSTRUCTION DATES 1990–97

IN THE LATE 1980s the Hong Kong government decided to move the old, congested Kai Tak Airport from the urban centre to rural Lantau, the largest island, which at the time was only accessible by sea. This called for the construction of a new crossing, now known as the Lantau Link, between Tsing Yi and Lantau. A key component of the Lantau Link is the Tsing Ma suspension bridge, which stretches across the Ma Wan channel.

The channel is a major shipping route into the Pearl Delta and requires a vertical clearance of over 62 metres and a horizontal clearance of 1,000 metres. The bridge Mott MacDonald designed, taking inspiration from the Forth and Severn bridges in Britain, is 206 metres high and 1,377 metres long. The 41-metre-wide bridge deck carries six lanes of road traffic. The lower level contains two rail tracks and two lanes of emergency carriageway.

The railway was one of the most challenging aspects of the bridge's design. Suspension bridge decks in the past had used movement joints located at the towers, with localised rotations too large for a railway to accommodate. It was therefore decided to make the deck continuous over the tower transverse supports. The bridge also has a rail movement joint at the Tsing Yi abutment.

Winds of up to 290 km per hour regularly batter Hong Kong. To mitigate this problem Mott MacDonald located two emergency carriageways and the railway on the sheltered lower deck, whose edges are shaped to resist the wind and assist aerodynamic stability. These two roads are used for maintenance access and as traffic lanes when severe typhoons strike Hong Kong. This design feature ensures the airport stays open whatever the weather.

The other immense challenge the project posed was an extremely tight deadline. The contractors, the Anglo Japanese Construction Joint Venture, had their work cut out. The link had to be ready in advance of the completion of the new Hong Kong International Airport, which was scheduled to open in 1998. However, the bridge was completed in time and residents and visitors have enjoyed a smooth transit from the airport to central Hong Kong ever since.

ICE 200

ST PANCRAS INTERNATIONAL AND HIGH SPEED ONE

THREE ENGINEERING FEATS IN ONE

LOCATION LONDON, UK
DATES OPENED 1868; REOPENED 2007

ST PANCRAS STATION was built by the Midland Railway Company to connect London with some of England's major cities. From the start the station had excellent passenger connections to the City via the Metropolitan Line, soon followed by through services to the south of London via what is now Thameslink. It is a marvel of Victorian engineering: the arched, train-shed structure, designed by William Henry Barlow, had the largest single-span iron roof in the world at that time. It was made up of a series of wrought-iron ribs resulting in a space 100 feet high, 240 feet wide and 700 feet long. Its design was copied across the world, most notably at Grand Central Station in New York.

The station sustained severe bomb damage in the Second World War. In the 1960s the late poet Sir John Betjeman led a successful campaign to save it from demolition (his statue now stands on the grand terrace). In 1967 the station achieved Grade I listed status and, in the early 1990s, the decision to build the Channel Tunnel Rail Link, now High Speed One (HS1), led to its extensive redevelopment. The £800 million scheme included plans to double the station in length and add six new platforms.

HS1 is an engineering marvel: a 109 km railway that links the Channel Tunnel with Kent and London. HS1 caters for domestic and international trains operating up to 300 km per hour and over 20 million passenger journeys a year. The railway took 11 years to complete. It involved the creation of more than 152 bridges and other structures and tunnels beneath the River Thames and more than 3,000 new London properties.

Now known as St Pancras International, the station is one of the central hubs for transport

and retail in Britain, with as many as 31 million passenger movements each year. Its 2007 reopening – together with the launch of HS1 – has had a critical impact on the regeneration of the wider area. It has brought world-class transport connections to Greater London, Kent and continental Europe. New platforms for Thameslink and the main line services to Sheffield, Derby and Nottingham were built and the station's home in King's Cross has been revitalised into a cultural and technological hub, home to Google, the British Library, the new Francis Crick Institute, and a thriving cultural and retail scene.

The frontispiece of the station is the St Pancras Renaissance London Hotel. It occupies much of the former Grand Midland Hotel designed by George Gilbert Scott, which had fallen into decline and closed in 1935. The old station's distinctive Gothic architecture was respectfully modernised with a new extension of glass, steel and aluminium. The building's undercroft, built in the 19th century to store beer, was transformed by cutting through the platform deck above to create a light and airy arcade with views of the station's glorious roof. The arcade and its rows of modern shops, cafes and bars have helped establish St Pancras International as a destination in its own right.

The rich architecture, history and art of St Pancras International today combine with the world-leading infrastructure and technology of High Speed One to create a connected station ready for the future. This is a station that is constantly evolving, with new links to Amsterdam and an expansion of high-speed services planned for 2018 and beyond.

THOMAS TELFORD'S ROADS

HOW "THE COLOSSUS OF ROADS"
MADE THE UK ACCESSIBLE

——————

LOCATION THROUGHOUT THE UK
CONSTRUCTION DATES 1790s–1830s

THE STORY OF the modernisation of Britain in the revolutionary years from 1750 is, in part, also the story of the modern road. "Good roads are … the greatest of all improvements," wrote Adam Smith in *The Wealth of Nations*, a book Thomas Telford adored, and his work was at the centre of those improvements. He was not the only road builder – nor was he the earliest or most prolific – and he turned his hand to many other engineering projects too. But he built the best and was famed for it.

In the 1820s, when the stagecoach network was at its height, the Tally-ho was famous for galloping the journey from London to Birmingham in half a day, thanks to a road made into an expressway by Telford. His route to Birmingham and on through North Wales to Snowdonia and Holyhead was the finest road built anywhere before the coming of the motorcar. It is the road remembered in George Eliot's *Felix Holt, The Radical*, and it won him enormous respect.

Before Telford – and before the work of the many other road builders who laid out Britain's turnpike routes, which Parliament authorised to help pay for repairs – travel was a slow and muddy business. It was said to take four days to get from London to Birmingham in the mid-17th century. A hundred years later that was down to two, but it was Telford's road that made it into something approaching a modern journey.

He did not set off in life to be a road builder, or even an engineer. The first part of his career saw him rise from stonemason to county surveyor and architect in Shropshire; the second part turned him into a builder of great canals. At the start of the 19th century others, such as John McAdam, had a much greater claim to be the master of modern roads. (McAdam's system was "macadamisation", which, when bound with tar needed to stop pneumatic-tyred vehicles sucking out fine particles, much later became "tarmac".)

But in the early 1800s the government sent Telford to survey the remote highlands of Scotland and then funded him to build a great network of useful roads and bridges, which made even the far north easily accessible for the first time. Telford and his team worked hard on the ground in tough, remote conditions. These roads survive today but are no match for the more magnificent routes he went on to build in England and Wales.

Asked to open a new route to Holyhead, Telford surveyed, widened and improved the existing route from London to Birmingham and built an entirely new route from there on to the coast. He was a perfectionist and he scorned quick fixes insisted on by some road builders – who often dumped rough gravel on to mud and did not install proper drains. Telford worked from the bottom up, with a series of large and then small interlocking stones, properly graded and drained, and a coating of smooth pebbles on top.

The method cost more but lasted better and made travel quicker. It worked on the Birmingham route. It would have worked on a route into South Wales, and along the Great North Road to Scotland, had he been able to transform his surveys into construction projects. But by then the train had arrived and the appetite for new roads was falling away.

Thomas Telford died knowing his schemes were incomplete. But he was still, as the poet laureate Robert Southey dubbed him, "The Colossus of Roads".

ICE 200
TITAN CRANE
A GIANT OF SCOTLAND'S ENGINEERING HERITAGE

_____

LOCATION CLYDEBANK, SCOTLAND, UK
CONSTRUCTION DATE 1907

IN THE 1900s about a fifth of the world's ships were built on the River Clyde, growing and sustaining international trade and the economy. These ships were built with cranes that had been designed by civil engineers, and the most famous of these was the Titan crane – also known as the Titan Clydebank.

This giant, 150-foot-tall cantilever crane was designed for the lifting of heavy equipment, in particular engines, boilers and ordnance, during the construction of ocean liners and battleships at the John Brown & Company shipyard. The crane was constructed in 1907 by Sir William Arrol & Co, whose chief engineer was Adam Hunter (1869–1933), a member of the Institution of Civil Engineers.

It was the largest of its type when it was completed. The design included a fixed counterweight and electrically operated hoists. A further 50 or so were built around the world. Around 20 survive, four on Clydeside, including the Finnieston Crane in central Glasgow. They have become iconic symbols of the engineering heritage of Glasgow and the Clyde.

The Titan fell into disuse in the 1980s but, in 2013, it was designated as an "International Historic Civil and Mechanical Engineering Landmark" by the American Society of Civil Engineers. Since 2007, more than 40,000 people, including many college and school children, have visited the Titan, taking the lift to the top and learning more about Clydebank's shipbuilding heritage.

ICE 200
ALDERNEY BREAKWATER
PROVIDING REFUGE FROM THE ELEMENTS

_____

LOCATION ALDERNEY, CHANNEL ISLANDS
CONSTRUCTION DATES 1847–64

BUILT OFF BRAYE Bay, this breakwater is an iconic structure. It was presented as forming a harbour of refuge for shipping, but was conceived as a naval harbour. The Royal Navy did not want the harbour to be visible from the French coast so the breakwater was constructed on the exposed north-west side of Alderney, which has resulted in an ongoing struggle between man and the elements. ICE President James Walker designed the breakwater, with Thomas Jackson as contractor.

The breakwater was originally built out to 1,430 metres long and in water depths of up to 40 metres. The masonry superstructure sits upon a mound of Alderney stone, which was transported along a purpose-built, two-and-a-half mile-long railway from the quarry, loaded into barges and tipped onto the mound. More than 1.8 million cubic metres of stone was used – enough to fill Wembley Stadium one and a half times over!

In the years immediately after its construction there were numerous instances of storm damage and, following an investigation by ICE past president Sir John Hawkshaw, the outer 560 metres was abandoned in 1873, leaving the breakwater much as it is today, protecting Alderney's commercial port and boat anchorage.

The most recent major breaches were in 1962 and 1990. Annual maintenance concentrates on the seaward face, both above and below water, to fill voids and cracks in the structure that storms might otherwise exploit.

ICE 200
CALEDONIAN CANAL
A BREATHTAKING WATERWAY THAT TRANSFORMED SCOTLAND

LOCATION GREAT GLEN, SCOTLAND, UK
CONSTRUCTION DATES 1803–22

THE CALEDONIAN CANAL, Scotland's longest inland waterway, is an audacious feat of engineering. Running from Fort William in the west to Inverness in the east, it carves through farmland and forest, marshland and mountains, as it follows the course of the Great Glen – the rift valley that provides the waterway with much of its breathtaking mountain scenery.

The proposal was bold: hewing a course through the UK's most mountainous terrain, as well as the mighty sea lochs of Oich, Lochy and Ness. However, with mass unemployment following the Highland Clearances and thousands leaving Scotland each year to seek employment, an epic engineering project – bringing jobs, income and vibrancy, and creating a new route for trade – was seen as a panacea for the region.

In 1803, Parliament passed an act commissioning renowned civil engineer Thomas Telford to take on the monumental task, with William Jessop consulting. However, the government's initial seven-year plan and the budget of £474,000 was too optimistic. It wasn't completed until 1822 – at a cost of more than £900,000. Recent appraisals by programme management experts attribute blame to the government, not Telford.

It was a nationwide effort with engineers and supervisors recruited from the entire country. Around 1,500 men carved the colossal locks and channels of the waterway by hand. Averaging 52 metres in length and 10 metres in depth, the locks were the largest ever constructed – vast chambers designed to hold the vessels of the coastal fishing fleet and Royal Navy, at the time still engaged in the Napoleonic Wars. More than 300,000 tonnes of earth and stone were hewn from the heart of the Great Glen to construct the canal's 29 locks – enough to cover a full-sized football pitch with a pile of rubble 25 metres high.

The canal transformed the Great Glen from an increasingly isolated yet epic landscape to a key driver in the Highlands economy. Today, thousands of visitors use the canal's towpaths and waterway each year to view Neptune's Staircase, the longest lock flight in Britain; to sail through the shadow of Ben Nevis, the UK's tallest mountain; or to go monster hunting on the waters of iconic Loch Ness. The Caledonian Canal is a unique example of Scotland's industrial heritage, an economically vital tourism destination, and a tribute to the transformational power of civil engineering.

ISLANDS BREED INNOVATION

NAME GEOMARINE
LOCATION GUERNSEY & JERSEY
WEBSITE GEOMARINE.GG

FROM OFFICES IN Guernsey and Jersey, Geomarine operates as a principal contractor or specialist sub-contractor providing a diverse range of capabilities. It maintains an agile multidisciplinary team with a wide range of technical knowledge and capability for its size. It offers expertise in geotechnics, deep drainage, utility installation, general civils along with marine and coastal work. "The Channel Islands might be geographically small," says co-founder and CEO Ian Gilmour, "but in terms of infrastructure needs it is a microcosm of a much larger jurisdiction, requiring the full spectrum of infrastructure. This makes it a highly varied and interesting place to work, while having its own challenges."

Ian Gilmour and Wedd Osmond co-founded Geomarine in 1998 to fulfil the need in the Channel Islands for a professional contractor, providing specialist services with local resources. It is now the largest civil engineering contractor in the Channel Islands, but engineering remains at the heart of its decision making.

Geomarine works on all of the seven inhabited Channel Islands as well as surrounding offshore structures. "Having limited access to resources breeds innovation," says Gilmour. "This is where the company's emphasis on teamwork comes into its own. That we are as good as our people is not a cliché to Geomarine, we encourage everyone to strive for excellence, in everything they do." This can mean upgrading Alderney's Commercial Quay (pictured left) providing a safe and sustainable port to secure Alderney's future, stabilising cliff faces in Jersey, or maintaining the foul-sewer network in Guernsey. All show a clear commitment to building, maintaining and upgrading the infrastructure of the Channel Islands, providing local business and employment.

"Our business model has always revolved around sustainability," says Gilmour. "It is imperative that skills and infrastructure knowledge are maintained locally to secure a sustainable future. Whether it's through the education and training of our own staff or supporting local initiatives to raise the profile of engineering for the wider population, we are constantly looking to improve the future of infrastructure for the Channel Islands."

FROM CHINA, WITH LOVE

NAME CHINA ROAD AND BRIDGE CORPORATION
HEADQUARTERS BEIJING, CHINA
WEBSITE WWW.CRBC.COM

WORKING ON THE world's biggest infrastructure projects is a tough job, but it's one relished by the China Road and Bridge Corporation (CRBC). "We let the work speak for itself," says Technical Manager Bang Tan. "We want to provide a high-quality service throughout the world."

CRBC is certainly a global enterprise. It operates under the umbrella of China's largest contractor – China Communications Construction Company Ltd – undertaking projects under the remit of the Belt and Road Initiative (BRI). This vast development strategy, initiated by the Chinese government in 2013, is intended to link China to the rest of the world and is supported by the British government. It promises a wide-ranging programme of infrastructure works including railways, roads and bridges in numerous countries around Asia, Europe and Africa. It's an exercise in soft power for China, fostering links with developing countries in particular.

"In Africa, for example, we send the management staff to train the local workforce," says Tan, "to build relationships and educate workers in building techniques, time management and more. And to the most talented construction supervisors we offer courses at university in China. We're not just building a bridge or a railway, we're future-proofing an international workforce."

In June 2017, CRBC completed the 472 km Mombasa-Nairobi Standard Gauge Railway (SGR) Project in Kenya, which included an "animal passage" for wild zebras to pass through. CRBC strives to innovate in this way for each project: for instance, the construction team of the Maputo Bridge in Mozambique – Africa's largest – had to provide anti-seismic protection and overcome the challenges of a long span and a tight construction programme.

In 2017, ICE named CRBC as NEC Contractor of the Year for the Tseung Kwan O-Lam Tin Tunnel (TKO-LTT) General Road P2 project in Hong Kong. CRBC HK also won awards for its work on other Hong Kong projects, including the Tuen Mun–Chek Lap Kok Link–Northern Connection toll plaza project, and it has won numerous awards for corporate social responsibility between 2016 and 2017. Its adoption of green measures, such as recycling concrete and waste water, shows a commitment to minimising the environmental impact of its work. It's clear that CRBC's reputation in construction is sure to rise.

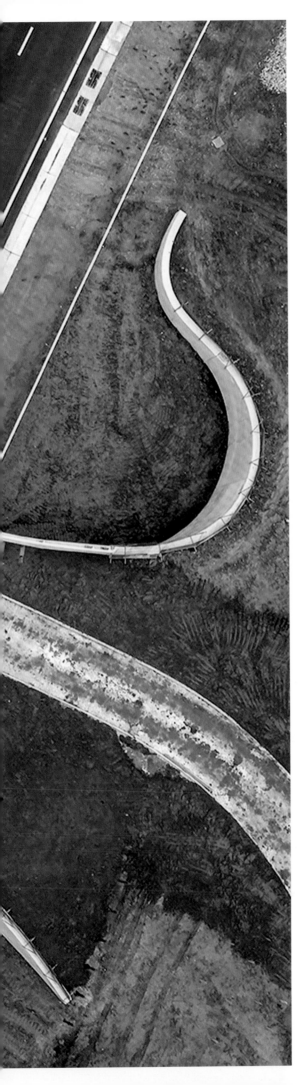

THE ROAD AHEAD

NAME HIGHWAYS ENGLAND
HEADQUARTERS GUILDFORD, UK
WEBSITE WWW.GOV.UK/GOVERNMENT/
ORGANISATIONS/HIGHWAYS-ENGLAND

EVERY TIME YOU travel on a motorway or major trunk road in England, you are under the care of Highways England. England's strategic road network encompasses some 4,300 miles of road and features more than 20,000 individual structures, from bridges and large culverts to tunnels and retaining walls. Carrying a third of the country's total traffic – that's around 4 million journeys each day – it has an estimated asset value of £99 billion to the UK economy.

"It's a significant engineering challenge," says Mike Wilson, Highway England's Chief Highways Engineer. "Part of that challenge is to improve the network while keeping that network flowing. It's a challenge that we faced in the past and face now."

England's strategic road network forms the economic backbone of the country. It is open 24 hours a day, seven days a week and is relied on by communities and businesses, connecting people across the country. The responsibility for maintaining, operating and modernising the network lies with Highways England – originally formed as an agency of the Department for Transport but now a company wholly owned by the Secretary of State for Transport.

Wilson is keen to stress the crucial role of standards in maintaining and improving the network. His directorate is responsible for the *Design Manual For Roads And Bridges* (DMRB), a weighty publication containing thousands of pages of technical advice and specifications. "The DMRB is the bible, if you will, for best practice in highway design," he says.

To ensure that the strategic road network continues to meet the country's needs, it is supported by billions of pounds of government funding.

"It is a mixture of road improvements, maintenance activities and the 24/7 operation of the network, all with a renewed focus on customers' needs," says Wilson. "In terms of maintenance, much of the network requires constant upkeep to ensure that it performs as well as it did in the 1970s and '80s. Better asset-management techniques, deterioration models, and asset condition knowledge allows us to be more precise about the maintenance the network needs."

Wilson cites an example of bridge inspections, traditionally carried out at set times, which have benefited from Highways England's smarter approach. "It's about making better use of the resources available to us, ensuring what we do is safe and delivers for the country."

FLOW CONTROL

Throughout all its work, be it improving existing roads or constructing new ones, Highways England is committed to improving safety. By delivering the road investment strategy, Highways England directly supports economic growth, creating jobs, connecting businesses and ensuring an environmentally sustainable future.

Simultaneously delivering road improvements and keeping traffic moving is one of Highways England's biggest challenges, but it is one made possible through a better understanding of advanced traffic modelling. This was key to the success of the Catthorpe Interchange improvement, completed in 2016, where the A14 meets the M1 and the M6 in Leicestershire. Highways England was able to carry out the improvement while keeping the complex junction open to traffic, something that Wilson describes as a "huge engineering achievement".

Another recent major development has seen Highways England move from mere environmental mitigation – essentially, doing as little damage to the landscape as possible – to identifying ways in which motorways and major roads can positively enhance the landscape for all users.

For Wilson this is about creating designs that respond to the location. "In some places this about creating a 'wow' factor, while in other places it's about hiding the road and being as unobtrusive as possible," he says. "It is a change of philosophy for most engineers, but we believe it is necessary. We are conscious that all our neighbouring communities need to benefit from the new infrastructure we build."

One example of these environmental improvements would be the 2011 work on the A3 in Surrey. Part of the road originally cut through a Site of Special Scientific Interest known as the Devil's Punch Bowl – a popular destination for ramblers – but the Hindhead Tunnel took us under the site, effectively reuniting two halves of the Devil's Punch Bowl. "It is about delivering a complex infrastructure project with a legacy," says Wilson.

Wilson identifies a couple of places where he feels motorways already do precisely that. Part of the A30 in Cornwall, for instance, incorporates traditional Cornish stone walls, helping it to blend into the surrounding environment. One of Wilson's favourite journeys is driving southbound on the M5. "Suddenly the Somerset levels open out and you see the sea for the first time," he says. "These are fantastic vistas and experiences for drivers, amazing bits of design and examples of the legacy we can create in the future."

FUTURE FOCUSED

Given that highway infrastructure will be used for decades, Highways England naturally looks to the future. "We are already exploring how roads will be used in the future and looking to design that capability into our future plans," says Wilson.

"We also monitor trends, like driverless cars or new forms of fuel, and invest in research to anticipate how people will use cars and roads in years to come." One example has been its collaboration with the University of Nottingham investigating whether sunflower oil can be used to help road surfaces effectively repair themselves.

Highways England has started work on three huge projects. The improvement of the A14 between Cambridge and Huntingdon started in 2016, while the Lower Thames Crossing to the east of Dartford is currently being designed. The third is the improvement of the A303/A358 corridor which includes a tunnel under Stonehenge, one of the world's most famous prehistoric sites. Upgrading this section of the A303 into high-quality dual carriageway will ease congestion, reduce the impact on the World Heritage Site and benefit local communities and businesses.

"All are projects which require significant feats of engineering and will leave lasting legacies," says Wilson of Highway England's groundbreaking work. "These present huge opportunities, not only for road users but for the country in terms of economic growth and development. It is truly a fascinating time to be a civil engineer."

BUILDING TOMORROW'S WORLD

NAME AECOM
HEADQUARTERS LOS ANGELES, USA
WEBSITE WWW.AECOM.COM

FROM THE LONDON Olympic Games of 2012 to the new World Trade Center in New York to the delivery of new cities in Saudi Arabia, few engineering firms can claim to have as interesting and diverse a portfolio as AECOM.

The global infrastructure services firm designs, builds, finances and operates infrastructure assets for governments, businesses and organisations all over the world. With global reach and local knowledge, the firm empowers its people and partners to provide innovation and technical excellence in order to solve complex problems. AECOM is constantly developing and adding new skills and strengths to its repertoire as it becomes one of the world's premier fully integrated infrastructure firms. As a result, it has been recognised by *Fortune* as one of the World's Most Admired companies, as well as being the world's top-ranked engineering design firm by revenue.

"We provide services across the life cycle of our clients' capital assets," says Lara Poloni, Chief Executive of AECOM in Europe, the Middle East, India and Africa (EMIA). "From upfront masterplanning and conceptual engineering to detailed design, engineering, procurement and construction. We also deal with management, operations, maintenance and even decommissioning after the expiry of a design life."

AECOM (an acronym for Architecture, Engineering, Consulting, Operations and Maintenance) was formed in Los Angeles in 1990, uniting several engineering and construction firms with more than a century of collective experience. Through organic growth and acquisitions, it has risen to become one of the world's leading integrated infrastructure firms,

with a passion for taking on the biggest challenges. Recent projects offer insight into its scope: the conception and delivery of the Lee Tunnel in east London (which prevents sewage overflow in the capital); the design of motorways in Sweden; the design, build, operation and maintenance of railways in the US and the UAE; and the design and engineering of the Sutong Bridge across the Yangtze in China.

The firm also designed and built the first two lines of the Riyadh Metro, bringing public transport to a city of six million, and provided masterplanning for the London 2012 Olympic Park with such success that it was asked to do the same job for the Rio 2016 Olympic Park and helped Los Angeles secure the 2028 Olympics.

STRENGTH IN DIVERSITY

This diversity has become the firm's strength. With vast expertise, AECOM operates in almost all market sectors and across all aspects of a project's development. "Whether it is a bespoke arts scheme or a large-scale urban regeneration development", says Poloni, "we can provide discrete standalone services or a complete integrated portfolio. In some cases it could see us joining the developer as a co-developer and placing our own equity into the project. Ultimately the advantage is to our client – they have access to some of the best talent and expertise from across the globe for any project. That ability to respond to projects as they develop, so they don't need to begin a whole new procurement cycle, offers great value."

The business has always had what Poloni describes as "a measured, intelligent" approach to acquisition. AECOM has brought in companies that have helped it extend its reach and expertise and increase the value to projects and clients, each with its own history of excellence to draw on. This valuable engineering legacy from the likes of Scott Wilson and Faber Maunsell complements the firm's commitment to innovation.

"We come together to develop innovative solutions," says Poloni. "We combine our celebrated design and consulting expertise, for instance, with our construction services to deliver buildable, effective and valued buildings and infrastructure. And our engineers are part of this. They intuitively challenge traditional solutions and push technical and creative boundaries. We know that our whole is greater than our sum of parts and with that we can bring some of the boldest ideas to life."

AECOM is the only engineering firm to have planned, designed and constructed a Hyperloop test track. The brainchild of Elon Musk, this groundbreaking transport system could one day move passengers and cargo at speeds of up to 760 mph. As well as work on the Hyperloop test track, the firm is supporting half of the winning teams for the new Hyperloop routes globally.

COLLABORATION AND INNOVATION

Nurturing creativity and innovation is a challenge, but AECOM addresses this with its annual Global Challenge, a competition that encourages teams from across the company to come up with disruptive, actionable ideas to make the cities of the future smarter, safer and better connected. The hope is that this will improve mobility,

resiliency and sustainability – and enhance the ways in which the world uses augmented reality, virtual reality, building information modelling and similar tools. Finalists present their business cases, products or solutions to senior executives and have the opportunity to receive up to $1 million in resources to incubate and launch their innovations. Such projects stand alongside another core company commitment – to safeguard its employees and to have a diverse, inclusive workforce with a work/life balance that allows them to deliver groundbreaking ideas.

The firm's current UK projects include Crossrail, HS2 and the Thames Tideway Tunnel section through central London. It is also working on Spire London, the tallest residential tower in Western Europe. It is a good example of how AECOM is able to combine its global reach with specific, local needs. "We are delivering Spire London for a Chinese developer," says Poloni. "It is no accident that we were given this opportunity. Through previous project experience with them globally – and with our respected record of delivery and expertise – we were able to go head to head with some of the biggest construction companies in the UK's residential market."

That ambition underpins everything AECOM does, and the firm's values include not just a desire to collaborate and think big but to inspire and to dream. "We know we can bring the boldest ideas to life and we are able to capitalise on our global reach and scale of expertise," says Poloni. "We strive to make the world a better place. We want to make dreams a reality."

BUILDING FOR THE FUTURE

NAME SIR ROBERT MCALPINE
UK HEADQUARTERS HEMEL HEMPSTEAD
WEBSITE WWW.SIR-ROBERT-MCALPINE.COM

IT'S EXTRAORDINARY TO consider it today, but one of the UK's most successful building and civil engineering companies owes its big break to a humble butcher in Motherwell. It was this unnamed trader who lent £11 to an ambitious young entrepreneur called Robert McAlpine in 1869, allowing the 22-year-old bricklayer to take on his first major building job. The company that he started is now one of the biggest names in engineering and will celebrate its 150th anniversary in 2019, having helped build Britain, improving public infrastructure and constructing some of the most important and groundbreaking buildings in the country.

"I always felt what a great thing that butcher did for me," Sir Robert once reflected. "He let me have the money on Saturday, although it was necessary for him to have it back by the following Wednesday in order to buy beef to supply his trade. That old butcher gave me a chance." It is fitting that a transaction based on trust and personal understanding should be the foundation stone for a company that has always understood the importance of these two factors in delivering for its clients.

Since Robert began the company that carries his name, it has been responsible for constructing many of the country's best-known structures and buildings, from the miraculous Glenfinnan Viaduct that carries the West Highland Railway over the Scottish Highlands, to the Olympic Stadium, a modern masterpiece of design and engineering, which was completed early and under budget and became the centrepiece of London's hugely successful 2012 Olympic Games.

It is a portfolio of projects which also includes the Dorchester Hotel, the first Wembley Stadium, Bankside Power Station, Canary Wharf, Birmingham Bullring, the Eden Project, the Millennium Dome and O2 Arena, the Emirates Stadium, the M74 Completion in Glasgow, the new US Embassy in south-west London and a new European headquarters for Bloomberg. In fact, a list of the projects completed by the company would fill a book, its track record encompassing many of the building blocks of our society.

This is a company that, throughout its 150-year history, has showcased its expertise across a range of sectors, establishing a reputation for technical excellence and client service that is second to none. As such, it has always attracted the most dedicated employees, renowned for their integrity, their commitment, and the relish with which they take on the most challenging of projects.

These are people who understand implicitly the factors that unite them and will bring future success: an unrelenting focus on client value and project delivery, an ever-evolving technical capability, a passion for innovation and an absolute commitment to excellence in everything they do.

FAMILY VALUES

All of which is underpinned, of course, by one of the company's core values – to act like a family: caring, trusting, celebrating successes and supporting one another to seize the opportunity to progress. Crucially, the company remains a family firm, with three fifth-generation McAlpines currently in senior roles.

Previous pages
Daniel Liebskind's
Imperial War Museum
(North) in Manchester

Right
The Eden Project
in Cornwall

New Chief Executive Paul Hamer believes this strong family ethos, and the fact that it extends beyond the confines of the company, is one of the great strengths of the business. "It's central to the way we operate and part of what makes us different," says Hamer. "Yes, we're a business and we've got targets and a job to do, but we're all in it together. And like a family, we function best when we are open and honest with each other and take the time to listen. When you buy into that ethos you quickly see how incredibly powerful it can be and it's why on every project we aim to treat our clients and our supply chain partners as part of our extended family."

The result is a company with relationships that in many cases span decades, says Civil Engineering Key Account Director Tony Gates, who joined the company last year. "I've met firms that have worked with the company for more than 30 years," he says. "That's a tribute not just to the company's track record of success but to that all-important mutual trust and understanding that has developed over the long term and which has been sustained through uncertain times as well as the good."

For Director of Business Development and Work Winning, Grant Findlay, nurturing and building on these long-term relationships is fundamental to the company's approach: "It's that sense of continuity. You know that when you're meeting a client you are part of a longer-term relationship, often established over many years."

This strong client focus has run like a spine through the company's history and been central to its approach through the delivery of the long line of complex projects that Sir Robert McAlpine has brought into existence since its foundation.

While the company is proud of its many achievements, its focus remains – as it has always been – on the future, working with all those involved in its projects to push innovation and improve efficiency in order to deliver ever more value for its clients.

CLIENT-LED AND PROJECT-CENTRIC

It is a foundation and an approach that Hamer is determined to build upon as the company looks beyond its 150th anniversary in 2019. "Our approach is quite straightforward and all the more powerful for that," says Hamer. "We are client-led and project-centric. We want to be the best at what we do and our focus is on the sectors where we know we can bring our wealth of technical expertise to add real value for our clients. Working hand in hand with our clients means that, as a business, we are continually moving forward with them, evolving and innovating, developing new and more efficient solutions which improve the services we offer."

This commitment to engineering excellence is integral to Sir Robert McAlpine's success, and is reflected in the fact that there are numerous engineers in senior management positions. The company's strong civil engineering capability remains, of course, a key strength, with an associated heritage that is a source of great pride. This, for example, is a contractor that designed 13 and built six of the original fleet of nuclear power stations, a sector involvement which continues today through its work to support a new generation of reactors.

Sir Robert McAlpine continues to be involved in major public infrastructure work, as evidenced by projects such as the completion of the M74

Left
McAlpine's major
infrastructure projects
include the completion
of the M74 in Glasgow

in Glasgow, one of the most complex civil engineering contracts undertaken in Scotland in recent years. Delivered eight months early, this hugely complex project set new standards for technical innovation, sustainability, health and safety, and community investment on major highways projects.

In addition to maintaining sections of the M74 /A74(M) and the A19 following construction works undertaken in the 1990s, current contracts also include the construction in joint venture with Bouygues and Volker Fitzpatrick of part of the HS2 rail link between London and Birmingham, a section which includes the Colne Valley Viaduct and the Chiltern tunnels.

"Our civil engineering capability has always been one of our core strengths," says Gates. "The heritage is there, the technical backing is there, and we've got the people who know how to make it work on the ground. And of course many of the iconic structures we deliver that are classed as building projects still have a big dose of civil engineering."

For every large-scale, high-profile project the company delivers, there is a host of less well known schemes of which it is just as proud. In fact the vast majority of its projects have a value of less than £50 million, allowing it to deploy self-delivery, spread risk and resources, and invest in tomorrow's engineering talent by providing development opportunities for young managers and engineers.

"The diverse scale and scope of projects we deliver provides remarkable development opportunities for our people," explains Director of People and Infrastructure, Karen Brookes.

"No matter where people come from or their background they can realise their full potential in a business with strong ethics and family values at its core. They can truly be part of projects that transform Britain's future heritage and in doing so progress their careers through early accountability, responsibility and opportunities to gain the necessary hands-on experience."

This broad portfolio has recently seen the company undertake jobs such as cancer support charity Maggie's new centre at St Bartholomew's Hospital in London. Working in the charity sector reflects the company's enduring commitment to contribute to wider society. In the case of Maggie's, with whom Sir Robert McAlpine has established a corporate partnership, it also highlights a willingness to undertake projects that will stretch and test its capabilities.

The company has delivered multiple centres for the charity in recent years. Designed by some of the biggest names in architecture, these are buildings renowned for pushing the boundaries of construction technology. "It really stretches the team to work with exciting designs and make them affordable while still realising the vision of both Maggie's and the architect," says Findlay. "Those constraints help us innovate. The communication and trust that builds up is incredible and the team get a lot of satisfaction out of delivering a project with a strong social aspect."

The company's close involvement with Maggie's reflects a responsible approach to business and illustrates another of the company's core values: a deep commitment to sustainability, which is often tied to innovation. This goes right

Opposite
Maggie's Cancer Care
Centre in Manchester

Below
The recently completed
Bloomberg project in
London

back to the company's earliest days, when the construction of the Great Ponsbourne tunnel on the train line between Cuffley and Hertford, between 1912 and 1915, required 30 million bricks, which the company made using clay from the excavation of the tunnel.

Today, the company continues to champion sustainability, working with its clients and supply chain to help reduce the environmental impacts of its projects. Its in-house embodied carbon and life-cycle impact-assessment capabilities inform the long-term sustainability strategy of its contracts. "As in any other part of our business we're determined to be out front leading the way," says the company's Head of Sustainability Anna Baker. "Sustainability is deeply interwoven into what we do and we see it as a driver for innovation and improvement, helping our clients achieve their goals."

Across the business, says Baker, Sir Robert McAlpine champions innovation and harnesses advances in technology. "A key focus is to devise new solutions that drive increased value for our clients," she says. Innovation often comes through the need to solve complex engineering problems one recent example being the construction of new delivery spaces beneath Selfridges department store, work which Findlay calls "the engineering equivalent of heart surgery".

Modern construction technologies such as BIM (building information modelling) are also helping the company de-risk projects and unlock value for clients by enabling problem solving in the virtual world, improving safety and quality, increasing predictability of outcome and saving time,

money and resources. With a dedicated and growing Centre for Excellence supporting the company's projects across the country, the added value BIM brings means that this is another area in which the company is looking to lead the way.

BUILDING A FUTURE HERITAGE
Embracing the latest technologies and looking to do things better has always been part of the modus operandi at Sir Robert McAlpine. As the company approaches its 150-year milestone it is embarking on the latest stage of its evolution through a business-transformation process designed to make sure it is delivering the very best service for its clients and harnessing to the full the engineering excellence and commitment to service which are at its core.

It's a mission Chief Executive Paul Hamer is absolutely committed to. "This is a fantastic organisation with a great heritage and a truly exciting future," he says. "We have a wealth of talented people within our business who share a passion for what they do and an ambition to see this company at the very top of the industry. We're building on solid foundations, planning for a future based around excellence in project delivery and developing strong and mutually rewarding relationships with our clients. Experience tells us that if we do this, there's nothing we can't achieve."

With 150 years of success under its belt and a strategy in place to see the business flourishing into the future, Sir Robert McAlpine can certainly look forward with confidence. And while it looks to write the latest chapter in its long history, proudly building Britain's future heritage, one thing is surely clear: there is much to thank that Motherwell butcher for.

VICTORY
IN ITS SITES

NAME JOHN SISK & SON
HEADQUARTERS DUBLIN, IRELAND
WEBSITE WWW.JOHNSISKANDSON.COM

"WE WANT TO be the 'go-to' construction company," says John Sisk & Son's CEO Steve Bowcott. "And we want to ensure we have a sustainable business from a community point of view." Although it is now an international operation with branches across Europe, the company started life as a small, local family concern in Ireland.

John Sisk, who set it up in 1859, was a 22-year-old apprentice plasterer when he founded the company with a view to becoming a major player in construction in and around the province of Munster. The first major building project Sisk is recorded to have undertaken was the Cork Distillery in 1868. Eventually, the firm took on the construction of schools, hotels, banks – and an astonishing 30 churches.

John Sisk & Son has not lost sight of its founder's original mission: to provide exceptional levels of construction expertise and customer service by employing, training and motivating capable staff. The company still places much emphasis on performance, quality, and teamwork and favours a hands-on management approach to ensure client satisfaction.

The company has been involved in major infrastructure development since the 1950s, building many of the Republic of Ireland's roads, bridges, power stations, airports and harbours – landmark projects that have both reflected and underpinned the nation's economic growth. In recent years this has included Limerick Tunnel, which involved the design, build, finance, operation and maintenance of approximately 10 km of tolled dual carriageway. Then came Luas

Cross City light rail extension, which required the construction in Dublin city centre of the equivalent of 13.4 km of track. It was one of the first projects of its kind to complete on time. Sisk has also built Croke Park and Aviva Stadium projects in Dublin; and made up part of the team that delivered the M17/ M18 motorway in County Galway.

John Sisk & Son opened offices in England in 1984 after the company had completed some work in Scotland and attracted the attention of an architect employed by the Scottish Development Agency. In those early days the challenge was to establish the company as a domestic contractor, in sectors where it could demonstrate its independent expertise, rather than as an Irish contractor in Britain. The hotel sector was the first to offer this opportunity. The contract to refurbish the Copthorne Tara Hotel in Kensington was quickly followed by a similar overhaul of the Royal Lancaster Hotel near Hyde Park.

By 1989, the company's British turnover had reached about £18 million; and by 2007 it had climbed to £250 million. In Britain, Sisk is now strongest in the industrial, commercial, rail, retail, highways, infrastructure and residential sectors; and it has developed expertise in specific markets like health, education and historic building restoration. Hub offices in Manchester, Bristol, Birmingham and St Albans are supported by smaller satellite offices to ensure the development of locally focused solutions for all its schemes. The company works with Network Rail and Highways England and has now built schemes for all the strategic road authorities in the UK and Ireland.

Sisk was engaged in the construction of London's Crossrail, Europe's largest infrastructure and engineering project. Crossrail's most major tunnelling scheme was awarded to the joint venture company formed by Sisk and Dragados. It involved the construction of three sections, which together represented almost 12 km of twin-bore tunnels. The award-winning contract was completed in late 2016.

Teamwork lies at the heart of Sisk's business culture. Its strategy is to achieve maximum value for customers, partners and others through its technical knowledge, ability and experience. The company collaborates with its customers and suppliers to provide technical and delivery solutions in an open and can-do way that meets the shared objectives of all parties.

Sisk employs 1,300 people across Ireland, Britain and Europe. The company is committed to investing in its staff and it is alone in Ireland in having its own training centre that takes on eight apprentice carpenters every year.

Safety is of paramount importance. The company has spelled out what it calls its "Zero Philosophy". "Some people in our industry think that whatever we do we will never stop accidents: we disagree," says Bowcott. "We think that to arrive at work with the possibility of being harmed or injured is wholly unacceptable. This belief runs through everything we do, through every level of the organisation. We plan, set up and manage our sites with the safety of our staff, subcontractors and the public at front of mind."

This sense of responsibility and integrity extends into John Sisk & Son's standards of construction. It applies rigorous quality control for the entire life of the project, eliminating snags and defects by planning, testing and inspecting as it builds. The primary aim is to achieve "Building Excellence", another of its mottos. This means delivering on time and on budget. "We took a hard, objective look at ourselves," says Bowcott, "during a time in which we had made very significant achievements in our health and safety goals. We wanted to be even better. We decided to raise the bar on our quality of delivery even though we were achieving phenomenal results. We knew that we could do more."

The "Zero Philosophy" and "Building Excellence" mission statements depended on a change in people's attitudes and behaviours. By establishing that it was in fact possible to prevent accidents and avoid construction snags, John Sisk & Son established a cultural, collective responsibility to be safe and to achieve the highest standards of excellence.

Next year John Sisk & Son marks its 160th anniversary but, rather than harking back to its foundation, the company is looking forward to future decades of high performance and quality in construction. "As the Institution of Civil Engineers celebrates 200 years," says Bowcott, "so Sisk can look back over its 160-year history and be proud of our achievements; while looking to the future with excitement and optimism."

END-TO-END SERVICE

NAME KIER GROUP
HEADQUARTERS SANDY, BEDFORDSHIRE, UK
WEBSITE WWW.KIER.CO.UK

SEAN JEFFERY AND Philip Miles have engineering in their blood. Their fathers were engineers and the pair – respectively, directors of infrastructure and pre-construction at Kier Group – have served a total of 48 years at the firm. They're well placed, then, to explain how it operates, which is not a straightforward task given its size and complexity.

Kier offers building and maintenance services in transport, defence, education, housing, energy and more. Its specialist business units offer clients a market-leading level of expertise and enabling the firm to take on some of the most challenging engineering projects in the world.

"What makes Kier a little bit different," says Miles, "is that we can invest in projects, build them and maintain them. It's an interesting collection of skills that we have around the business."

"It gives us strength in depth and resilience," says Jeffery. That resilience has seen Kier through 90 years of trading. Founded by expat Dane Olaf Kier in 1928, it made a key contribution to the war effort with the "Mulberry" portable harbours that were vital to the D-Day landings. It also engaged in numerous postwar reconstruction projects.

Headquartered since 1967 at Tempsford Hall in Bedfordshire, Kier is now a FTSE 250-listed company with an annual turnover above £4 billion. Its workforce of over 21,000 has grown both organically and through strategic acquisition to make up an enviable roster of engineering talent, deployable across the supply chain.

Invest, build and maintain: these words best sum up the end-to-end service Kier offers, from concept to delivery. The range of partnerships with clients and other contractors is huge but these collaborations are selected very carefully.

"We tend to look at projects on a case-by-case basis," says Jeffery, "to see if they're the right profile."

Kier's work with Network Rail is an example of such fine-tuning. In one area of collaboration, via the Solum Partnership, railway stations such as Twickenham, Walthamstow Central and Haywards Heath are being reimagined as mixed-use public spaces, including housing, hotels, car parks and retail spaces. "We're looking to reinvigorate large stations," says Jeffery, "and get the residential and retail benefits of the land, working with Network Rail as an investor. But we are also a contractor in that environment."

The possibilities as contractors are indeed varied under the wider Network Rail framework, from design and installation of building and earthworks projects to signalling, train care and even emergency repairs. "We're involved in some niche areas," says Miles.

Yet Kier's outlook is not merely to sit within a framework agreement and tick off projects as they arrive and are fulfilled. What sets it apart is a willingness to innovate. Crossrail serves as a prime example of high-level problem solving.

"Crossrail put out two tenders," says Jeffery, "one for the Western Running Tunnels – from Royal Oak to Farringdon – and another for Tottenham Court Road station. We said 'Look, these two tenders will mean loads of trucks, lots of disruption. We can put them together, reverse the construction order, then you can take the muck from the station out through the tunnel, take 90,000 lorries off the road and speed up the programme in the process.' It just shows how, with a forward-looking client, you can change their procurement and bring advantages."

What then happens with "the muck" is also revealing about Kier's approach. Two-thirds of the excavated material from the Crossrail tunnelling has been donated to the RSPB to create a 1,500-acre nature reserve at Wallasea Island in Essex. It helps to compensate for habitat loss elsewhere in England and to combat threats from climate change and coastal flooding. "Environmental impact is massively important to us," says Jeffery. "We spend a lot of time looking at the bigger picture of sustainability."

It's a delicate balance for a company so heavily invested in major building projects and also steeped in the energy market. Kier is involved right across the energy spectrum: in nuclear, gas-fired power stations, wind farms and, for many years, coal mining. Its highest-profile presence in recent years has been at the new nuclear power station at Hinkley Point C in Somerset, where Kier has been engaged since 2012.

The project has attracted controversy due to potential consumer costs. But EDF Energy has been a model client for Kier and its joint-venture partner BAM Nuttall, according to Jeffery. "There are some fantastic things going on at Hinkley," he says, "but it suffers a bit from sensationalism in the press. EDF is a very progressive client, looking to make step changes in improvements in working practices and workforce diversity. And you see the same sort of collaboration between contractors that has worked so well on Crossrail also working at Hinkley. We're all sharing the good things we're doing on other projects."

Safety is, of course, paramount on such heavy engineering projects – especially nuclear installations – and the group boasts a fine record there. Kier Group's annual measure of accidents per one million man-hours stands at 91: significantly less than the industry average of 397, according to figures from the Health and Safety Executive.

Best practice for safety only comes with training, and among the firm's softer initiatives is the deployment of Kieran, its safety mascot, in schools around Britain to encourage children to think about the dangers of building sites. Pupils are given safety equipment to try on, while books and poster-making activities support the national curriculum.

Education, training and the fostering of a new generation of engineers are central to Kier's mission for the future. "A company is all about the people," says Jeffery. "And it's quite typical for staff to stay here – like us – for 20 years or more. So we're doing a lot to encourage graduate intake and to get graduate employees to go back out to schools as ambassadors and promote engineering as a career."

Kier also runs schemes to encourage women back into the workforce after career breaks; and to attract applications from ex-forces personnel. "People from the services bring advantages," says Miles, "in showing us different ways of working."

As innovative efforts continue on projects ranging from HS2 construction to highways maintenance in Australia, Kier shows no signs of slowing in its scope or ambition, for its projects or its staff. And as Jeffery and Miles attest, it's a vision for generations to come.

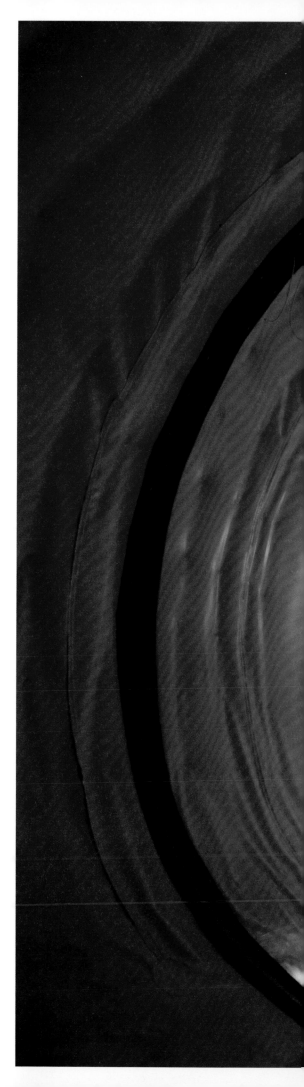

NORTHERN LIGHTS

NAME RJ MCLEOD (CONTRACTORS) LTD
HEADQUARTERS GLASGOW, UK
WEBSITE WWW.RJMCLEOD.CO.UK

SINCE ITS FOUNDING in 1951, the engineering firm RJ McLeod (Contractors) Limited has made a substantial contribution to Scotland's infrastructure, and has grown to become the country's largest privately owned civil engineering contractor. "The company still bears the name of our charismatic founder," says Bruce Clark, Joint Managing Director. "Affectionately known as 'RJ', he was noted for his unbounded optimism and pioneering spirit."

In 1953, Bruce's father Sandy Clark joined the company and it is said that RJ handed him a pile of drawings and a £20 float, with instructions to build the Cowal Hydro Power Scheme in Argyll. The aplomb with which Sandy carried it out left RJ in no doubt about his contracting ability and the two men forged a longstanding friendship, culminating in Sandy succeeding RJ.

From its early work on hydroelectric schemes, RJ McLeod built a reputation for innovation in complex areas of contracting. Now, with more than 100 wind farm projects under its belt, RJ McLeod is Scotland's leader in the renewables field. "We are equally at home on Highland hillsides and salmon rivers as we are on busy trunk roads and city centres," says Clark.

RJ McLeod's successful early work on Scottish new towns and Highland roads led to commissions for ports, harbours and urban streetscaping across Scotland. The company now has a turnover of more than £125 million. Its standing and reputation across the civil engineering spectrum are reflected in repeated recognition at the ICE Scotland's annual Civil Engineering Awards, held in partnership with the Saltire Society.

Simplicity is central to the RJ McLeod philosophy. "Some might regard our commitment to employing our own workforce – we own all our plant and transport and avoid subcontracting – as old-fashioned," says Clark. "But being a company that self-delivers means that when you employ RJ McLeod, you get RJ McLeod." All the principal shareholders are directors, which enables the company to be flexible and swift in decision-making.

RJ McLeod has developed into something of a national institution in Scotland. In the six decades since it began, the sight of its familiar yellow-and-black logo around the landscape has come to represent the highest values of reliability and healthy enterprise.

PLAN BAY

NAME YMGYNGHORIAETH GWYNEDD CONSULTANCY (YGC)
HEADQUARTERS GWYNEDD, WALES, UK
WEBSITE WWW.YGC.UK.COM

YGC IS THE largest public sector-owned infrastructure consultancy in Britain, with 21 years' experience in planning, coastal and flood management, infrastructure and transport. Operating across north and mid-Wales, 90 per cent of its 120 workforce is bilingual in English and Welsh.

YGC recently led the successful regeneration project of Plas Heli on the Lleyn Peninsula. This £8.9 million project to establish the Welsh National Sailing Academy and Events Centre is now a centre of excellence for sail training, and hosts a large number of dinghy events of national and international standard. "This state-of-the-art facility," says Huw Williams, Project Director, "meets the needs of sailors at all levels of ability; and also the needs of the community". Since the official launch, the facility has hosted events attracting more than 40,000 visitors and run competitions for competitors from over 37 countries.

The development comprised three main components: a new road and other infrastructure, the Marina extension and the iconic Academy building. Despite a challenging budget, the integrated project team embraced a highly collaborative approach to deliver this transformation. In recent years it has won an ICE Sustainability Award, a RIBA Client of the Year Award, a Royal Town Planning Institute (RTPI) Wales Planning Award and a Local Authority Building Control (LABC) Best Public Building award. Plas Heli has also been rated excellent under the Building Research Establishment Environmental Assessment Method (BREEAM).

Another challenging undertaking is managing climate change and its impact on Fairbourne's natural coastal processes – and on its community of 1,200 people. "The unprecedented strategy for decommissioning the entire village and coordinating a 36-year multi-agency programme needs vast knowledge and expertise for what is a change-management project," says Williams. Governance within Fairbourne Moving Forward is about decision-making and accountability within a process of interaction and long-term collaboration. "Working closely with the Fairbourne community and the disciplines of climatology and sociology," says Williams, "means we are able to maintain flood and coastal defences for as long as possible. This project is an innovative and catalyst for informing policy-making in Wales and the UK."

STREET SMART

NAME FM CONWAY
HEADQUARTERS SEVENOAKS, KENT, UK
WEBSITE WWW.FMCONWAY.CO.UK

LEADING INFRASTRUCTURE SERVICES company FM Conway has taken the mantra of self-reliance and turned it into a management ethos. It has delivered huge benefits not only for the business, but also for communities and the environment.

Launched by Francis Michael Conway in 1961, the family-run construction company has grown to become a nationally recognised, tier-one contractor, employing over 1,300 people and with a turnover of more than £252 million. Designing, constructing and maintaining roads across London and the south of England, it currently holds contracts with around half of the London boroughs, and an increasing number of local authorities and customers outside the capital. Alongside a range of value-added services, such as programme management, asset management and stakeholder consultation, FM Conway is also targeting sustained growth in the rail industry, having won its first major construction and civil engineering contract with Transport for London last year.

Michael Conway, CEO of the firm launched by his father, is clear that its success is down to two key factors – the company's people, and its groundbreaking self-delivery model. "I have always said that people are at the heart of our business," he says. "Without the continuing hard work of our employees, we would not be where we are today – I see the pride and passion they put into their work. Family values remain at the heart of our business, not just in terms of its ownership, but also in its whole ethos. More than 75 employees now have family members working within the business, and I hope many more will join us in the years to come."

With the industry suffering from a major skills shortage, FM Conway has worked hard to attract young, enthusiastic people into construction and change the perception of what it can offer

as a long-term career. The company has its own higher-education scholarship programme to help young people studying for an engineering or construction-related degree, and also supports the London Construction Academy, which gives youngsters the skills they need for a career in the highways industry.

"Training and developing our own in-house talent is part of our self-delivery model – and self-delivery is what sets us apart from our competitors," says Michael Conway. "From manufacturing our own materials to operating and owning our own plant and machinery, the ability to deliver projects in-house means that we can react quicker, pass on savings and deliver better projects for our customers."

This self-delivery model also drives both innovation and environmental efficiencies. In a sector that has traditionally been materials intensive, FM Conway was one of the first construction businesses to recognise the commercial and environmental advantages of recycling, and adopted a "circular economic" approach to materials, recycling everything from aggregates to asphalt, kerbs and paving. The result is an impressive 98 per cent recycling rate for waste generated by the company. It has also become the first highways materials manufacturer and contractor in the UK to produce its own Polymer Modified Bitumen, which, when added to asphalt, can significantly improve the durability of highways assets.

"Self-delivery of skills and materials is at the heart of our long-term vision," says Michael Conway. "As well as making commercial sense, it supports our aim to create a sustainable model of road construction and maintenance that can serve the needs of communities for decades to come."

GROUND CONTROL

NAME BRILLIANT IDEAS LTD
HEADQUARTERS ASHBOURNE, DERBYSHIRE, UK
WEBSITE WWW.BRILLIANTIDEASLTD.CO.UK

IT'S SAID THAT necessity is the mother of invention. In the case of Beresford's Flooring, the need to prevent the kind of accidents that are seen as a fact of life in the construction industry has inspired several creative solutions.

"We don't just accept that these things happen," says Managing Director Chris Massey of his predominantly precast flooring company. "We like our lads – I play rugby with most of them. I don't want them to have accidents."

After one of Beresford's workers put his foot through an unprotected service hole, Massey patented the Hole Cover: a slimline, highly visible, non-slip plastic board. When one member of staff trapped his fingers under a stair using normal shims, Massey invented interlocking blocks that form a safe and stable structure, called Stacker Packers. "A bit like Lego," he says.

It was after a crane nearly toppled over on site that Massey came up with one of his most ingenious inventions, the Alimat. This interlocking crane stabiliser mat was purpose-built to spread outrigger loadings. "We searched all over the world for something to assist in moving cranes around a site," says Massey, "but there was nothing. So, we invented something."

Last year, Massey and his team brought all of these solutions under one umbrella, the aptly named Brilliant Ideas Ltd. Industry recognition soon followed, winning them the British Precast Health and Safety award.

Massey hopes that such recognition can raise the profile of the company's product offering even higher. "It's about getting good old British engineering and problem-solving out to the rest of the world," he says.

To that end, Stacker Packers are now being used in the construction of Tottenham Hotspur's new football ground. They have also been used at Barcelona's iconic Sagrada Familia cathedral. Beresford's Flooring recently sent shipments of Alimats to Abu Dhabi, Angola and Sierra Leone. And when Shell built a new refinery recently, it insisted on using Alimats for all crane usage.

Not bad for a series of inventions which Massey, a kind of Heath Robinson of the construction industry, formulated in his shed. "I guess I'm like a nutty professor," he laughs. However, for his staff at Beresford's Flooring – and responsible employers in the wider construction and engineering industries – his inventions are no laughing matter.

AHEAD OF THE CURVE

NAME CORDEK
HEADQUARTERS HORSHAM, WEST SUSSEX, UK
WEBSITE WWW.CORDEK.COM

THE NET RESULT of a well-managed construction project might be a new building, tunnel or structure, but – before this point can be reached – there are a number of puzzles to solve. This is where technical solutions specialists Cordek come in.

"We don't just provide building materials," explains Simon Poole, Cordek's Business Development Manager, "We solve problems and provide the solution." Founded in 1973, Cordek takes a consultative approach to finding these solutions, working across key areas such as ground heave, volatile organic compounds (VOC) and ground gas protection, as well as structural fill, bespoke formwork and patterns and moulds.

"We ask the right questions and we use that information to propose a concept," says Poole. "That concept may in turn result in a standard product or a bespoke product, depending on what really fits the job in hand. We have an open-minded approach to the most suitable materials and systems based upon over 40 years of knowledge and experience in specialist fields."

These projects can vary hugely in scale, from supplying products for use in a residential extension right up to delivering structural fill, protective membranes and specialist formwork systems to the London Bridge Station Redevelopment. Among other projects in the capital, Cordek has been heavily involved in Crossrail, Battersea Power Station and Farringdon Station.

Cordek also played a key role in the London Aquatics Centre, designed by Zaha Hadid for the 2012 Olympics. Cordek specialises in creating curved concrete and conceived a bespoke formwork solution to create six concrete diving platforms that could be constructed on-site. "It was a complex process," says Poole. "We knew what they wanted to achieve structurally and aesthetically, so we took that information onboard, along with drawings, dimensions and other requirements around the finish and materials. We then designed, tested and supplied a sectional glass-reinforced plastic (GRP) formwork solution."

As for the future, "Cordek is committed to investing in new technology to ensure we can continue to provide innovative solutions and stay at the forefront of an ever-changing construction industry," says Poole.

CONCRETE POETRY

NAME MPA BRITISH PRECAST
HEADQUARTERS GLENFIELD, LEICESTERSHIRE, UK
WEBSITE WWW.BRITISHPRECAST.ORG

"YOU'LL FIND PRECAST concrete products in every engineering and construction sector – from small-scale housing to major infrastructure, and everything between," explains Andrew Minson, Executive Director of MPA British Precast. "It's an absolutely critical resource." It's why this manufacturers' trade association wants to maintain precast concrete's status for years to come, focusing on durability, sustainability, and ethical and responsible sourcing.

As the organisation approaches its own centenary, Minson and his team remain committed to encouraging manufacturers to adopt the highest possible standards, as well as acting as an advocate for its members, and a vital source of information for industry and customers.

British Precast recently published its latest Sustainability Matters report, featuring sustainability data from 2016, which highlights how far the industry has advanced. Since the first report in 2008 the precast sector has reduced manufacturing carbon emissions by 26 per cent, mains water consumption by 31 per cent and factory waste to landfill by over 95 per cent. The report also enables members of British Precast to use the data captured – and the

targets set by the industry – to help demonstrate their conformance with the Responsible Sourcing of Materials standard, BES 6001.

"Because we've done those things, and because we're a progressive and forward-looking industry, we've recently published our first set of Environmental Product Declarations, or EPDs," says Minson. "It covers areas such as concrete flooring, concrete paving products and concrete blocks." British Precast worked with sustainability consultants to develop a lifecycle assessment tool for products to enable them to produce EPDs.

The organisation also offers a valuable online resource for those looking to make contact with British manufacturers, listing all members and the products they offer. "If you're a responsible designer or contractor," says Minson, "you should be choosing a responsible supplier, and to do that, you can come to us."

So, what does the future hold for MPA British Precast? "We'll continue to raise the bar in relation to sustainability, health and safety, and responsible manufacture," says Minson, "so that we can play our part in delivering to the construction sector."

THE LIMITS OF POWER

NAME OMEGA RED GROUP
HEADQUARTERS NOTTINGHAM, UK
WEBSITE WWW.OMEGAREDGROUP.COM

PROTECTING PEOPLE AND property from the devastating effects of power surges and lightning strikes has been Omega Red Group's core business for the past 30 years, and the company's commitment to high levels of safety and service has seen them become the UK's market leader. But for Managing Director Neil Shailer, there's another key message for the construction sector – bringing the specialists into a project early can also deliver real architectural and cost benefits.

"Lightning protection and earthing is often considered part of the electrical package, and by the time we're involved, the structure is often out of the ground," Shailer explains. "If we're part of the civil engineering stage, we can use the groundworks and structural features of the design, rather than having to add external, often highly visible conductors. It's value engineering in practice."

The prestigious Mersey Gateway project was one example of this approach, where Omega Red liaised closely and at an early stage with its client, Merseylink CJV. "Given the size and span of the structure, our main focus was on protecting the pylons, and the supporting cables descending from them,"

says Shailer. "Because it's such an iconic structure, we worked very closely with the client to ensure that the lightning protection system is both functional and as discreet as possible." The company has also been involved in other iconic projects, including Hinkley Point C, Crossrail and HS2. However, Omega Red's 16,000 customers are incredibly diverse, and range from blue-chip construction companies to small businesses and schools.

With headquarters in Nottingham, the company's 250 staff operate from a UK-wide regional structure. Construction, power and rail are Omega Red's key markets, although the company also provides a full turnkey testing and maintenance service for a large number of existing installations (including the Shard, Tate Modern and Wembley Stadium) and offers a range of height safety solutions and safe working training.

"I'm proud of our employees," says Shailer. "We've built a strong, proactive, safety-first culture, and actively develop and promote from within. Around 30 per cent of our employees have been with us for 10 years or more, which I believe is outstanding in the modern construction industry."

CONNECTED THINKING

NAME HEWSON CONSULTING ENGINEERS
HEADQUARTERS GUILDFORD, UK
WEBSITE WWW.HEWSON-CONSULTING.COM

AS A SPECIALIST in bridges and transport infrastructure, Nigel Hewson, founder of Guildford's Hewson Consulting Engineers, speaks with pride about his area of expertise. "Rightly or wrongly, structural engineers tend to think they are the elite of civil engineering, and, rightly or wrongly, bridge engineers see themselves as the cream of structural engineers," he laughs. "So bridge-building could be seen as the pinnacle of our industry."

Hewson smiles as he says this, but it's with a note of seriousness. Hewson Consulting Engineers was formed in 2005, with fellow director Andrew Hodgkinson joining in 2006. Between them, the pair have copious experience on bridge and infrastructure projects throughout the world. Originally, work largely took place abroad but the company now has numerous projects in the UK – where it employs around 25 people, all but two of whom are engineers – as well as abroad, where it has sister companies in Malaysia and Hong Kong.

"We put a lot of effort into bringing our expertise back to UK projects and now all our engineers work both in the UK and overseas, so we cross-fertilise knowledge and experience," says Hewson. "Our engineers are able to take whatever is thrown at them. It's about adaptability – one day they could be working on a viaduct in Kuwait, the next it could be a footbridge in Scotland. We bring the same enthusiasm and expertise to everything we do."

Fellow director Hodgkinson admits a passion for bridges, particularly relishing the different challenge each project provides. "With bridges, you can't simply regurgitate what you've done before but you can adapt it so it can be applied to a different situation, culture or client," he says. "That's a key feature of our business, and of over

200 years of the Institution of Civil Engineering: British engineering has always been adaptable, going to new cultures, environments and markets. It sees how things are done, it absorbs that and it provides solutions suited to local needs. That's a skill that has stood the test of time."

Hewson Consulting Engineers does everything, from major spans to small footbridges. Major projects include the construction of elevated railway viaducts in Malaysia, Jakarta and Dubai, but Hewson and Hodgkinson take equal satisfaction from schemes such as the Pont Briwet viaduct in Wales and the Edinburgh Gateway transport interchange. The latter two required innovative solutions to technical problems.

"We are constantly looking for ways of advancing bridges, to make them more efficient and reduce the burden of maintenance," says Hodgkinson. "It's real innovation and it comes with technical challenges that some consultants might shy away from." The company collaborates with academics at the nearby University of Surrey to research new engineering solutions.

As the firm grows, both directors look forward to future challenges, eager to further their knowledge and experience. "Bridges and viaducts are always unique and challenging, so from an engineering point of view they are always very interesting," says Hewson. "A lot of people think they can do it but there aren't that many engineers who understand the nitty-gritty and are able to apply it to a particular structure or environment. When you finish, you can see what you've done – you can drive over a bridge or take a train. They become a very prominent part of the landscape and you get a lot of satisfaction out of that. There is a huge legacy that goes with the work we do."

RISING STARS

NAME DAVIES MAGUIRE
HEADQUARTERS LONDON, UK
WEBSITE WWW.DMAG.COM

THE TROUBLE WITH tall cranes, explains Des Mairs of the structural engineering design consultants Davies Maguire, is that they become unsafe to use in high winds. "In bad weather, you can lose vital days on a build," he says. "That can cost time and money." To overcome this issue, the contractor Mace, in conjunction with the team at Davies Maguire, came up with a novel concept – the "rising factory". The system, currently being used by Mace on a project in Stratford, East London, is a first in the UK construction industry. It resembles a steel exoskeleton and encloses the entire footprint of the multi-storey building under construction. As the building rises during the building process so too does the steel frame – jacks elevate it by another floor level each week.

"The frame acts as a series of platforms," says Mairs. "It's a much safer and more efficient system. Just the interior of the building needs finishing once the outside is complete. This is the future of the industry."

The London-based structural engineering consultancy was founded in 2010 by Mairs along with fellow directors Gareth Davies and Seamus Maguire. As well as developing innovative construction solutions, it has a track record in "adding value" to existing schemes. As working practices change, companies seek to adapt office space to meet the needs of staff better, which can involve altering how the lifts work or the floor plans.

"There's always scope for making a building more efficient," says Davies, "and our team has the depth of knowledge to spot an existing structure's scope for improvement. The skill in engineering sometime lies in asking what clients, such as developers and private home-owners, want to achieve, not in asking what they want. Our expertise includes unlocking hidden potential."

Numerous prizes, including Engineering Excellence and an Editors Choice pick in the 2017 NCE100 Companies of the Year Awards, are testament to Davies Maguire's ability to deliver practical and commercially astute design. From bespoke bridges to high-rise developments, the company's belief is that anything is possible through working collaboratively with architects, technicians and contractors. Every client presents an opportunity for a new challenge, and the knowledge gained is used in the company's next project, enabling it to continue scaling the heights of success.

A BREADTH OF BENEFITS

NAME MORGAN SINDALL CONSTRUCTION & INFRASTRUCTURE LTD
HEADQUARTERS RUGBY, WARWICKSHIRE, UK
WEBSITE WWW.CONSTRUCTION.MORGANSINDALL.COM

WHETHER IT'S THE impressive construction of the Clackmannanshire Bridge over the Firth of Forth (pictured above) or a current scheme, such as the joint venture to deliver the Infrastructure Strategic Alliance contract to provide essential infrastructure assets to the Sellafield nuclear site, construction and infrastructure company Morgan Sindall has a customer-focused philosophy to ensure that all work delivers a local benefit.

"We constantly look at how the finished scheme will benefit the end user," says Engineering Director Tony O'Donnell. "Whether that's a rail tunnel, a relief road, a bridge to link a local community or a wastewater treatment facility upgrade, we want to ensure that what we do improves the UK's infrastructure."

Part of Morgan Sindall Group plc, one of the UK's leading construction and regeneration firms, the construction and infrastructure division prides itself on delivering complex projects that create a real difference across the commercial, defence, education, energy, healthcare, industrial, leisure, retail, transport and water markets. The company works for private- and public-sector clients on projects and frameworks from £50,000 to more than £1 billion. Activities range from small works and repair and maintenance, to the design and delivery of complex infrastructure projects. It can provide specialist design, tunnelling, utilities, building, civil engineering and mechanical and electrical services.

Current work includes a joint venture to deliver the west section of the Thames Tideway Tunnel – a major infrastructure project to upgrade London's sewers – and three Crossrail projects as part of the overall scheme to provide a world-class railway across the capital. Past works include constructing the bored tunnelling works for Heathrow Airport's new Terminal 5 and the most complex structures on the Channel Tunnel Rail link, which included the 3.2 km North Downs Tunnel, the largest and deepest twin-track railway tunnel in the UK.

Whether delivering an iconic structure or a more utilitarian asset, Morgan Sindall's attention to detail ensures that each project works for its customer, the local community and the end user. "We're working on Smart Motorways," says O'Donnell, "which maximise the capacity of the existing road space in times of heavy traffic but avoid encroachment onto adjacent land." Technology and civil engineering in harmony – a premise intrinsic to all Morgan Sindall endeavours.

KEEPING THINGS MOVING

NAME WENTWORTH HOUSE PARTNERSHIP
HEADQUARTERS ESHER, SURREY, UK
WEBSITE WWW.WENTWORTH-HOUSE.COM

LONDON BRIDGE IS one of the UK's busiest stations, handling 50 million passengers a year, and is in the final stage of an internal reconstruction that has created a huge new concourse. Since the project began in 2013 the station has remained open, a feat made possible by the Surrey-based specialist engineering design consultancy Wentworth House Partnership.

"All the works had to allow sufficient space for the pedestrians who flow through each rush hour," explains Wentworth House Director Stuart Vaughan. "With 170-year-old masonry structures, you don't really know what you're dealing with until you start to investigate. The weight of the demolition machinery posed a serious risk, as did the live rail.

"People die if things go wrong in demolition, so you have to get it right to avoid uncontrolled collapse," continues Vaughan. "The key challenge was to maintain the stability of historic arches supporting live train lines, through a series of demolition phases. The works included the support and restraint of sections of quadripartite arches." Vaughan and his colleagues drew on their own specialist technical expertise but also

consulted with other engineering firms such as Tony Gee for independent verification of their work.

Set up in 1999, Wentworth House specialises in providing temporary works such as shoring up basements, façades and deep excavations. "We tend to work with historic rather than modern structures," says Vaughan. "If you bought steel today you'd know it will have a certain strength. But if you're dealing with a 1920s building it could be made of anything."

The skill lies in using existing structures – where they are structurally sound – alongside modern designs and materials. As with the London Bridge station project, the most important requirement is to ensure the safety of construction workers and all who use the building at every stage of the project.

"What we do is of high consequence," says Vaughan. "Getting it wrong can result in expensive project delays and put lives at risk." But construction workers and train passengers alike can be confident that their safety, like Wentworth House's expertise, is based on solid foundations.

SCHEME LEADER

NAME CLANCY CONSULTING
HEADQUARTERS ALTRINCHAM, GREATER MANCHESTER, UK
WEBSITE WWW.CLANCY.CO.UK

CLANCY CONSULTING'S VERSATILITY in collaborating with all members of the construction and property industry has been demonstrated across many sectors of the built environment. Established in South Manchester in 1972, the business has since expanded greatly and now, in its 46th year, offers a range of multi-disciplinary engineering services from 10 regional offices across the UK. "We remain an SME," says Chief Executive Alan Bramwell, "which is very important to us. And we're an owner-managed business, in control of our own destiny, so we have no external funders or shareholders to satisfy."

Clancy values the old and the new, overseeing preservation projects as well as new-build schemes. The company's £12 million transformation of Liverpool's listed but derelict Royal Insurance building into the Aloft Hotel has been widely admired. But it has succeeded equally in renovating a 1960s concrete-frame student accommodation block at the University of East Anglia. "Our strength is our ability to adapt to market requirements, whilst still doing what we do best and doing it well," says Bramwell. "For example, during the construction of the Channel Tunnel, we were involved with all the

Euro-terminals that were built to serve the new tunnel." Clancy continues to be involved in significant infrastructure schemes as well as commercial and retail projects. It also focuses on the education, healthcare and leisure sectors, assisting in the delivery of government-funded projects.

Its strongest sector continues to be residential, currently delivering over 18,000 student accommodation units, 1,500 units for the elderly and vulnerable adults, along with a number of prestigious and high-value 30+ storey towers. Current projects include the £12 million redevelopment of central Manchester's Piccadilly Gardens, and nearing completion is a £100 million biomass conversion scheme at Lynemouth Power Station in Northumberland.

Clancy prides itself on keeping a high proportion of loyal repeat business clients while growing in line with its strategic plan. "We're on course to our turnover target," says Bramwell. "But the growth is not just about having a bigger business. With both long-serving staff and younger recruits, it's about maintaining a diverse and inclusive culture, creating dynamic career opportunities for our staff and for people who wish to join us."

ELEVATED THINKING UNDERGROUND

NAME GALL ZEIDLER CONSULTANTS
LOCATION CROYDON, SURREY, UK
WEBSITE WWW.GZCONSULTANTS.COM

WHILE BRIDGES MAY capture the imagination of poets, politicians and the public, the tunnel design and engineering specialists at Gall Zeidler Consultants believe that it is the roads and railway tracks below the surface that are the vital arteries serving the hearts of most major cities.

"People use tunnels every day, often without noticing them or recognising the work that goes into developing them," says Kurt Zeidler, who launched the international tunnel engineering company in 1999 and teamed up with Vojtech Gall in 2002. "With surface space increasingly scarce in urban areas, people are looking not only to put their transport links in tunnels, but also to develop major infrastructure projects, such as water-treatment plants and storage facilities, below the surface. It's why there's been such a remarkable boom recently."

With more than 60 years' experience of tunnelling and underground construction between them, it's no surprise that the expertise of Gall and Zeidler is in demand. Gall Zeidler Consultants has been involved – as designers and consultants – in many of the sector's major developments around the world, from the East Side Access project in New York to the Sentosa Gateway in Singapore, and the Riyadh Metro Project in Saudi Arabia. GZ Consultants has also won a fair few awards along the way, including the NCE Tunnelling and Underground Space Award in 2014, the ITA Tunnelling Award in 2016, and an Excellence in Automation Award from the American Society of Civil Engineers (ASCE).

"Being well established in the international market, and able to work across a range of projects in a number of countries at any one time,

is certainly one of our strengths," says Zeidler. "We have to be international because our work is so specialised, it wouldn't be economically viable to rely on the market in any one country. Historically, when countries faced financial difficulties, the first projects cut to save budgets were always tunnels, because they were expensive. But, over the years, politicians around the world have realised that you need to invest in infrastructure to help cities, regions and countries develop, otherwise you will be falling further behind. And while we're proud of our international success, the continuity of the workload in tunnelling in the UK over the past eight to 10 years is pretty unprecedented."

Many of the company's most significant projects have been in London, where GZ Consultants has been a partner in a number of underground station upgrades (including King's Cross, Green Park, Vauxhall and Victoria), as well as the development of Crossrail.

"Crossrail presented many of the challenges we face regularly – tunnelling underneath areas of major structures and listed buildings, in the historic centre of a large city," says Zeidler. "It means we must design the construction, excavation and support in a way that minimises ground movements, settlements and the impact on people's lives, while maintaining existing services. We feel privileged to have served the project through every stage, from design to completion."

With the boom in tunnelling and underground development continuing, and the company's teams in Europe, North America, South America and Asia increasingly in demand, it's clear that GZ Consultants will be unearthing interesting underground challenges for many years to come.

TRANSFORMING TOMORROW

NAME ARCELORMITTAL
HEADQUARTERS LUXEMBOURG
WEBSITE CORPORATE.ARCELORMITTAL.COM

"WE BELIEVE THE latest innovations in steel sheet piling solutions will inspire design engineers to look at steel solutions in a new light for tomorrow's major civil engineering projects," says Amit Sengupta, Chief Marketing Officer, ArcelorMittal Europe Long Products. "We want to deliver value engineering to the client and meet today's requirements for the circular economy."

Sheet piles are steel profiles with longitudinal clutches at each side creating a mechanical connection – an interlock – between the profiles allowing the construction of continuous retaining walls in a simple clean and fast way. They are used worldwide for the construction of quay walls in harbours, flood defences, retaining walls for rail and highways, underground car parks and basements, and as temporary cofferdams in land or water. ArcelorMittal has been producing hot rolled steel sheet piles for more than 100 years to build reliable and cost-effective permanent and temporary soil retention and water containment structures.

Continuous innovation and investment has resulted in more sophisticated steel grades and a unique new range of sheet piles with optimised geometry to enable wider, lighter sheet pile solutions, which are weight- and cost-efficient. "Our engineers engage with clients and their designers in the early stages of a project," says Sengupta. "We want to understand their needs and share our technical expertise to provide high-end technical solutions."

With designs also considering the end-of-service-life scenario, an important advantage of steel is that it is recyclable. "Steel sheet piles can be recovered using the same method and equipment used to install them, which is why the recovery rate for steel sheet piling is 99 per cent," says Sengupta. The life cycle inventories of steel sheet piling products are documented in an accredited Environmental Product Declaration. ArcelorMittal also offers the rental of steel sheet piling for temporary works, with a short lead time. When piles are returned they are cleaned, repaired and made ready for re-use.

ArcelorMittal is the world's leading steel and mining company, committed to producing safe, sustainable steel. "Our research and development ensures a future of safe and sustainable steel solutions for tomorrow's civil engineering projects," says Sengupta. "It's why our slogan is 'transforming tomorrow'."

EXPLODING THE MYTH

NAME EPC UNITED KINGDOM PLC
UK HEADQUARTERS ALFRETON, DERBYSHIRE
WEBSITE WWW.EPC-GROUPE.CO.UK

EXPLOSIVES ARE A risky business. But in the right hands, such as those of Dr Rob Farnfield, Head of Explosives Engineering at EPC-UK for the last 20 years, those risks can be controlled. "Using explosives in an uncontrolled manner comes with extremely high risks," he says. "However, the strict regulations and high levels of safety training and competence EPC-UK insists upon result in a very low residual risk."

A French-owned firm, EPC-UK has been manufacturing and deploying high explosives for more than 100 years and enjoys a worldwide reputation for safety, security and technological innovation. Often the challenge is in countering public perception of risk, as projects that require blasting services are often located within or near housing. One such project was the widening of the A5 near Snowdonia in 2006/7, where 104,000 tonnes of rock needed to be drilled and blasted, within 100 metres of a 250-year-old stone bridge and two houses. Previous efforts had raised local opposition but, through consultation with farmers, residents and local schools, EPC-UK was able to allay fears, and the expertise of its engineers kept vibration and noise to a minimum.

Dr Farnfield cites improvements in technology and training as the key advances in his time at EPC-UK, and the company has interests that are diversified into fuel additives, logistics, security and even farming. "One of the basic principles in the explosives industry around the world is safety distances between storage facilities and the public," he says. "Companies like ours often own large areas of land, so we farm it."

The firm owns more than 2,000 acres of farmland in Essex and Derbyshire, producing wheat, rapeseed and peas – an unusual brand extension, but in keeping with EPC-UK's wider philosophy. "By taking environmental responsibility for the protective barrier of countryside around us, we're making a difference," says Dr Farnfield. "It's the same in civil engineering, where projects are often very near housing and we monitor, predict and control the environmental impact. That's where we have unparalleled experience."

EPC-UK has a global footprint in the explosives market, but a focus on conservation that speaks to the care required when each project needs a personal, local solution.

FROM DEMOLITION TO EXPANSION

NAME KELTBRAY GROUP
HEADQUARTERS ESHER, SURREY, UK
WEBSITE WWW.KELTBRAY.COM

KELTBRAY WAS FORMED in 1976 as a small earth and groundworks company. Over the past four decades it has been transformed into a £369 million group of companies that plays a key role in maintaining and developing Britain's built environment by providing a multitude of services These include engineering design, demolition, piling, environmental management and reinforced concrete structures. It also specialises in rail services, including overhead line electrification design and build and other track and civils work.

The group is still privately owned by Chief Executive Brendan Kerr, who became sole shareholder in 2003. "At Keltbray we have developed our capability as a specialist contractor to support our clients' evolving needs," he says. "The result has been a greater diversification and an increased integration of our services which are delivered by our own expert people, and by utilising high-value and specialist equipment. This self-delivery model requires continuous investment in plant capability and means we employ, manage and train our own people. The result is larger, longer-term and more technically complex contracts with a higher risk profile."

Keltbray sees its people as integral to the group's success. The company provides direct employment for around 1,500 people, and at the core of its philosophy is the belief that anyone, with the correct attitude and aptitude, should be given the opportunity to fulfil their potential. To realise this potential, and be fit for future growth, Keltbray invests over £2 million per annum in training and development.

For Kerr, Keltbray has a set of family values that have helped shape the company and create a strong sense of identity. "These have resulted in a low turnover of staff and been key to our stability and growth," he says. "While retaining staff is essential, we are also focused on attracting the best skills and talent to future-proof our business. One in 13 of our people is now an apprentice, graduate or trainee, but we've got to keep on working to get the message across to more young people that construction offers great job prospects, job security and a range of opportunities."

Keltbray's client list reads like a *Who's Who* of the development and infrastructure world and includes Land Securities, Balfour Beatty, Network Rail and Crown Estates, to mention but a few. Its companies' signs can be seen on cranes and construction sites across the UK and current projects include Earl's Court (pictured), Chelsea Barracks and Battersea Power Station in London, as well as long-term contracts for Crossrail and Great Western Mainline for its rail division. The company's engineering design house and environmental materials business have also secured work on the Thames Tideway Tunnel and Crossness Sewage Treatment Works.

The group's performance has resulted in a slew of awards. In 2017 it broke into the top 50 private mid-market growth companies, ranking 45th in the annual *Sunday Times* Grant Thornton Top Track 250. It was also named Specialist Contractor of the Year in the Building Awards, while Kerr was presented with a Roll of Honour award by *Construction News*.

Looking ahead, the company is focused on its continued prosperity and a turnover growth target of £400 million. "Keltbray has survived and thrived by continually aiming to be the best," says Kerr. "We see ourselves as the Rolls-Royce of the industry, and we will always go the extra mile and ensure we provide excellent quality."

STRONG FOUNDATIONS

NAME ABBEY PYNFORD
HEADQUARTERS HEMEL HEMPSTEAD, UK
WEBSITE WWW.ABBEYPYNFORD.CO.UK

AFTER WORKING TOGETHER for several years on a number of projects, engineers Paul Kiss and Phil Jones joined forces in 1988 to form Abbey Foundations. They were keen to bring to the profession a fresh integrity and transparency that it had sometimes lacked.

Abbey specialised in underpinning, repairing foundations, and mini piling projects. When the established engineering firm, Pynford, ran into difficulties, Kiss and Jones – keen to benefit from Pynford's expertise and pioneering reputation – took it over, and the business became Abbey Pynford. Pynford had developed a technique for creating concrete structures beneath an existing building, using support stools that remain permanently in place. "Relying on the sturdiness of the platforms thus created, it is possible to lift and move entire buildings," says Head of Business Development Tim Casalis de Pury.

Abbey Pynford's flagship project thus far has been moving the Belle Tout Lighthouse atop Beachy Head, East Sussex. Due to severe erosion of the chalk cliffs, the decommissioned landmark was in danger of sliding into the English Channel. "We put in a new reinforced concrete foundation under the structure and laid down steel railway-type tracks," says Casalis de Pury. "We then jacked the building up a bit and simply slid it along on to a new concrete bed."

The lighthouse's foundation has also been specially designed to make another move possible with further erosion. "It's the haute couture of civil engineering," he says. "The project was undertaken more in the spirit of an artistic exercise than as a commercial venture, and it didn't return enormous profits." However, the prestige that it has garnered, and the discoveries made during the process have more than repaid its time and expenditure.

Much of Abbey Pynford's work is in piling, new foundations and retrofit basement construction – installing new spaces under existing structures. Its specialisation is in creating bespoke designed solutions to individual situations, taking into account the characteristics of each site and its specific ground conditions. It thrives on fresh challenges, and the company is constantly looking forward and experimenting. "There is a special excitement for us, as well as for our clients, when something we try out for the first time actually works," says Casalis de Pury. "It's a fantastic feeling."

CHANNEL SURFING

———

NAME HALFEN
UK HEADQUARTERS DUNSTABLE, BEDFORDSHIRE
WEBSITE WWW.HALFEN.CO.UK

"HALFEN'S MOST RECOGNISABLE product is the cast-in channel, a structural connection which enables you to connect steelwork to reinforced concrete," says Mark Smith, Technical Director of Halfen Ltd. "People tend to refer to these types of fixings as 'Halfens', due to the strong brand name and long heritage." Halfen originally launched the channel in 1929 when the company was founded. "Casting a C-section of steel into concrete," says Smith, "creates an anchor channel connection that is ideal for fixing and adjusting assembly-friendly installations. Applications include facades, precast concrete elements, lift guide rails, stadium seating, pipe fixings, signs and balustrades." One example is the Warner Stand at Lord's cricket ground (pictured, left), where Halfen, Arup, Populous and BAM worked closely to find the best solution for the balustrade fixing.

While the channel remains Halfen's signature product, these days it is just one of 20,000 different items manufactured by the company, which now has 1,100 employees worldwide. "We have diversified into many different construction products – dealing with reinforcement, framing, thermal connections and so on – but most are related to steel connections that are cast into concrete," says Smith. "Because of this diversity, if one product does not suit a particular application, we can try another. We have a lot of flexibility."

New technology has raised the expectations of what is achievable in the world of construction. "Structural designs are now optimised," says Smith, "which often means less concrete to fix to. Loads are also getting bigger, particularly as more components of the building are now modular and produced offsite." Halfen finds connection solutions to these problems that will allow for both adjustment on site and for any possible future connections.

"We work closely with architects, engineers and consultants from the early stages of each project," says Smith. "We try to ensure the most appropriate Halfen products are specified and used. We're currently working on Hinkley Point nuclear power station, manufacturing bespoke channels to meet the particular and exacting requirements. We have done this on many similar hi-spec projects, including Heathrow Terminals 2 & 5, Crossrail and the Kingdom Tower in Saudi Arabia, utilising Halfen's production facilities to produce specific channel solutions to meet the customers' demands."

HIRE GROUND

NAME SPEEDY HIRE
LOCATION HAYDOCK, MERSEYSIDE, UK
WEBSITE WWW.SPEEDYSERVICES.COM

EMPLOYING MORE THAN 3,700 people, based in over 210 depots across the UK, Ireland, Middle East and Kazakhstan, Speedy is a leading tool and equipment hire and services company. "Our vision is to provide safe, reliable services to enable customers to successfully deliver their projects," says Marketing Director Karen Whittingham. "Our customers range from large, multi-site corporate businesses, through to small, family-run enterprises, operating in the construction, infrastructure, industrial and utilities markets."

In four decades as a market leader, Speedy has expanded to offer over 3,000 product lines, as well as services such as product and consumable sales, training, and testing inspection and certification, through the acquisition of Lloyds British in 2016. Delivering service excellence to customers is a key strategic priority. This resulted in the launch of the company's same-day delivery promise; any order for a key product received by 3pm will be delivered the same day. The company is also well known for its innovation, whether in being first to market with sustainable, cutting-edge new equipment, or in IT systems which enable customers to view their activity on-line,

and transact via a mobile app. Surveys show that 90 per cent of customers are satisfied or very satisfied with Speedy's service, which includes a full end-to-end solution. "We offer a range of connected services and hire products," says Whittingham. "If we're hiring out excavators and powered-access machines, we can provide the fuel management and relevant product training. For customers that purchase their own plant and equipment, we can carry out testing inspection and certification services through Lloyds British."

"Through working with key customers on projects such as Thames Tideway, Crossrail, Hinckley Point and HS2, we know the importance of logistics, availability and speed of response," says Sales Director Neil Newsome. "The industry is increasingly under pressure to be more efficient and deliver projects within timescales and budget. We are committed to supporting our civil engineering customers by supplying everything from tools and consumables, through to powered-access and power-generation equipment, with reliable, guaranteed deliveries, and backed up by an emergency out-of-hours service for those unforeseen project requirements."

FORGING CONNECTIONS

NAME PICK EVERARD
HEADQUARTERS LEICESTER, UK
WEBSITE WWW.PICKEVERARD.CO.UK

PICK EVERARD BELIEVES that the construction industry can do better by delivering more collaboratively and with better outcomes for clients, stakeholders and communities. Its collaborative ethos, range of technical expertise and early adoption of innovation ensures it delivers value for money for clients and positively contributes to the industry as a whole.

Operating for more than 150 years, Pick Everard has 11 offices across the UK, interconnected to deliver a local service with the benefits of national scale. Its broad suite of services include civil and structural engineering, architecture, building services, quantity surveying, project and facilities management, energy consultancy and more.

"A multi-professional offering means we can draw on any service that a project needs by working collaboratively between the various disciplines within the practice," says Partner Mark Colby. Colby joined the firm in 1986, specialising in the field of water management, and he's now responsible for civil engineering and structural disciplines within the practice. Colby can attest that co-ordination across the group is helped by strong staff retention.

"We create a culture that makes people want to stay," he says. The firm is looking to grow, with a 2020 Vision which outlines a strategy to achieve a £50 million turnover and employ more than 500 fee-earning staff in the next five years. Gender equality will play a large part in that process.

"We have STEM (science, technology, engineering, maths) ambassadors who go into schools and promote engineering subjects to young people," says Colby. "We champion women's role in construction, encouraging them to bring their talents and ideas to plug the industry skills gap. This is why we work with local universities to offer placements and work experience. We're growing our own graduates and extending our apprentice scheme."

Pick Everard's diverse projects include legacy work such as the Commonwealth Games in Glasgow, redeveloping Leicester Cathedral Gardens and upgrading Severn Trent's largest sewage treatment works. Collaboration is the key. "The partnership approach is at the heart of everything we do," says Colby. "We believe what sets us apart is our commitment to enhancing how we improve communities through our work."

THE ROAD AHEAD

NAME BAM NUTTALL
HEADQUARTERS CAMBERLEY, SURREY, UK
WEBSITE WWW.BAMNUTTALL.CO.UK

THROUGHOUT BAM NUTTALL'S distinguished 153-year history there is a common theme that unites the diverse projects that the civil engineering contractor has carried out. From iconic infrastructure developments such as the Manchester Ship Canal in 1894 to today's astonishing King's Cross regeneration, BAM Nuttall welcomes a challenge. Whether constructing Liverpool's emblematic Liver Building or creating sub-stations in remote parts of Scotland, undertaking demanding projects is ingrained in the company's DNA.

"The way our engineers are wired up, they particularly like complex, challenging jobs," says BAM Nuttall's CEO Steve Fox. "Many of the projects we've delivered recently have involved a lot of innovation and we work with new techniques and new technology to bring about a solution."

Such a mindset is neatly captured in the company's ethos: "Building the present, creating the future by bringing engineering to life." With the advent of digital technology, civil engineering is rapidly changing and impacting upon how the company does business.

"In a very short period of time we're going to see a complete step change in the industry," says Fox. "We'll see the use of robotics on site; an increased use of 4D and 5D modelling, where we can demonstrate to a customer exactly how we're going to build their piece of infrastructure, and new and evolving roles for people on site. It's like a second industrial revolution. The good news is that BAM Nuttall is very much at the vanguard of that."

As the civil engineering arm of Royal BAM in the UK, BAM Nuttall delivers services across all sectors across the country, from rail to road and beyond. The company is one of the largest providers of civil engineering rail services to Network Rail, and works closely with Highways England. Other vital projects include implementing flood defence schemes with the Environment Agency, and the company also specialises in marine projects, having recently completed work for Peel Ports' Liverpool2 expansion programme.

Besides pioneering a collaborative approach to early contractor involvement – something BAM Nuttall achieved at the beginning of this century with the A500 Stoke Pathfinder project – the company displays remarkable feats of innovation in other areas. It recently completed a world-first Gravity Base Foundation project off the coast of Blyth for a new wind farm in Northumberland, which paves the way for greater flexibility as to where such structures can be installed in future.

Other notable recent schemes include the reopening of the Borders Railway line between Galashiels and Edinburgh for Network Rail; the Leeds Flood Alleviation Scheme for the Environment Agency and Leeds City Council; the Ordsall Chord in Manchester, which links the city's Piccadilly and Victoria train stations; and the northbound bore of the Blackwall Tunnel.

But in a rapidly changing working environment, Fox is particularly proud of BAM Nuttall's commitment to bringing more young people, particularly women, into the industry. "We have recognised the need to bring people in from all parts of the country and at different levels," he says. "Give them the tools to do their jobs, give them interesting projects to work on, and a stimulating working environment, and retain them."

In an era of great change, this philosophy will see BAM Nuttall forge ahead for another 150 years.

GREEN AND BEAUTIFUL

NAME MANNINGS (ASIA) CONSULTANTS LTD
LOCATION HONG KONG, CHINA
WEBSITE WWW.MANNINGSASIA.COM

FOR MARK CHEUNG, Managing Director of Mannings (Asia) Consultants Ltd (MACL), the company's recent detailed design of a road-noise-reduction project incorporating living "green" walls and roof is a classic example of his desire for infrastructure projects to be innovative, effective and attractive.

"I think we're one of the few engineering companies in the region who approach projects using this sort of innovation," explains Cheung. "If the infrastructure we put in place is not attractive, people living here will consider it an eyesore, and in some cases they won't use it. So our main purpose is to make sure that all our infrastructure designs are accepted by local people, effective, and easy for them to use. That's our design philosophy."

In the 12 years since MACL was launched in Hong Kong, Cheung and the now 200-strong team of this engineering consultancy have built a strong reputation for delivering on those principles. Established by experienced professional engineers with a wide variety of expertise, the company has undertaken projects in China, Southeast Asia and Africa, offering services ranging from infrastructure, traffic and building to drainage, geotechnical

and environmental. The firm's contracts have included traffic improvement and noise reduction initiatives, environmental impact studies, bridge construction reviews, and the design and construction of disabled access facilities.

"Hong Kong is a congested city with a growing population and lots of buildings close to roads," says Cheung. "We're involved in a number of projects retrofitting barrier-free access to facilities such as footbridges and subways, as well as pedestrian access and noise reduction." But innovation and appealing design remain a high priority – and not just for the benefit of the community.

"Because our projects are quite innovative and attractive, young engineers often join the company looking to achieve something special," says Cheung. "We make sure they understand that, as well as sound engineering, we need to come up with designs that improve people's living environment, and encourage them to use facilities more. This means that engineers enjoy their work more. When people talk about engineering, they often don't mean the things that affect us every day. If we can repackage engineering so that people understand it can look beautiful, and is part of daily life, that would make a big difference."

THE ART OF THE STEEL

NAME AMP CONSULTANTS
LOCATION DARLINGTON, COUNTY DURHAM
WEBSITE WWW.AMPCONSULTANTS.COM

FROM ITS LOCATION in the engineering heartlands of the North East, AMP Consultants has been embedded in structural design and the steel industry since it was formed in 1992. The company was founded following the demise of the Conder Group, and was set up by three former technical directors at Conder, picking up where the old company left off. "We've maintained all our major clients since then," says Managing Director David Hodgson. "We work with steel fabricators of all sizes, from small local companies here in the North East to some of the biggest in the country."

AMP specialises in designing and advising on the construction of steel frame structures of all types, working from the foundations upwards to develop structural engineering solutions. It has constructed buildings in just about every sector, including health, education, commerce, retail and leisure, industrial, residential and transport, bringing with them decades of success and a senior team of experienced and imaginative engineers.

"When we receive a design-and-build project, we engineer all the designs," explains Hodgson, an ICE member who has worked in structural

engineering since 1980. "It can be any project of any size, from an aircraft hangar to a school building; a distribution centre to an office block."

Hodgson emphasises AMP's expertise but also the commitment to innovation. The company has long embraced 3D modelling and has been working with BIM (building information modelling) for many years. This experience with BIM means that AMP is able to provide clients with improved design, shorter build times and ultimately reduced costs.

"We wanted to be at the forefront of structural analysis and design," says Hodgson. "We've managed to reduce steel weight by 30-40 per cent for our clients' projects – a substantial saving which is good for the industry and good for continuous employment. We've done so much work in the structural steel industry born out of fierce competition, because if steel fabricators weren't innovative they wouldn't survive. There isn't that sense of innovation and competition anywhere else in Europe that I can see. It's a vital part of what we do." AMP is now engaged with Fondazione Promozione Acciaio in Italy to promote structural steel as the preferred method of construction.

A COLLABORATIVE LEGACY

NAME BARHALE
HEADQUARTERS WALSALL, WEST MIDLANDS, UK
WEBSITE WWW.BARHALE.CO.UK

WITH A PORTFOLIO offering a full spectrum of services to infrastructure clients, Barhale has a reputation for flexibility, collaboration and innovation. It delivers whole-life-cost, low-carbon, digitally enabled solutions in a variety of fields, from major civil-engineering structures, tunnels, pipelines and bridges, to capital maintenance and advanced optimisation of water-system operations.

"We are the civil engineering contractor with the expertise to take on projects that others might find difficult," says Samantha Barratt, Business Development and Communications Director. "We have the ability to design, fabricate and install footbridges, deliver electrical substation infrastructure, or undertake new and refurbished utilities while also delivering major infrastructure projects. The more challenging the problem, the more we like it."

The family-run company was founded in 1980 by Chairman Dennis Curran as a specialist tunnelling contractor. It has since become a major force within the construction industry through innovative development, and works nationwide for major clients across water, energy, rail and the built environment. "Barhale is a £150 million-plus company," says Barratt. "It is not the biggest, but it has a well-

developed direct employment model, and punches above its weight. We have an enviable reputation in the water industry, working alongside major tier-one contractors, sometimes in close collaboration, sometimes in competition. One of our biggest challenges has been the 25 km water pipeline for Severn Trent, a key element of the £300 million Birmingham Resilience programme."

Barhale has been fully integrated in Anglian Water's progressive @One Alliance since 2000. Agility and transparency makes Barhale adept at working collaboratively. "It's inherent in our culture and we're comfortable leading or being led on projects," says Barratt.

"People are core to Barhale's strategy, and 38 years after being founded we still retain a family feel through our strong values and cultural ethos," says Matthew Behan, Barhale's CEO. "Our 'Source Train Retain' programme is fundamental to the success of our business sustainability model. The focus on our people is visible through our commitment to direct labour and heightened level of training and development across technical and non-technical areas, coupled with bespoke health and wellbeing programmes, ultimately satisfying our clients' needs."

CASTING DIRECTORS

NAME GOODWIN STEEL CASTINGS
LOCATION HANLEY, STOKE-ON-TRENT, UK
WEBSITE WWW.GOODWINSTEELCASTINGS.COM

"GOODWIN IS A family-controlled build-to-print manufacturer, and it is very passionate about its projects," says Brian Quinn, Sales Director of Goodwin Steel Castings. Founded in 1883, Goodwin is now owned and run by the sixth generation of the Goodwin family. The company originally manufactured castings for the local mining and pottery industries in Stoke. Now Goodwin makes steel castings up to 35 tons for many different industries internationally, including many construction and architectural projects.

Its recent international successes include the Oakland Bay Bridge in San Francisco, for which Goodwin provided all the structural steel castings for the main cables, and the Hardanger Suspension Bridge in Norway. In London, Goodwin manufactured the high-tensile steel castings that support the Wembley Arch; at the Cabinet Offices in Whitehall, Goodwin manufactured the steel columns and the glazing arms for the walkway canopy. In the refurbishment of Paddington Station, Goodwin supplied castings for the roof structure. "They were manufactured in super-duplex steel," says Quinn, "to be aesthetically pleasing, yet maintain the structural integrity of the roof."

A key priority is to engage with project engineers at the design stage. "The engineers work with the foundry to design something manufacturable," says Quinn. "Goodwin adds value by providing solutions that architects and design engineers don't necessarily conceive at the early stages. Rather than expensive fabrications, castings can be an aesthetically pleasing solution to many problems."

New technology plays a key role. "The sole source of information used to be 2-D drawings," says Quinn. "Today's customers are more discerning in their requirements for the projects and the design of their components. They want castings to be identical to their computer models. We now take the customer-generated 3-D models and incorporate them into our methods of manufacture, guaranteeing the component's geometric shape and tolerance. We also use the latest laser-scan technology for geometry verification."

Goodwin recognises that investment in people as well as technology is key for long-term growth, and set up an engineering apprentice school in 2012. The first graduates are now employed in varying roles within the group, and the school's success enhances their engineering capability.

DESIGN-LED INNOVATION

NAME CAREY GROUP
LOCATION UK
WEBSITE WWW.CAREYSPLC.CO.UK

"AS A COMPANY, we focus on providing solutions for our clients," says Steve Regan, CEO of Careys Civil Engineering, a Carey Group company. "We're always striving to do things better for each project we work on, which is something our clients really appreciate."

The companies that make up the Carey Group provide specialist construction services – design, asbestos removal, demolition, civil engineering, dry lining, new homes and resource recovery across multiple sectors. The group offers these disciplines as integrated, digitally planned packages, winning them numerous contracts on some of the UK's most prestigious and complex construction projects.

Carey Group offers clients end-to-end solutions to overcome key industry challenges. "Normally, our clients would need to go to a different contractor for each service they need," says Regan. "But with us, they can utilise Careys Design Team to plan their project and then deploy resources from Scudder Demolition through to Careys Civil Engineering and Seneca Resource Recovery to complete the project."

Careys Design Team was established to enhance the group's ability to work on increasingly complex projects. "Our Design Team plays a key role in our ability to plan projects before we get to site," says Regan, describing how it has transformed the company's business model. A team of engineers analyses a project proposal to identify and overcome key challenges, before working with building information modelling (BIM) technicians and 4D specialists to visually model and test the methodology.

These models are used throughout Carey projects, including during presentations to clients. "Both our clients and project teams have seen real value from our ability to explain and demonstrate how we overcome project challenges," says Regan.

At Rathbone Square in central London, where Careys Civil Engineering was principal contractor during construction of the basement, pre-construction visualisation played a key role in overcoming project challenges inherent in urban developments. The project entailed the partial demolition of the decommissioned, seven-storey Royal Mail building, located amid tourist-filled shopping streets and luxury hotels. The 4D modelling developed for the project enabled the team to overcome the logistical challenges of part-demolishing an original 1950s building in addition to providing the design of the complex temporary works used to complete the project.

Alongside proactive investment in new technology and specialist equipment to enable safer, more efficient and sustainable methodologies, Careys invests in its people and their ongoing training. "It's about lifelong learning," says Regan. "From our in-house academy that trains our people in a range of operational skills to our 'Black Hat' supervisor programme that develops their management and people skills, our teams undergo continual development from the first day they start their career with us. Creating the right environment is so important to everyone at Careys. All members of the team, both site and office based, are encouraged to become 'better every day'. No stone is left unturned in the pursuit of better solutions for our clients."

The world of construction and resource recovery keeps presenting new challenges. With its pre-construction visualisation capabilities, high standards of client engagement and expert teams empowered to find better ways of working on the ground, Careys is well placed to meet these challenges – and to continue to play a vital part in future UK construction projects.

GERMAN EFFICIENCY SINCE 1873

NAME HOCHTIEF
LOCATION ESSEN, GERMANY
WEBSITE WWW.HOCHTIEF.COM

HOCHTIEF IS A leading global construction and services group. The group is present in the transportation, energy and urban infrastructure sectors as well as in the contract mining, public/private partnerships and services markets. With around 54,000 employees and a sales volume of about €23 billion in 2017, Hochtief's global presence is focused on developed markets. Through the CIMIC Group, it is the market leader in Australia. In the US, Hochtief is the number-one general builder through its subsidiary Turner; while another Hochtief subsidiary, Flatiron, ranks among the most important players in the field of civil works, mainly in the transportation infrastructure sector.

"Since its beginnings transportation infrastructure has been at the core of Hochtief's portfolio, delivering highways, railway, stations, airports, ports, harbours, bridges and tunnels," says Lawrence Jackson, Managing Director Hochtief UK Business. Recent projects have included the on-going Champlain Bridge in Montreal (a 3.4 km, triple deck, cable-stayed road bridge), Gotthard Base Tunnel in the Swiss Alps (a 57 km rail tunnel, the longest in the world), Crossrail C310 Thames Tunnel (twin 2.6 km, 6.2 metre-

diameter bored tunnels beneath the River Thames) and Queensferry Crossing, Scotland (a 2.7 km cable-stayed road bridge).

The Queensferry Crossing – a Guinness World Record holder for the longest pair of free-standing balanced cantilevers at 643.9 metres – was a technically challenging scheme that involved thousands of operatives, engineers and specialists. The elegant structure has the suspension cables in the centre of the bridge deck providing a sleek and unobstructed view.

Hochtief maintains a rigorous focus on economic, ecological and social aspects in its work, recognising that long-term success is driven by the interplay of these factors. In September 2017, Hochtief was recognised for its sustainable corporate management for the 12th year in a row and was included in the internationally renowned Dow Jones Sustainability Index. "Five guiding principles represent our values: integrity, accountability, innovation, delivery, and sustainability, underpinned by the precondition of safety," says Jackson. "As a future-oriented company, we assume accountability for society and the environment."

STEELING BEAUTY

NAME CLEVELAND BRIDGE UK LTD
HEADQUARTERS DARLINGTON, COUNTY DURHAM, UK
WEBSITE WWW.CLEVELANDBRIDGE.COM

CLEVELAND BRIDGE GROUP is a global leader in the design, engineering, fabrication and construction of steel structures. Founded in the UK in 1877, the company has a long track record of innovation in steel construction. In 1905, it built the iconic Victoria Falls Bridge over the Zambezi River, in 1911 the Middlesbrough Transporter Bridge and in 1932 the famous Sydney Harbour Bridge. Many more milestone bridge projects followed, including the Forth Road Bridge in Edinburgh, the Bosphorus Bridge in Turkey and Hong Kong's stunning Tsing Ma Bridge. More recently, it has played a key role in the construction of the Wembley Stadium Arch, the Shard in London and the Burj Al Arab in Dubai.

It is now part of the Al Rushaid Group, producing high-quality structural steel components at advanced manufacturing centres in the UK, Dubai and Saudi Arabia. Its network of sales offices covers Europe, India, China and the Middle East.

The combination of highly skilled designers and engineers with technically advanced manufacturing facilities enables Cleveland Bridge Group to produce up to 150,000 tonnes of precision-engineered steel every year. Its products are engineered to fulfil the most demanding applications in the highways, rail, built environment, power, oil and gas and nuclear sectors.

"We design, manufacture and install steel bridges of every type, including beam, truss, cable and modular bridges," says Managing Director Chris Droogan. "Our knowledge and expertise enables us to bring innovation and value engineering to any project, helping to solve problems, save time, costs and resources for clients, while improving safety and environmental performance."

"Our job is also to prove steel's worth in areas like sustainability, flexibility, speed to market and aesthetic finish," says Droogan. "Sustainability is not merely a question of environmental responsibility. It's also about a sustainable business; about health, safety, well-being and service quality. It's about being active in the community and running an ethical business." A sustainable business also includes a commitment to apprenticeships that is helping to address the skills shortage. "We're identifying talent and making sure apprentices have a solid career path onwards and upwards," says Droogan.

KING OF THE HILL

NAME FRASER CONSTRUCTION CO. LTD
LOCATION WONG CHUK HANG, HONG KONG
WEBSITE WWW.FRASERCONSTRUCTION.COM.HK

"HONG KONG IS very hilly," says Ringo Yu, Managing Director of Fraser Construction Co Ltd. "For some work you can't use sizeable machinery on the slopes, so we have to resort to manual labour or clever lifting methods to convey construction materials."

Fraser Construction's work involves stabilising hillsides and laying the foundations for buildings on the slopes of Hong Kong. The island is densely populated and most of the works are in the vicinity of occupied buildings. For Fraser Construction this means that careful planning and cooperation with the neighbourhood is important in order to have the least impact on local people and to remain complaint-free during course of a project.

"We have to liaise and coordinate with neighbours around the construction site to make sure they know what we're doing," says Yu, "and so that things like the noise don't interfere with their daily activities. There may be a school, there may be children having classes. Sometimes we have to stop the work to let them take their examinations." In addition to being a considerate neighbour, Fraser Construction strives to be environmentally

friendly. "This means not just keeping noise and pollution to a minimum but also generating less waste," says Yu.

An average job for Fraser Construction would require 40 management personnel and about 200 labourers. The company runs a sound safety-management system, with managers taking every precaution to protect labourers and staff.

"We have to plan our method or sequence of construction carefully in order to protect nearby properties and not to trigger landslides," says Yu. "We carry out a risk assessment to identify hazards. When stablisation of a slope is in progress, we cover the bared slope surface with tarpaulin sheets to protect the soil from being washed away during heavy rainfall. We also construct temporary drainage to divert rainwater to proper discharge points."

The adoption of soil nails, which are driven into the soil to stabilise it, has eliminated the removal or recompaction of large amount of soil. "This has reduced risks, improved safety and transformed our work," says Yu.

CONSTRUCTIVE SOLUTIONS

NAME IMC WORLDWIDE LTD
HEADQUARTERS REDHILL, SURREY, UK
WEBSITE WWW.IMCWORLDWIDE.COM

A CYCLE LANE that cuts across a main thoroughfare, a poorly connected railway line, vast windows that flood a school with light yet leave children shivering in winter – we're all familiar with the realities of poor planning. None more so than Gavin English, Managing Director of the international development consultancy, IMC Worldwide. "All too often, mistakes are made because the right people haven't been consulted on change," he says.

English's company is different. It carefully balances the development of "hard" infrastructure – such as roads and bridges – with "soft" infrastructure, such as the institutions, systems and skills required to support economic growth. "You've got to understand how people will use new structures and services," he says. "For example, following the 2004 tsunami in Indonesia, locals told us that the new houses we built had to be orientated a certain way. And everything had to be yellow because that's the colour of hope."

Formed in 1997, IMC grew from the successive mergers and expansions of firms dating back to 1856. In 2011, English led a buy-out, and today IMC is an independent, multi-disciplinary business. Working with governments, NGOs, multilateral donors and private corporations across 40 countries, the company has expanded from 80 permanent and contract staff to over 400 in just six years. "People who work for us want to help the world's disadvantaged in a professional yet compassionate culture," says English. "It's about giving back."

One ongoing success has been the UK Aid-funded Rural Access Programme (RAP) in Nepal. Since 1999, IMC has built over 1,000 km of roads that have improved rural communities' access to markets, education and health facilities. RAP won a British Expertise International Award in 2014 and an award from ACE in 2017, and has changed the lives of 625,000 people. "Road works are undertaken by 8,000 locals drawn from the poorest sectors of society, so they gain paid work," says English. "We're building livelihoods and educating communities on financial management, agriculture and livestock. On average, incomes have grown by 220 per cent and school enrolment by 80 per cent. Kids from these areas never had the chance to go to university. They now do."

RAP shows how the company's "hard" and "soft" aspects work in tandem. "It's a long-term approach," says English. "Real change takes time."

FORENSIC INVESTIGATORS

NAME HAWKINS
HEADQUARTERS LONDON, UK
WEBSITE WWW.HAWKINS.BIZ

IT'S OFTEN SAID that "accidents happen". But, when it comes to the built environment, Andrew Reeves, Principal Associate of Hawkins, takes an opposing view. "Nearly all construction-related failures are down to poor workmanship, lack of supervision or defective design – and often a combination of all three."

Hawkins is a firm of forensic investigators that began with a single office in Cambridge in 1980, focusing on fire investigation. It now has eight UK offices, plus Dubai, Hong Kong and Singapore, investigating a wide range of failures. When the dust settles after a collapse, fire or flood, it falls to industry experts such as Hawkins to assess what happened, how it happened and why.

Reeves leads the civil engineering and construction team and cites the collapse at Didcot A Power Station in 2016 to explain how Hawkins operates. "I've been to site about 25 times over the past two years and taken detailed measurements and photographs, carried out surveys using laser scanners and drones, and performed a detailed back-analysis to understand exactly how the structure failed," he says. "We've prepared technical reports and videos to assist the legal team, the police and the Health & Safety Executive."

More recently, the firm has been investigating the aftermath of the Grenfell Tower fire in west London and these two examples give you an idea of the complexity, timescales and sensitivities involved in Hawkins' work. In dealing with issues of liability and the potential for legal proceedings, forensic work requires a cool head alongside academic and technical excellence, especially as most cases are taken on individually.

That said, Reeves also cites a strong team ethic in the company. "It's a great place to work because we all own it and we have such a diverse range of expertise including geotechnical, structural, fire and acoustic engineers, that invariably someone will know the answer," he explains. "But what really differentiates us is our ability to respond rapidly in order to preserve evidence – when the City Gates Church in Ilford collapsed during construction in 2012 we had a team, equipped with a drone, on site within the hour."

At a time when building safety is at the forefront of public awareness, Hawkins has a key role to play in ensuring the technical questions around failures are answered and lessons from previous mistakes are learned.

CHAPTER TWO

ENVIRONMENTAL IMPACT

Today, two of the key issues that civil engineers are being forced to face are combating the effects of climate change, and increasing access to clean water. Too many of the world's population are denied access to a clean water supply, sufficient energy and effective waste management. At the same time, the pressure we are putting on our planet's resources is immense. A solution lies in engineering and building on the already huge strides that have been made over the past two centuries in areas such as hygiene and healthcare, environmental protection, sustainable fuels and greener living.

ICE200

ICE 200
THAMES BARRIER
THE CAPITAL'S FAMOUS FLOOD DEFENCE

LOCATION LONDON, UK
CONSTRUCTION DATES 1974–82

IN 1953, THE east coast of England and the Thames Estuary felt the full force of a disastrous flood. Over 300 people lost their lives. If the flood had got all the way to the highly populated, low-lying areas of Central London, the results would have been even more horrific. This flood led to a dramatic rethink in the way in which flood defences were built to protect London.

Following a 1966 report by Sir Hermann Bondi, it was decided that the best solution was to raise the banks together with a flood barrier with movable gates built across the river at Woolwich Reach. The Greater London Council appointed Rendel, Palmer & Tritton to design the Thames Barrier. Charles Draper, an engineer in the design team, is credited with the idea of "rising sector gates". There are four large gates that span across 61.5 metres, and weigh 3,300 tons each, and two smaller gates spanning 31 metres. The floodgates are circular segments in cross section that are turned by enormous, hydraulic rocker beams.

The water levels of the Thames rise and fall by an average of 7 metres every tidal cycle. The Thames Estuary is also vulnerable to an increase in water levels caused by a North Sea "surge" tide that happens when a band of low-pressure moves across the Atlantic towards the British Isles. The sea under it rises above the normal level, creating a hump of water. These circumstances caused the 1953 floods.

It took eight years to build the barrier. Construction started in 1974 and was completed in October 1982. It was first used in February 1983, and formally opened by Queen Elizabeth II on 8 May 1984. It cost £535 million which was met through central government funding (75 per cent), with the remainder provided by local government. It costs around £8 million a year to maintain and operate.

An individual gate can be closed in 10 to 15 minutes, and to close the whole barrier for a flood defence closure usually takes one and half hours. This provides enough time to check the equipment and stops the potential of a reflective wave. Between 1983 and 2017 the gates had been used 179 times to protect London from fluvial or tidal flooding, a credit to the foresight of those who commissioned it.

ICE 200
DRAINING OF THE FENS
BRITAIN'S BIGGEST LAND-DRAINAGE SCHEME SINCE THE 17TH CENTURY

LOCATION NORFOLK, UK
CONSTRUCTION DATES 1954–64

THE RIVER GREAT Ouse drains rainfall from 13 English counties. In March 1947, the river burst its banks and inundated nearly 60 square miles. The existing flood defences were unsuitable for further improvement: raising them would cause them to sink further into the soft ground below. Instead, it was decided to lower flood levels in the rivers.

Sir Murdoch MacDonald & Partners designed a scheme which partly echoed proposals made by John Rennie in the 19th century and Sir Cornelius Vermuyden in the 17th century. It comprised a relief channel for the Great Ouse between the Denver Sluice and King's Lynn; widening the Ely Ouse upstream of Denver; and installing a cut-off channel around the eastern edge of the Bedford Level. The scheme was approved in parliament in December 1949, but it was August 1953 before agreement was reached with the King's Lynn Conservancy Board about the protection works required in the Wash. Work was eventually undertaken in stages between 1954 and 1964.

The Relief Channel is a 17 km embanked channel that runs alongside the existing tidal outfall channel of the Great Ouse. It can store a large volume of diverted floodwater and discharge it rapidly to the outfall channel at low tide, close to the Wash. Five road bridges and a railway bridge run across it. A head sluice, which admits floodwater from the Ely Ouse above Denver Sluice, and a tail sluice, which controls the outflow of floodwater.

The Cut-Off Channel is a 54 km catchwater, from Mildenhall in Suffolk to Denver in Norfolk, which diverts floodwaters from the rivers Lark, Little Ouse and Wissey before they enter the fens. Its construction required three railway bridges, 28 road bridges, four footbridges and concrete structures to house siphons and sluices where the channel crosses the Little Ouse and Wissey.

In 1971, the Cut-Off Channel was ingeniously modified by a sluice erected across the downstream end of the channel at Denver to reverse the flow during dry periods. Surplus water from the Great Ouse is thus pumped into the headwaters of the rivers Stour, Colne and Blackwater to help meet increasing water demand in Essex. The Ely Ouse to Essex Transfer Scheme takes water from Denver through a 20 km tunnel, two rivers and two pipelines to Abberton and Hanningfield reservoirs in Essex,

LANDSLIP MITIGATION
AN URBAN PROGRAMME THAT AIMS TO SAFEGUARD BOTH LIFE AND ECOLOGY

LOCATION HONG KONG
DATES 1977–

HONG KONG IS A densely urbanised city in hilly terrain. Its combination of substandard man-made slopes and vulnerable natural hillside, together with intense seasonal rainfall, has caused severe landslide problems. Since the 1940s, these have cost 480 lives and caused considerable economic losses.

Commendably, in 1977, the Hong Kong government launched a Landslip Prevention and Mitigation Programme. The plan was – and still is – to retrofit those slopes that posed an undue risk to critical infrastructures and bring them up to modern safety standards. The slopes in need of urgent attention are identified through a risk-based priority ranking system.

The works have improved the lives of millions of citizens by reducing the chance of landslide casualties and minimising community disruption. The scheme is also one of the key components of the Hong Kong government's strategy for climate change adaptation against extreme weather impact.

The programme embraces a range of innovations to promote sustainability and enhance the quality, efficiency and cost-effectiveness of the works. For example, soil nails are used extensively as a robust and versatile measure to upgrade substandard slopes. They are a sustainable and low-maintenance solution and can minimise earthworks and tree felling. Use of time-domain reflectometry (TDR) has been adapted to check the quality of the embedded steel reinforcements and grout columns in soil nails.

Digital and information technology is used routinely to facilitate risk assessment and streamline the design process. Technical breakthroughs have also been made in natural terrain landslide risk management and in the design of debris flow risk-mitigation works. As part of the upgrade effort, the slopes are improved as far as possible with vegetation cover. Apart from enhancing their appearance, this has ecological benefits and promotes biodiversity through the judicious selection of native plant species.

The upgraded slopes are also more resilient against intense rainstorms and the impact of climate change. The slope-retrofitting programme has greatly improved public safety. Quantitative risk assessments have demonstrated that the overall landslide risk has been reduced by more than 75 per cent, a huge credit to the ingenuity of geotechnical engineers. The slope greening and landscaping works have also created a more attractive environment for the citizens of Hong Kong.

HYDROELECTRIC POWER IN NEW ZEALAND
A HYDRO POWER PIONEER

LOCATION THROUGHOUT NEW ZEALAND
DATES 1886–

WITH ITS MOUNTAINS and rivers, New Zealand was an early adopter of hydroelectric power over 100 years ago when the Bullendale gold mine in the hills of Otago in the South Island built a small hydro scheme to power equipment in 1886.

Between 1903 and 1992 the government invested heavily in a number of significant hydroelectric power schemes throughout New Zealand. Early schemes included the Waipori scheme in 1903 and the Lake Coleridge power station, serving Christchurch in 1914. The success of these, along with a rapidly growing population in the 1950s led to construction of the Manapouri power station in the South Island and the ambitious Tongariro Power Scheme comprising three power stations Tokaanu, Rangipo and Mangaio in the North Island built 1964–83.

The Manapouri power station is New Zealand's largest hydro station and second largest power plant. The potential of the site for hydro power had been noted as far back as 1903 because of the steep fall between Lake Manapouri and Doubtful Sound some 10 km away. By building the power station underground by the lake and a tailrace or tunnel down to the sound, water would flow quickly through the turbines to create electricity more efficiently.

Although hydro power is one of the cleanest ways of producing electricity, the large dams and power stations have not been without critics, concerned about the effects on the landscape and wildlife. Manapouri was the first scheme to attract a massive environmental protest, and a plan to build a dam to raise the level of the lake by 30 metres was abandoned.

New Zealand now has over 100 hydroelectric generating plants including five major schemes: Manapouri, Clutha and Waitaki in the South Island, and Tongariro and Waikato in the North Island, as well as numerous other smaller dams throughout the country. Although eight new plants have been built since 2000 and more are planned, these are all small, mainly run-of-river schemes that have less environmental impact than creating large lakes. The last large plant was at the Clyde Dam, South Island, in 1993. This again caused a public outcry as homes and orchards were flooded.

Today hydro power continues to provide over half New Zealand's electricity, having peaked at providing 84 per cent of the country's total demand in 1980. The country has committed to renewable energy and has invested in geothermal, wind, solar and marine energy.

ICE 200

LONDON SEWERAGE SYSTEM

HOW SIR JOSEPH BAZALGETTE BROUGHT SANITATION TO THE CAPITAL

———————

LOCATION LONDON, UK
CONSTRUCTION DATES 1859–66

THE WC, THE water closet, has a lot to answer for. It was in the 1830s that it became the must-have home improvement for many Londoners. The city's excrement, previously collected by "night soil" men, was now flushed into the storm sewers, then on into rivers such as the Fleet and the Wandle and thence into the Thames.

The Thames was tidal and the capital's effluent flowed up and down without ever escaping into the sea. The smell was bad enough, but citizens were also drawing their drinking water from the Thames. And, in an unhappy coincidence, this was also the decade in which the water-borne bacterium, cholera, arrived from India – between 1831 and 1854 it killed more than 20,000 Londoners.

The mistaken orthodoxy of the time was that cholera was spread in a "miasma" through the air. As the abnormally hot summer of 1858 became known as "The Great Stink", something had to be done. As the stench invaded the House of Commons and threatened the health of MPs, self-interest finally led to action.

The Chancellor, Benjamin Disraeli, allowed the Metropolitan Board of Works to borrow £3 million to construct a revolutionary sewage system, independent of the river network. It had been drawn up by the board's newly appointed Chief Engineer, Joseph Bazalgette, the grandson of an immigrant French tailor (the referee for his job application had been another engineer of French extraction, Isambard Kingdom Brunel). He's been rightly called the "Drain Brain".

Over the course of nine years, Bazalgette dug up London to create six "interceptor" sewers 82 miles long and 1,300 miles of main sewers feeding into them. It was a project of breathtaking ambition and extraordinary technical acumen. It had to cross countless canals, railways and roads. And always with a gradual incline from west to east, so that gravity propelled the ordure.

Bazalgette pioneered the use of quick-drying Portland cement and high-baked Staffordshire Blue bricks to build his beautiful vaulted tunnels. At the time, London's population was around 2.5 million. He designed the scheme to accommodate growth to 4.5 million. Today, 150 years later, with successive extensions in 1910, between the wars and in the 1950s, it successfully serves around 10 million.

The destination of London's effluent, sliding west to east, was two enormous pumping stations downstream, at Abbey Mills (now next to the Olympic Stadium) and at Crossness beyond Woolwich. There the waste was held, 40 feet below ground, and pumped up by massive steam engines to be dumped into the retreating tide – not acceptable today but an ingenious solution at the time.

You can visit a massive, restored beam engine at Crossness, now a museum with beautiful Victorian wrought iron. It's a cathedral of sewage designed by Bazalgette's team to demonstrate their pride in great public works. In addition, Bazalgette built the Thames embankments to house his low-level sewer and the new District Line. He constructed three of London's great bridges, introduced thoroughfares such as Charing Cross Road and Shaftesbury Avenue and laid out Battersea Park and Clapham Common. In short, he saved London from terrible disease, improved its transport and communications and made it a more pleasant place to live. A good example of how engineering improves our wealth and health: with inspiration, tenacity, innovation and technical expertise.

SECTION OF OVERFLO

CHAMBER AT JUNCTION OF NORTHERN HIGH & MIDDLE LEVEL SEWERS.

CALDER HALL NUCLEAR POWER STATION
THE WORLD'S FIRST NUCLEAR POWER STATION

LOCATION SELLAFIELD, CUMBRIA, UK
CONSTRUCTION DATES 1953–56

ON 17 OCTOBER 1956, Calder Hall was opened by Her Majesty the Queen in a ceremony that was attended by scientists and statesmen from 40 countries. It was the world's first full-scale nuclear power station, and was billed as the start of the "new atomic age". "This new power," announced the Queen, "which has proved itself to be such a terrifying weapon of destruction, is harnessed for the first time for the common good of our community." The power station was originally designed to last for 20 years but it actually operated safely for 47 years before closing in 2003.

Forming part of the larger Sellafield site, the Calder Hall buildings covered an area equivalent in size to that of Buckingham Palace and its grounds. Engineer Christopher Hinton supervised construction, while the contractor Taylor Woodrow was responsible for the build.

Although the power station was promoted as generating electricity too cheap to meter, in reality most of the electricity produced was used on site with less than 25 per cent fed into the national grid. At its most productive it only generated 196 Megawatts of power, compared with 1200 Megawatts produced by the modern water pressure reactor at Sizewell B. However, Calder Hall was also designed for a military purpose and up until 1995 it produced plutonium for the atomic weapons programme. This process did not produce energy efficiently.

Calder Hall had four Magnox reactors – named after the metal containers used to store the fuel, which were made of magnesium-aluminium alloy. It became the pattern for a series of 11 more power stations around the UK.

By 1976, the first advanced gas-cooled reactors (AGR) began operating. These were built with the sole purpose of producing electricity, making them more efficient. By 2003, years of exposure to high levels of radiation had distorted the fittings at Calder Hall, which put the safe loading and extraction of fuel rods at risk. As it would have been uneconomic to repair, the power station was finally closed.

Calder Hall employed 300 people, many of whom were later involved in removing the fuel from the reactors. The programme to remove the spent fuel rods began in 2011 and is scheduled for completion in 2019.

ICE 200
GOLDFIELDS WATER SUPPLY SCHEME
AN IMMENSE PIPELINE, DELIVERING RUNNING WATER TO THE DESERT

LOCATION WESTERN AUSTRALIA, AUSTRALIA
CONSTRUCTION DATES 1898–1903

THROUGHOUT THE 19TH century, many areas – including South Africa, California and Canada – experienced gold rushes. The discovery of gold at Coolgardie in 1892 and in Kalgoorlie a year later in 1893 were two of the biggest. These events created a massive population explosion in Western Australia, as thousands flocked to the goldfields in this sparsely populated state.

However, a lack of fresh water resulted in poor sanitation, and many deaths were recorded from diseases such as typhoid. With an urgent need for a continuous potable water supply, the state's premier invited an Irish-born civil engineer, Charles Yelverton O'Connor, to supervise the design and construction of the necessary infrastructure to support the growing colony.

O'Connor's solution was a scheme to pump water from an impounding reservoir at Mundaring in the forested Perth Hills, across the arid Wheatbelt, to the Mount Charlotte Reservoir, overlooking Kalgoorlie-Boulder. The scheme was expensive and was initially met with political resistance and criticism by the media.

Nevertheless, the project was carried out between 1898 and 1903. Mundaring was chosen as the best site for a dam. It had a river in a narrow

valley with steep sides, bedrock for the foundations and a large catchment with a reliable rainfall. The pipes were laid mainly in trenches, to limit expansion and contraction caused by the fluctuating temperatures, and were made from steel plate, using an innovative locking bar system invented by Mephan Ferguson. This replaced the need for rivets (thus minimising leakage) and rivet heads (which would have slowed the flow of water).

Eight pumping stations were built along the pipeline, pushing the water over the Darling mountain range, a lift of 340 metres. It was the world's first continuously welded above-ground water-supply pipeline, and – after more than a century of upgrades, repairs and reconstruction – is still the longest water-supply pipeline in the world. Around 90 million litres of water are pumped daily for agricultural, domestic and mining purposes, through 8,000 km of pipe mains. It takes between five and 11 days for the water to reach Kalgoorlie.

Tragically, O'Connor never saw the success of his scheme. On 10 March 1902, he took his own life – riding on horseback, into the sea south of Fremantle, where he shot himself.

HYDROELECTRIC POWER IN SCOTLAND

HOW HYDROELECTRICITY REVOLUTIONISED THE HIGHLANDS

LOCATION THROUGHOUT SCOTLAND, UK
DATES 1900–

SCOTLAND'S HYDROELECTRIC REVOLUTION
has delivered clean electricity across the country,
dramatically improving the lives and businesses of
hundreds of thousands of Scots and pioneering
the use of renewable electricity production since
the early part of the 20th century.

This was a significant engineering challenge.
It involved the construction of dams, aqueducts,
pipelines and power stations, and a network of
power lines connecting the plants to the National
Grid across Scotland's rugged territory.

It began when the burgeoning aluminium
industry, driven by the need for a large source of
cheap electricity, made large-scale hydroelectric
power a reality. The Kinlochleven scheme was
constructed in 1907, while the Laggan Dam for
the Lochaber Plant followed in the 1930s.

The Lanark Hydro Scheme was developed
in the 1920s taking water from the Falls of Clyde
and was the first of its kind. The development of
the Galloway Hydro Scheme was undertaken in
the early 1930s both located in Southern Scotland
and first hydro schemes drawing lowland river
water supplies.

The Grampian Electricity Supply Company
was created to develop power stations at Tummel
and Rannoch and formed the basis of future
developments. Following the publication of the
Hydro-Electric Development Act in 1943, Tom
Johnston, then Secretary of State for Scotland,
nationalised the company in 1948 and formed
the North of Scotland Hydro-Electric Board with
Johnston as its first chairman and engineer Edward
MacColl as Chief Executive. The board's first two
developments at Sloy and Tummel Valley became
the model for many further developments (Sloy
Power Station remains the largest conventional
hydroelectric power station in the UK).

Hydroelectric development brought
employment to the north of Scotland in the postwar years. At its peak, more than 12,000 people
were employed, with workers from Ireland,
Germany, Italy, Poland and Czechoslovakia joining
many native Highlanders and local firms in its
construction. During the construction of the Loch
Sloy scheme in Ben Vorlich in 1949 the 'Tunnel
Tigers' excavating the principal rock tunnels
received wages some 10 times that of local estate
workers. During the excavation of the St Fillans
tunnel in 1955 they set the world rock tunnelling
record – 557 feet in just seven days.

By the time major hydroelectric development
ended in the mid-1960s, Scotland had 56 dams,
connected by over 600 km of rock tunnel, aqueducts
and pipelines to 54 power stations. Over 90 per
cent of the north of Scotland was now on grid,
up from about 40 per cent in 1944.

It would take more than 40 years for another
large conventional hydro station to be built in
Scotland. SSE (Scottish and Southern Energy),
which now operates most of the schemes
built during the time of the "Hydro Board",
commissioned the 100 megawatt Glendoe
scheme in 2009. The other major hydroelectric
plant in the Highland area is the 440 megawatt
Cruachan scheme at Loch Awe, now operated
by Scottish Power. This is one of only four similar
schemes in the UK that operates as a pumped
storage rather than a traditional gravity scheme.
Cruachan was one of the first reversible pumped-
storage systems, where the same turbines are
used as both pumps and generators.

Before and during the construction of the
Pitlochry Power Station in the 1960s, opponents
of the scheme believed it would be "the ruination
of tourism in Highland Perthshire". Now half a
million people visit the Pitlochry Dam and Fish
Ladder each year, and with a new visitor centre
opened in 2017, these and other developments
have become a resounding endorsement of
hydroelectric power's continuing economic and
environmental achievements.

MANGLA DAM

ONE OF THE WORLD'S LARGEST DAMS

LOCATION MIRPUR DISTRICT, PAKISTAN
CONSTRUCTION DATES 1961–67

THE MANGLA DAM in northern Pakistan was one of the greatest reservoir projects of the 20th century. Designed by British consultants Binnie & Partners and supported by US consultants Harza Engineering, its planning and construction, financial management and diplomacy were a triumph of transcontinental collaboration.

As well as being a great feat of civil engineering, Mangla Dam was also a vital part of an international treaty between Pakistan and India. In 1947, partition had split both the people and the waters of the Indus River Basin. In 1960, after years of difficult negotiations, the Indus Waters Treaty was signed. Mangla Dam was the first of two huge dams needed to fulfil its terms. The 250-sq-km reservoir holds about 6.5 cubic km of water. Mangla Dam, which crosses the Jhelum River, is a maximum of 138 metres high, 2.5 km long and built with more than 100 million tonnes of earth fill. In addition to this, the Mangla hydropower station provides up to 1,000 megawatts of electricity.

Background work and design on the project began in 1957, led by the British civil engineer Geoffrey Binnie. There were numerous challenges to overcome along the way, including a short war, but the first hydropower went into supply in July 1967, with the dam becoming fully operational the following year.

One of the most extraordinary features of the project is the spillway, which must pass about 28,000 cubic metres per second down a fall of 100 metres: about twice the height and 10 times the flow of the Niagara Falls. The world's largest tunnel-boring machine at the time was used to drive the five tunnels – each nine metres in diameter – that are used to divert the river. The construction was made more problematical not only by the quality of the ground, which was a mixture of clay and crumbly sandstone, but also because the area is prone to earthquakes and is situated 30 miles away from a major fault.

The project was not without controversy, and many people were displaced to make way for the reservoir. But the dam has served the nation of Pakistan well by providing clean electricity and water for irrigation for the past 50 years, and should continue to do so for many more to come.

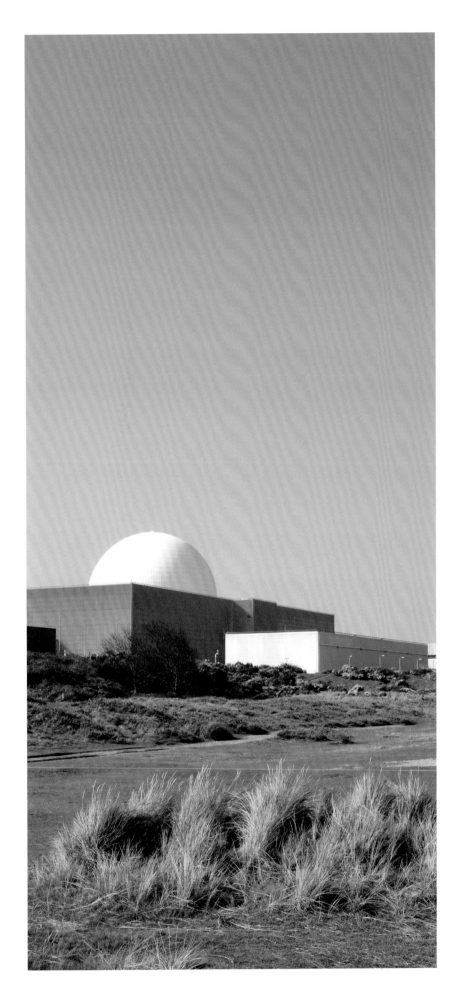

SIZEWELL B

BRITAIN'S FIRST PRESSURISED WATER REACTOR

LOCATION SIZEWELL, SUFFOLK, UK
CONSTRUCTION DATES 1987–95

SIZEWELL B NUCLEAR power station was the first pressurised water reactor (PWR) to be built in the UK. The earlier Magnox reactors (like Sizewell A) and the current Advanced Gas Reactor (AGRs) use carbon dioxide gas to cool the reactor and transfer energy to the boilers, which generate steam for the turbo-alternators that generate electricity, whereas a PWR uses pressurised water for the energy transfer.

Preliminary construction work began in 1987 and the project took nearly eight years to complete at a cost of £2 billion. Around a quarter of this cost was for the civil engineering works. Before construction of the permanent works could begin, engineers had to build a world-record-breaking diaphragm wall, 1,259 metres long, 56 metres deep and 800 mm thick constructed around the perimeter of the site (an area equivalent to 13 football pitches). It gained the record for the largest diaphragm wall (70,000 square metres) in just 95 days and was completed in 135 days. Its function was to protect the natural water table from the dewatering process required to allow excavation to take place for the foundations in the dry.

Once the dewatering or pumping was completed the main civil engineering works could begin in earnest. An early concrete pour for the reactor building's 3.8-metre-deep reinforced concrete circular base became one of the UK's largest non-stop pours, placing 5,200 cubic metres in 55 hours. In total, the project required half a million cubic metres of concrete to be poured (enough to fill the Royal Albert Hall five times over) and 70,000 tonnes of steel bar reinforcement.

At the time of construction a "buy British" policy for the project ensured that over 90 per cent of Sizewell B was manufactured or constructed by UK firms, thereby safeguarding thousands of jobs. John Laing Construction was the main contractor and Nuclear Design Associates the lead design engineers. Its main contribution to society is the fact that Sizewell B has been reliably producing 1,200 megawatts of low-carbon electricity to meet the demands of 2.5 million homes and businesses for the past 22 years, and is expected to continue doing so until at least 2035. It also currently employs around 520 full-time staff and more than 250 full-time contract partners.

In 1994, the project won the prestigious British Construction Industry Award and the Supreme Award.

ICE 200
TSUNAMI SUPPORT IN INDONESIA

THE REBUILDING OF IRRIGATION
AND HOUSING

LOCATION ACEH PROVINCE AND
NIAS ISLAND, INDONESIA
PROJECT DATES 2005–06

ON 26 DECEMBER 2004, an earthquake struck the coast of Sumatra, Indonesia. With a magnitude of 9.1 it was the most powerful the world had seen since 1964 when a quake hit Prince William Sound, Alaska. The earthquake caused a tsunami – a series of massive waves – along the coasts of several countries in the Indian Ocean. Indonesia was hit the hardest, followed by Sri Lanka and India. The tsunami reached the north Sumatran coast – including Aceh province – around 15 minutes after the quake. Almost 228,000 people were listed as missing or dead in 14 countries after the disaster. Around half the total deaths caused by the tsunami were in Aceh province, mostly among fishing and rice-farming communities. Aceh City was almost entirely destroyed in minutes, while large areas of coastal land and whole communities were inundated, changing the morphology of the landscape. A later quake in March 2005 caused widespread damage and killed 1,000 people on the nearby island of Nias. Material losses were estimated at around £7.4 billion.

The earthquakes destroyed or damaged much of the infrastructure in Aceh and on Nias, including bridges, weirs, canals, embankments and irrigation schemes. The tsunami had a disastrous effect on the paddy fields, covering them in sand and building material – including glass – from destroyed houses. The Earthquake and Tsunami Emergency Support Project (ETESP), funded by the Asian Development Bank (ADB), addressed many cross-sector issues with some 25 different packages, including an irrigation component. The latter was set up by civil engineering consultants Black & Veatch after they had been contacted by the ADB in June 2005 to assist in preparing an irrigation recovery project. The firm had worked in Aceh on UK Official Development Assistance (ODA) and ADB projects from 1976 to 1995 and was in the middle of carrying out a similar project in North Sumatra Province, so it was able to act rapidly.

The programme – which was managed by a special Indonesian government unit with support from the consultants – saw the reconstruction of 93 irrigation schemes over 58,000 hectares of rice fields. It used some local competitive bid contracts, favoured by government staff, but the bulk of the on-farm systems were community contracts carried out through water-user associations (WUAs), most of which were completed to good standards of construction. An important aspect was to design earthquake-resistant structures, using mainly reinforced concrete rather than masonry, which had universally failed.

Fifteen months after the disaster, however, most families around Aceh were still living in temporary shelters, and required rehousing. The Canadian Red Cross (CRC) were one of the main agencies involved in the rehousing programme, and turned to IMC Worldwide for technical expertise. Many logistical problems had to be faced. Land had disappeared under water, and new sites had to be identified and environmentally assessed. Government records had been destroyed, so there was often no evidence of property rights.

Local people were involved in the design for a core house that could be modified by its owners without compromising structural integrity. Each had 44 square metres of living space, and an earthquake-proof reinforced concrete frame construction, with brick infill. Each had two bedrooms, a bathroom and a kitchen, with the latter sited on the external rear veranda, in accordance with local custom; and easy-maintenance, durable zinc roofs.

IMC engaged five Indonesian consulting firms and four major Indonesian contractors to construct the houses. The IMC team in Aceh was multidisciplinary, multicultural and multinational, with professional skills that covered planning, management, engineering, surveying and social analysis. The range of skills and the cultural sensitivity were of great value working within a complex multinational disaster-recovery effort.

ICE 200

WOMEN IN THE WATER INDUSTRY

HOW FEMALE ENGINEERS ARE TAKING THE LEAD AT SEVERN TRENT WATER

LOCATION MIDLANDS, UK
DATES PRESENT DAY

"OUR PEOPLE WILL always be our most important asset," says Jane Simpson, head of Capital Programmes at Severn Trent Water. "With 66 per cent of our new graduates and a quarter of our apprentices being female, it's really important that we have strong and talented female role models in the water industry."

Midlands-based water company Severn Trent has a proud record when it comes to diversity, and especially female representation as operational leaders and engineers. Women make up 44 per cent of Severn Trent's board, 60 per cent of its executive committee and 27 per cent of its senior leadership team. The company can point to its CEO Liv Garfield and commercial director Helen Miles as key roles that have gone to women in recent years. Many other senior roles – including business leads – have also been filled by women.

For this company, challenging the traditionally male-dominated world of engineering has been key to driving change and creating a culture of inclusivity. "Having female leaders at every level of our business inspired me to follow my chosen career path," says Hannah Black, who started at Severn Trent as a mechanical maintenance engineering apprentice and is now a

programme engineer, completing a higher national diploma in preparation for a mechanical engineering degree. "I'd urge other young women to look at engineering opportunities."

Currently a team of 150 in-house engineers and a further 1,000 people across Severn Trent's supply chain are working to deliver key water and wastewater infrastructure projects for the 4.5 million households and businesses they serve.

"We work on projects of all sizes," says Simpson. "These include the Birmingham Resilience Project, our largest ever investment programme, to create a new back-up water supply for Birmingham and surrounding areas. It also includes smaller projects like pumping station renewals or eel screens. Often we are carrying out maintenance on assets that were created by engineers 150 years ago, which shows you what an amazing legacy engineering can have. Water underpins every part of our day-to-day lives. As culture, technology and the environment change, our business needs to change too. A key part of this is having a workforce that truly reflects the communities we serve."

ICE 200
CHERNOBYL NEW SAFE CONFINEMENT

CLEANING UP AFTER THE WORLD'S WORST NUCLEAR ACCIDENT

LOCATION CHERNOBYL, UKRAINE
CONSTRUCTION DATES 2007–16

THE 1986 ACCIDENT at the Chernobyl power plant – the worst nuclear disaster in history – left behind a dangerous, difficult and costly legacy. The traces of radioactive contamination were recorded as far west as the UK and Ireland, and resulted in the displacement of 200,000 people from the surrounding areas. The immediate remedial measures constructed in an incredibly short time at a great personal risk to the Soviet workers involved had a design life limited to 30 years and the time came to implement a more durable solution to protect the environment while dismantling and making safe the infamous Chernobyl Reactor Number 4.

VINCI Construction Grands Projets and Bouygues Travaux Publics formed a joint venture known as NOVARKA and were awarded a design and construction contract in 2007 funded by more than 40 countries and organisations, including the European Bank for Reconstruction and Development who manage the account. Innovative engineering solutions were necessary as the construction over the existing reactor would be dangerous and lengthy due to limitations on working time for labour exposed to the reactor's radiation. The ingenious solution was to construct a massive 36,200-tonne arch built to the profile of the nuclear plant's remaining structures. This was erected 330 metres away from the final location and was the largest structure ever built on land to be moved. It was pushed into place on sliding bearings ahead of schedule in November 2016. Reactor Number 4 is now contained and, for the first time since the accident, a clear path for safe, long-term decommissioning at Chernobyl has been established.

ICE 200
MUNDRA ULTRA MEGA POWER PLANT

INDIA'S MOST ENERGY-EFFICIENT COAL-BASED THERMAL POWER PLANT

LOCATION GUJARAT, INDIA
CONSTRUCTION DATES 2007–13

INDIA'S URGENT NEED to increase power production has led the government there to plan a series of ultra mega power projects (UMPP), scheduled for completion by 2022. When the first of these, at Mundra, was completed in 2013, it was the largest thermal power station in India. Coastal Gujarat Power Limited (CGPL), a subsidiary of Tata Power, built and runs it.

Although the most viable fuel for these large power stations is coal, there is a commitment to using renewable energy as far as possible and steps have been taken to reduce fuel use and pollution. Mundra is the first power plant in India to use supercritical technology, whereby steam temperatures in excess of 600 degrees Celsius are reached. This improves efficiency and reduces carbon emissions by up to 20 per cent compared with conventional methods.

The project has created 5,000 construction jobs. It is expected to benefit around 16 million domestic customers and to supply competitively priced power to industry and agriculture across five of India's most fuel-starved states.

As part of the project, CGPL has improved local infrastructure and water supply and has set up various initiatives to support local communities. It has also planted nearly a million indigenous trees to absorb pollution and reduce dirt and noise.

NEW ORLEANS – CLOSING THE FLOODGATES

ENGINEERS RESPOND TO THE AFTERMATH OF HURRICANE KATRINA

LOCATION NEW ORLEANS, LOUISIANA, USA
DATES 2006–

HURRICANE KATRINA LEFT a trail of devastation when she hit New Orleans in August 2005. The levees and barriers extending for 350 miles were breached at multiple points, resulting in the flooding of around 80 per cent of the city. The floodwaters penetrated up to six miles inland, causing more than 1,000 deaths and destroying or severely damaging more than 200,000 homes and businesses. More than 800,000 people fled the area.

In 2006, the Dutch firm Royal HaskoningDHV was commissioned to advise and assist the United States Army Corps of Engineers (USACE) on the redesign and rebuilding of the entire Hurricane Storm and Damage Risk Reduction System (HSDRRS). The work included strengthening levees and pumping stations on the 133-mile Greater New Orleans perimeter system, as well as the largest surge barrier of its kind at Lake Borgne and the largest drainage-pumping station in the world at the GIWW-West Closure Complex. Royal HaskoningDHV has since provided expertise in hydraulic modelling and design, flood forecasting, GIS-based mapping and risk management. It has established baseline data, analysed flood-defence performance and developed and applied innovative modelling and data-management tools.

"Five days before a storm a lot of decisions have to be made," says Royal HaskoningDHV's Resident Director, Maartje Wise. "People may need to be evacuated and emergency services deployed in the right locations. More than 300 floodgates need to be left open, or closed at the appropriate time. Closing them is not simple: they might close off access to streets or transport links and prevent the movement of emergency vehicles. We developed a Levee Information Management System that brings together all the information the decision makers need onto a high-level dashboard, with the ability to drill down to detailed technical information for each section of levee."

The Danish engineering firm COWI was responsible for the detailed design of the flood barrier, which included a concrete swing-barge gate. The barrier was used to regulate navigation, tidal flows and storm surge in New Orleans' inner harbour navigation canal. Costing $1.3 billion, it was the largest civil works design-build project ever awarded by USACE. It won the American Society of Civil Engineers' highest design honour in 2014 and served as example of innovative design and fast-track construction.

ICE 200
SAN TONG WATER SUPPLY SYSTEM
HOW A SMALL RURAL COMMUNITY ACHIEVED CLEANER WATER

LOCATION GUANGDONG PROVINCE, CHINA
CONSTRUCTION DATES 2012–13

ICARE IS A group of Hong Kong civil engineers founded in June 2011 that uses its professional and technical knowledge to help improve the living standards of other, often remote communities. Even a small-scale amenity like a well, a septic tank or a mini-incinerator can make an enormous difference.

ICarE's first project was to construct a water supply system in San Tong, a rural village about an hour from the centre of the prefecture-level city of Qingyuan. After the villagers there requested improved water quality in the existing wells, samples that were taken and laboratory tested showed the water was polluted because of inadequate waste treatment. ICareE designed and constructed a new system to bring fresh water to the village for domestic use and agricultural irrigation.

The team developed several components to make the system cost effective, low maintenance and sustainable. They installed a filter feature for purity and a double storage chamber for easy maintenance. It also used gravity instead of a pressure pump to save on construction and operation costs.

Construction began in October 2012 and finished in early 2013, with the team making weekly inspections to check the quality of the work and monitor progress. Since completion, about 200 local households have enjoyed access to clean water, something that is taken for granted in many communities but that in San Tong represents a valuable gift.

Civil engineers have a long tradition of supporting humanitarian projects (see Engineers for Overseas Development; Engineers Without Borders; RedR). Those who participate in bringing the benefits of civil engineering to many, not just those who can afford to pay, are fulfilling the ethos of the objectives enshrined by those young engineers who founded the Institution of Civil Engineers in 1818.

The focus then was on routes for trade and tapping into new sources of power. Later, public health engineering drove another wave of advances. The work of ICarE reminds us that many communities still lack the basic rights that civil engineering can bring.

ICE 200
THE TRIO
THE STORM WATER STORAGE SCHEME BURIED UNDER GREEN GROUND

LOCATION HONG KONG
CONSTRUCTION DATES 2001–17

THE TRIO IS an urban flood protection scheme based on the innovative idea of temporarily storing upstream run-off. Storing water temporarily means it does not overwhelm drainage systems downstream, which used to be one of the most problematic areas in Hong Kong. The Trio system has eliminated flood risks and garnered praise for its engineering innovation and effectiveness.

Years of rapid development and changes in land use have resulted in significant increases in surface run-off in Hong Kong. By the turn of this century, the existing drainage system could no longer cope with severe rainstorms. To address the problem long term, the Drainage Services Department and the Government of the Hong Kong Special Administrative Region joined forces with the engineering company Black & Veatch. They devised a plan that was less disruptive and more economical than digging up roads and upgrading existing drains. It involved building three underground storage tanks in the heart of the city to collect storm water temporarily and stop it flooding the urban areas below.

Three sites were chosen at Tai Hang Tung (2001–04), Sheung Wan (2006–09) and Happy Valley (2012–17). Built underneath a rugby pitch and a football pitch, the Tai Hang Tung scheme was Hong Kong's first large-scale storage tank. Its pump house is covered in greenery, with vertical climbers and ground planting that help it blend in with the environment.

The Sheung Wan scheme is located at the waterfront of Victoria Harbour, where there is limited underground space. A smaller tank was designed and equipped with pumps of a high flow rate to meet this challenge, while a diversion chamber and penstock was constructed to prevent any backflow of seawater. The open space on top of the tank has been landscaped and turned into a large park and recreation ground.

The Happy Valley scheme is characterised by innovative features including smart moveable weirs and a water harvesting system. Groundwater underneath the storage tank, together with rainwater and irrigation water, is collected around the clock through subsoil drains. The water is treated and reused for flushing toilets, street cleaning and further irrigation, so reduces the consumption of valuable drinking water.

KOLKATA SEWERS

REHABILITATING THE CITY'S VICTORIAN-AGE SEWERS

LOCATION KOLKATA, INDIA
PROJECT DATES 2007–13

THE CITY OF Calcutta (now Kolkata), a "crowning glory" of the British Raj, was the administrative capital of continental India for more than a century until the capital was shifted to New Delhi in 1911. Situated on the Hooghly River, a tributary of the Ganges, it has witnessed phenomenal growth and evolved into a sprawling metropolis since its inception in 1690.

Triggered by the city's growth as a commercial hub and its insalubrious sanitary conditions, the planning of sanitation and drainage was initiated in the early 19th century by then Governor-General Lord Wellesley. The unhygienic conditions and high rates of disease propagation and sickness were comparable to London's infamous "Great Stink" of 1858, and that same year – around the time when Sir Joseph Bazalgette drew up plans to address the British capital's sanitation problems – a sanitation scheme proposed by William Clark was adopted for implementation in Calcutta.

The system served the city for more than a century before showing signs of major distress in the late 20th century. The Kolkata Municipal Corporation embarked on an ambitious project in 2007 to rehabilitate major brick sewers in its oldest section, which were more than 130 years old.

The first phase of this project involved the refurbishment of trunk sewers with a total length of 27 km. The long-term issues addressed included the retention of discharge capacities of sewers, regaining their structural integrity, a reduction in water logging, protection against corrosion, future cleaning and maintenance, and socio-environmental aspects.

The cost of the project was around £70 million, and the refurbished sewers were recommissioned in 2015, representing one of the world's most successful brick-sewer rehabilitation projects using glass-reinforced plastic (GRP) "slip-lining" technology.

The execution of this project in one of the most congested urban areas on the planet was made possible through the adoption of trenchless technology. The project had to overcome several hurdles, such as restricted access, reduced working hours, the presence of utility lines, uncharted body connections, high combined flow and logistical challenges. The rehabilitation of Calcutta's sewerage system is a perfect example of municipal asset management and sustainable urban renewal in a city that has existed for more than 300 years.

ICE 200
SNOWY MOUNTAINS HYDRO ELECTRIC SCHEME
THE LARGEST RENEWABLE ENERGY GENERATOR IN AUSTRALIA

LOCATION NEW SOUTH WALES, AUSTRALIA
PROJECT DATES 1949–74

THE SNOWY MOUNTAINS Scheme (the "Snowy") is the largest engineering project ever undertaken in Australia and one of the most complex in the world. It took 25 years to complete, mostly under the supervision of Sir William Hudson. It attracted over 100,000 workers from over 30 countries and was completed under budget and before time.

At the launch of the project, Prime Minister Ben Chifley presented it as a national milestone, not only in terms of its ambition but also for the drought relief it would bring to inland Australia and the power it would supply to the whole country.

The purpose of the scheme is to collect water from melting snow and rain in the Snowy Mountains. The water is diverted from the Snowy and Tumut rivers, stored in reservoirs to create electricity, and then directed into the Murray and Murrumbidgee Rivers via tunnels through the mountains. The project also supplies irrigation to the arid farming areas of New South Wales and Victoria. It consists of 16 major dams, seven power stations, two pumping stations, and 225 km of tunnels and aqueducts. Only 2 per cent of the entire construction is visible above the ground.

The majority of the work involved difficult and dangerous tunnelling through rock. Conditions were harsh. The workers' temporary camps in the mountains were not built adequately for the freezing weather. Although over time the project introduced safer construction techniques with improved standards of health and safety, more than 120 workers died during the process.

The original scheme did not consider the area's ecosystem needs and, over time, concern has grown about the reduction of the flow of the Snowy River to just 1 per cent of what it was previously. In 1998, the New South Wales and Victoria governments agreed to restore 21 per cent of the water flow to the Snowy River to address environmental degradation (reached in 2017), with an option of increasing this to 28 per cent under certain conditions.

In 1967 the American Society of Civil Engineers rated the Snowy Mountains Scheme as one of the civil engineering wonders of the modern world. The scheme was also added to the Australian National Heritage List in October 2016. A proposal to add 50 per cent to the generating capacity was announced in March 2017.

ICE 200
ENGINEERS FOR OVERSEAS DEVELOPMENT

A CHARITY ENGINEERING POSITIVE CHANGE IN AFRICA

LOCATION CARDIFF, UK
ESTABLISHED 2000

ENGINEERS FOR OVERSEAS Development (EFOD) has helped to develop young civil engineers and members of the construction industry by challenging teams to deliver development projects in sub-Saharan Africa. Over 18 years, £1 million has been spent on 30 projects involving 800 volunteers from the United Kingdom, who have raised funds, designed and supervised the construction of schemes to help alleviate poverty.

EFOD started at an evening lecture in Cardiff in 2000, when ICE Wales Chairman Ian Flower accepted the challenge to build latrines in The Gambia. Six graduate civil engineers volunteered, designed community latrine blocks and raised £6,000. They visited the site in pairs for a fortnight to buy materials, hire labour, train local staff, commission and supervise construction. Initially a subgroup of ICE Wales, EFOD branches soon formed in Bristol, Birmingham, Manchester, London and South West Wales. EFOD became a charitable company with the aim of building for the benefit of the urban and rural poor of Africa. Run by three ICE fellows, it was closely linked to nearby ICE committees.

The complexity of its projects increased in 2010 when EFOD Cardiff built a 16-room medical centre offering low-cost treatment for the poor and an orphanage for 83 street children, both in Soroti, Uganda. The Bristol group built a sewing school for a women's cooperative in Ghana, while the West Midlands group worked on a development for Koutulai Widows' Cooperative in Uganda, including a grinding mill, grain store, village hall, latrines and a borehole.

EFOD North West completed a grain store for a women's cooperative and a centre for the women of Mayuge, while EFOD London secured the water supply at Kumi Hospital, all in Uganda. Recently EFOD Cardiff installed a solar-powered pump in a borehole to supply 4,000 villagers and 10,000 cattle, while a group of mainly apprentices from South West Wales completed a grain store and a new unit to improve maternity provision in Kachumbala, Uganda.

Sustainability is key to EFOD's schemes, which are regularly monitored and maintained. Boreholes provide water to build and supply the local community; blocks are pressed from local materials on site; solar power provides lighting; and rainwater is harvested from buildings. Local communities benefit from the provision, local staff benefit from the training provided and EFOD volunteers benefit from delivering a complete project at an early stage in their career.

ELAN VALLEY RESERVOIRS

BRINGING FRESH WATER TO INDUSTRIAL BIRMINGHAM

LOCATION ELAN VALLEY TO BIRMINGHAM, UK
CONSTRUCTION DATES 1893–1904

WHEN THE INDUSTRIAL Revolution transformed Birmingham in the 19th century, demand for water outstripped the supply from local rivers and wells. These became increasingly polluted and caused outbreaks of typhoid, cholera and dysentery.

In 1892, the Birmingham Corporation Water Department commissioned civil engineer James Mansergh to construct a system to bring fresh water to the city. He decided the Welsh Elan Valley was the ideal source: it averaged 1,830 mm of rainfall each year; the shape of the valley would facilitate the building of dams; and the bedrock was impermeable so water would not drain away. Better still, the reservoirs would be 50 metres higher than the waterworks at Birmingham, so gravity alone would propel the water through the pipes.

Four reservoirs were built in the lower valley between 1893 and 1904. An additional one in Claerwen was built between 1946 and 1952 and opened by the Queen in one of her first official engagements. The 118-km-long aqueduct opened in 1904. It carried the water through

21 km of tunnels, 38 km of conduits or channels, and 59 km of pipes to a reservoir at Frankley on the outskirts of Birmingham.

Some 50,000 jobs were created during the construction of the dams and a village was built for the workmen or navvies. The Nant-y-Gro dam, originally built to bring water to the workers' village, was used as a secret testing venue during the Second World War in preparation for the Dam Busters raids on Germany in 1943.

The reservoirs bring recreational and economic benefits as well as water. Tourism is estimated to contribute a further £0.5 million to the local economy. Since 1997, hydro-electric turbines installed at the base of the dams have been producing electricity.

Although the Elan aqueduct has served the city of Birmingham for over 100 years, the Birmingham Resilience Project is currently creating an alternative supply from the River Severn and other parts of the network to allow the aqueduct to be maintained. At present it cannot be shut for more than five days as Frankley Reservoir has only five days' worth of storage capacity.

CARSINGTON WATER

ONE OF ENGLAND'S LARGEST RESERVOIRS

LOCATION CARSINGTON, DERBYSHIRE, UK
CONSTRUCTION DATES 1979–92

THE CARSINGTON SCHEME was conceived in the 1960s to address a potential shortage in the water supply to the East Midlands. Following a detailed appraisal and a rigorous challenge, permission was granted to build a reservoir at Carsington in mid-Derbyshire.

Although the reservoir has a local catchment, most of its water travels – via a major pumped storage project – from the River Derwent 6.5 miles away. It has a capacity of 36 million cubic metres. The system abstracts water from the river at times of high flow for storage in the reservoir. Water is released back into the River Derwent when it is at low flow, for abstraction and treatment further downstream. Water can also be abstracted directly from Carsington for treatment at Ogston Water Treatment Plant.

Construction of the original dam, which was more than 1 km long and 35 metres high, began in 1979. It was constructed with a rolled clay core in an unusual "boot" shape, supported by earth-fill shoulders. As the dam neared completion in June 1984, a crack was detected in the crest near the upstream face, which led to a dramatic partial collapse of the structure. Specialist geotechnical and geological advisers undertook painstaking

investigations into the failure, while consultants Babtie, Shaw and Morton and Professor AW Skempton were commissioned to determine its cause. Using advanced finite element modelling they attributed it to a lens of weathered clay that had severely weakened the embankment. This error demonstrated the need for a comprehensive site investigation before undertaking a project of this kind.

Given the importance of the scheme to the local water supply, an independent expert, RE Coxon, was appointed to report on the failure to the Environment Secretary. The original dam was demolished and Babtie, Shaw and Morton designed the current structure. A review panel was established, chaired by Coxon, to oversee the project and give technical advice. The new dam was completed in 1991 and officially opened by Her Majesty the Queen in 1992.

Severn Trent Water, the dam's operator, has retained a review panel to oversee the management of the reservoir and ensure its safety. The continued existence of the panel inspires confidence in the management of Severn Trent reservoirs as well as monitoring the region's water supply.

ICE 200
DERWENT VALLEY RESERVOIRS
A RESERVOIR AREA OF ENTIRELY MAN-MADE NATURAL BEAUTY

LOCATION NORTH DERBYSHIRE, UK
CONSTRUCTION DATES 1901–45

TOURISTS VISITING THE Derwent Valley Reservoirs today may not be aware that the landscape is almost entirely man-made. With its deep, narrow sides and high rainfall, the Upper Derwent Valley is an ideal location to store water in a series of reservoirs to serve neighbouring Derbyshire and South Yorkshire, as well as cities as distant as Leicester and Nottingham.

The first two dams and reservoirs were designed by Derwent Valley Water Board chief engineer Edward Sandeman and constructed between 1901 and 1916. A temporary village called Birchinlee – more commonly known as "Tin Town" due to its corrugated iron huts – was built to house up to 1,000 workers. The village was dismantled in 1909 when the dams were completed.

The top reservoir is the Y-shaped Howden, built between 1901 and 1912. The border between Derbyshire and South Yorkshire runs down the middle of the reservoir. The reservoir is held by Howden Dam, a cyclopean concrete dam (concrete with large stones or "plums" mixed into it) dressed with masonry, and is 36 metres tall and 330 metres long. Leaving Howden Reservoir, the River Derwent flows to the middle reservoir, the 2-km-

long Derwent Reservoir. Construction of the Derwent Dam started in 1902 and the reservoir was filled in 1916. During the Second World War, the reservoir was used by pilots of 617 Squadron practising low-level flying for the Dambuster raids as the towers were a similar distance apart to the towers on the dams that they were targeting in Germany.

Work on the lowest reservoir and Ladybower Dam, designed by GH Hill & Sons, began in 1935 and continued during the war. The River Ashop also flows into Ladybower Reservoir, although surplus flows from the Ashop and its tributary, the River Alport, had been diverted through a tunnel into Derwent Reservoir in the 1920s. Ladybower is 46 metres high and 363 metres long and is an earth-fill dam with a puddle clay core.

Like many reservoir projects, Ladybower involved some resettlement due to the controversial flooding of two villages – Derwent and Ashopton. The remains of these villages occasionally reappear when the water level is particularly low. Together, the three Derwent Valley reservoirs and surrounding forests attract more than two million visitors each year, and in 1993, the Upper Derwent Valley became one of the Forestry Commission's first Centres of Excellence.

ICE 200
COW GREEN RESERVOIR
HOLDING WATER ATOP BRITAIN'S HIGHEST WATERFALL

LOCATION UPPER TEESDALE, UK
CONSTRUCTION DATES 1967–71

BETWEEN 1892 AND 1915, three reservoirs in Teesdale, County Durham, were built in response to demand in consumption, primarily from the development of the iron and chemical industries on Teesside. Following a slackening of demand during the recession of the 1930s, demand for water began to increase again and, in the 1950s, ICI decided to construct a major complex at Wilton, on Teesside. This led to the construction of three new reservoirs: Selset, completed in 1960; Balderhead in 1965; and Cow Green, the last to be built in Teesdale, with work finishing in 1970.

Cow Green was one of the highest major reservoirs in England, at an altitude of 480 metres, and formed the second river regulatory reservoir for the River Tees, alongside Balderhead. The reservoir is situated at the point where an extensive flat meandering section of the Tees crosses the Cow Green barytes mine area. This created a large reservoir store with a 25-metre-high, 550-metre-long dam. The dam feeds back into the river via Cauldron Snout, Britain's longest waterfall.

Cow Green holds 40 billion litres of water, has a surface area of 3,219,000 sq metres, a water depth of 25.8 metres and serves a catchment area of 59 sq km.

It offers a reliable yield of 186 millions of litres per day (Ml/d). The engineer was MF Kennard and the main contractor was Mitchell Construction.

After the completion of Cow Green, the Tees Valley was deemed to have reached maximum reservoir capacity, but the Tees can also be served by the Kielder Transfer System. This can not only feed the Tyne from Kielder Water in Northumberland but also, through a network of underground pipes, support the Wear and the Tees. As the Tees flows towards Teesside, it is further served by Selset, Grassholme, Balderhead and Hury, before reaching Northumbrian Water's Lartington Water Treatment Works at Barnard Castle.

Further downstream, it reaches the Broken Scar Water Treatment Works in Darlington, one of the company's principal water treatment works, with a nominal capacity of 180 Ml/d, which serves Darlington and the surrounding areas. The area was also previously served by Tees Cottage Pumping Station since 1850. However, this site was taken out of use and turned into a museum after the population of the area grew from 11,000 in 1850 to more than 84,000 in 1980.

ICE 200
KIELDER WATER SCHEME
NORTHERN EUROPE'S LARGEST MAN-MADE LAKE

LOCATION KIELDER VALLEY, NORTHUMBERLAND, UK
CONSTRUCTION DATES 1975–82

THE NEED FOR a major water storage scheme in the north east of England goes back to the mid-19th century when expanding industries on Tyneside and Teesside were demanding more water. Reservoirs were built in the late 19th and early 20th centuries but, by the 1960s, it looked like demand would outstrip supply, encouraging local schemes on the Derwent and the Tees. Industries such as British Steel, however, required much greater volumes, while domestic water usage was also rising due to growing prosperity.

The answer was the Kielder Water Scheme, a transfer system that can store and release water from a reservoir in Northumberland's North Tyne Valley into rivers across the region. Designed by Babtie, Shaw & Morton, it was the first example of regional water grid designed to supply a wide area rather than a single town or city.

Kielder Water now attracts more than 250,000 visitors a year. It is also the largest man-made lake in northern Europe, holding 200,000 million litres, and houses England's largest hydroelectric power station. The 1.2 km-long and 52-metre-high Kielder Dam, built by a Balfour Beatty Fairclough joint venture, used glacial clay originally deposited more than 15,000 years

ago. Water is released to the river below the dam via the valve tower. The concrete tower is 70 metres high (the height of a 23-storey building), although only the top is visible above the water level. Releasing the maximum 1,300 million litres per day can produce enough power to illuminate a town the size of nearby Hexham (population 11,000).

It takes around 24 hours for water to travel the 36 miles to Riding Mill pumping station. From there, it either continues down the Tyne for use on Tyneside or is pumped into a 40 km underground system, main contractor Tyne Tees Tunnelling, that takes it beneath the Durham Fells to the rivers Derwent, Wear and Tees. The water is discharged into each river by a cascade spillway that reoxygenates water that may have been stored for some time.

The scheme was an enormous project involving up to 1,500 engineers and construction workers, and was designed to meet the demands of the region well into the future. In recent years, while the south has suffered droughts, the North East has retained a plentiful supply thanks to the foresight that created the Kielder Water Scheme.

TEES BARRAGE

THE TAMING OF THE RIVER TEES

LOCATION STOCKTON-ON-TEES, UK
CONSTRUCTION DATES 1991–95

WITH A HISTORY of flooding, which has seen the water rise by a metre in just 15 minutes, the River Tees has required numerous engineering interventions. The most impressive is the Tees Barrage, which, along with 22 km of the river, is operated and maintained by the Canal & River Trust.

Completed in 1995 and costing £55 million, the barrage was considered the largest British civil engineering project of its time. Designed by Ove Arup and the Napper Partnership, it was built by Tarmac Construction using 16,500 cubic metres of reinforced concrete and 650 tons of structural steel.

The 70-metre-wide barrage controls river flow, maintains water levels and prevents localised flooding. The four hydraulic gates can be independently raised or lowered via a computer in the on site control tower according to water levels, flow rate and weather conditions. A team of engineers works around the clock to manage the effects of tidal change every day of the year.

In addition to holding local water levels steady the Tees Barrage has improved the local community, wildlife and economy. Migratory fish such as salmon and sea trout are found there, and can be seen leaping over the gates, up the fish pass and through the navigation lock. The Canal & River Trust's ecologists work with partners from the Environment Agency, angling organisations and other waterways groups to assess how fish move through all parts of the barrage. They also monitor the impact of the seal population, carrying out regular observations and scientific research. The findings can be translated into operational and even structural changes at the barrage, such as the installation of a special gate on the lock to allow fish through and the use of sonar to deter the seals from predating them.

Since the barrage was built, the Stockton area has enjoyed a new lease of life. Housing, commercial and leisure developments have sprung up and the cleaner river is used for pursuits like angling, boating, canoeing and jet ski. A free park run is held every Saturday.

"Tees Barrage is not only an incredible feat of engineering," says Team Leader Lee Butler, "but it is also a hive of activity for locals and visitors and wildlife. It's the perfect place for walking, jogging, getting on the water or simply watching the seals, fish and birds."

ICE 200
HARBOUR AREA TREATMENT SCHEME (HATS)
DEALING WITH SEWAGE IN A CITY OF SEVEN MILLION

LOCATION HONG KONG
PROJECT DATES 1994–2001, 2009–15

THE HARBOUR AREA Treatment Scheme (HATS) was implemented to collect the 2.45 million cubic metres of sewage generated daily on both sides of the Victoria Harbour in Hong Kong and convey it to Stonecutters Island Sewage Treatment Works (SCISTW) to be treated before being released into the harbour. The scheme included the construction of 44 km of deep sewage tunnels, expansion and upgrading of the SCISTW and 16 preliminary treatment works. The work was carried out in two stages spanning two decades at a total cost of HK$25.8 billion (about £2.5 billion).

Stage one, completed in 2001, treats 75 per cent of the sewage discharged into the harbour. The works consist of a 23.6 km underground tunnel to transfer 1.7 million tons of sewage from Kowloon and north-east Hong Kong Island to the treatment plant. The second stage, competed in 2015 removes the remaining 25 per cent of sewage from the northern and south-western parts of Hong Kong Island via 21 km of tunnels. The scheme also included upgrading all the preliminary treatment works and installing disinfecting works at Stonecutters Island.

The scheme has improved water quality in the harbour, creating a more pleasant harbourfront for the public. As a result, the annual cross-harbour swimming race resumed in 2011, attracting hundreds of entrants and thousands of spectators to the area.

ICE 200
RIVINGTON RESERVOIRS
BRINGING FRESH PENNINE WATER TO LIVERPOOL

LOCATION FROM RIVINGTON PIKE, LANCASHIRE, TO LIVERPOOL, UK
CONSTRUCTION DATES 1846–57

OVERCROWDED LIVERPOOL IN 1846 was one of the unhealthiest towns in England, and there was little doubt that the "impurity and deficiency" of the water in its wells was a major cause. Enter celebrated water engineer Thomas Hawksley, an advocate of using pressurised distribution systems for universal access to public water. His vision for Liverpool was to pipe in "wholesome" river water 27 km from the Pennine uplands around Rivington Pike, near Wigan.

But Hawksley's expensive plan for a group of three reservoirs the largest water-supply scheme yet conceived, became a sensational battle, pitting the Liverpool Corporation against colourful local surveyor and famous map maker Michael Gage. The ensuing debate between "Pike-ists" and "anti Pike-ists" ended with Gage in prison for falsifying a petition and the endorsement of Rivington by railway entrepreneur Robert Stephenson.

Hawksley's reservoirs – Anglezarke, Upper Rivington and Lower Rivington – are as spectacular today as they were when built. Unusually, all the water was filtered before arriving in Liverpool. Despite that, when water first arrived in August 1857, it was brown and needed mixing with well water.

Rivington was a hive of building by other water engineers and, by 1867, the group totalled seven separate reservoirs. Today, those reservoirs are managed by United Utilities and store more than 18,000 million litres from a relatively modest catchment of 9,710 acres.

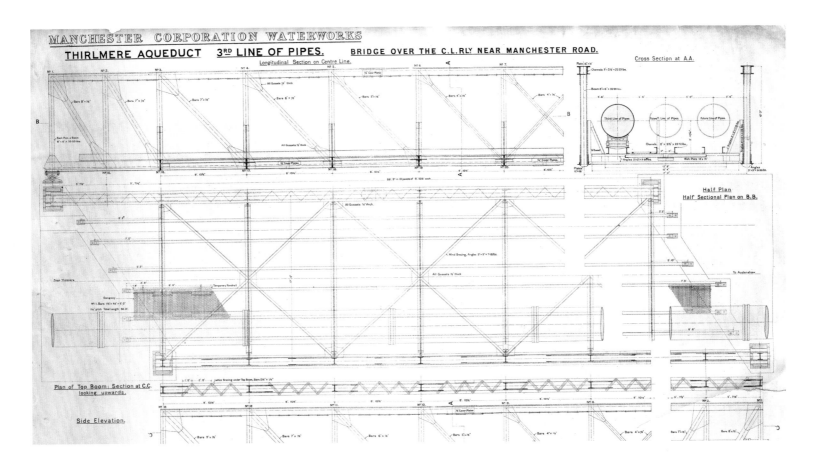

ICE 200

THIRLMERE RESERVOIR AND AQUEDUCT

A 96-MILE AQUEDUCT PROVIDING WATER TO INDUSTRIAL MANCHESTER

LOCATION THIRLMERE, CUMBRIA TO MANCHESTER, UK
CONSTRUCTION DATES 1886–94

THE BEAUTIFUL RESERVOIR in the Thirlmere Valley looks natural but was created as the second major water supply to sustain the growth of Manchester's Industrial Revolution. It is still the longest gravity aqueduct in England today at 134 km. More than 120 years later Thirlmere Reservoir will soon feed a new £300 million aqueduct system for the west of Cumbria – the largest pipeline project currently underway in England.

The original Thirlmere scheme was designed by civil engineer John La Trobe Bateman, with his assistant George Henry Hill, when Bateman's earlier Longendale Valley scheme was being outgrown by Manchester's needs. It was commissioned by Manchester Corporation Waterworks to supply 220 million litres of water to the city per day.

The chairman of the Waterworks Committee noted that "there were not more than 200 inhabitants" in the catchment area and, as for local objections, "he was himself a native of the district where this water was to be found, and … no man with common sense would say that, in the works they were contemplating, they were destroying any of the beauties of the place." The chairman had underestimated the strength of opposition to the scheme and it was not until a series of droughts, when 80,000 Mancunians died from waterborne diseases, that the scheme was finally granted parliamentary approval.

Construction began in 1886 and was completed eight years later. On 12 October 1894, at the south draw-off tower, an opening ceremony was held. Prince Albert was supposed to be in attendance, but he could not make it at the last minute. However, a great gathering of prestigious gentlemen of the Manchester Corporation were in the draw-off tower to see the water flow for the first time. Twenty-four hours later, after a hurried train journey, the same gathering reunited outside the Town Hall at Albert Square in Manchester to see the water arrive by gravity from Thirlmere for the first time, into a specially built fountain in the square.

The original fountain is now located at Heaton Park on the edge of Manchester, but there is a replica located in the same spot in Albert Square. Anyone visiting the grand historic centre of Manchester can take a moment to consider the water flowing through the fountain and its non-stop journey from Cumbria for more than a century.

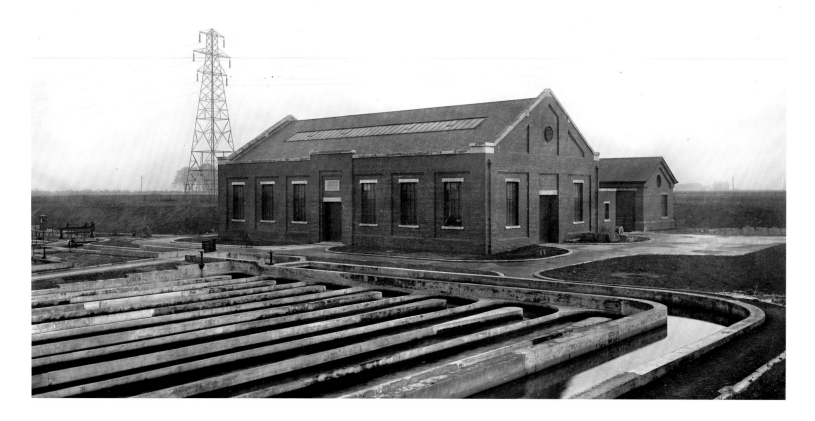

DAVYHULME WASTEWATER TREATMENT WORKS

MAKING ECO-FRIENDLY ENERGY FROM MANCHESTER'S SEWAGE

LOCATION TRAFFORD, GREATER MANCHESTER, UK
DATES OPENED 1894, ACTIVATED SLUDGE PLANT 2014–18

SITUATED ON THE banks of the River Irwell, Davyhulme Wastewater Treatment Works has led the world in the treatment of sewage for nearly 150 years. In 2018 the plant's owner, United Utilities, is completing the biggest upgrade in its history, a four-year, £200 million project. This will allow the site to treat Manchester's wastewater to even higher standards while continuing to meet the growing population needs of a thriving 21st century city.

Manchester, like other fast-growing Victorian industrial towns, struggled to cope with the disposal of human excrement. Much of this waste found its way into natural watercourses where it combined with industrial effluent to make Manchester's rivers some of the most polluted in the country by the second half of the 19th century.

By the 1880s it was decided to collect the sewage via a network of branch sewers leading into main sewers which transported it to a site at Davyhulme. Here it was possible to build a municipal sewage farm where the waste could be drained and separated into liquid and solid waste.

The site was alongside the newly built Manchester Ship Canal which offered a means of transporting treated sewage sludge by boat for discharge in Liverpool Bay. The journey was later shortened by the construction of a sludge pipeline to Liverpool.

Traditional sewage farm techniques were very wasteful of land. Under the leadership of city engineer Thomas De Courcy Meade the sewerage network was expanded greatly. While more land was acquired a new technology was required to enable the works to function effectively. Bacteriological treatment came in 1904–7. In 1914, Manchester University scientist Gilbert Fowler and Davyhulme engineers Edward Ardern and William T Lockett announced their discovery of activated sludge, the space-saving biological treatment process now used around the world. It enabled faster treatment of raw sewage to create a sludge with many of the more harmful bacteria removed and helped solve many of the public health problems of Manchester and other cities.

Davyhulme today is energy self-sufficient following completion of its award-winning sludge-recycling centre in 2014. Using a process known as "thermal hydrolysis" the centre converts wastewater sludge into high-quality agricultural fertiliser and biogas used to generate 12 megawatt-hours of green energy. The operation now helps to support 1.2 million people.

CONNSWATER COMMUNITY GREENWAY

A LIVING LANDMARK TO THE BENEFITS OF CIVIL ENGINEERING

LOCATION BELFAST, NORTHERN IRELAND, UK
DATE 2017

THE CONNSWATER COMMUNITY Greenway is a £40 million project that has transformed East Belfast's tired landscape into an infrastructure system offering numerous environmental, economic and social benefits. The initiative has improved 16 km of footpaths and cycle paths and 26 bridges; and with them access to local services such as schools, hospitals and shops. It has cleaned three rivers, planted native trees and connected 379 acres of green open space to the area's urban streets.

The project has also fulfilled a key civil engineering goal: to turn unexpected challenges into drivers of added benefit. After repeated severe flooding in East Belfast, the Greenway plan was revised to include widening culverts, realigning rivers and constructing floodwalls and embankments. These improvements have protected 1,700 homes and businesses.

A principal aim of the project was to promote a more active lifestyle in local residents. The Greenway has succeeded in doing this by creating vibrant, attractive, safe and accessible parkland for leisure, recreation, community events and activities. There are numerous trails to follow, some leading to monuments to local heroes such as Van Morrison and CS Lewis.

Local people support the Greenway enthusiastically: the number of hours put in by volunteers exceeded targets by 44 per cent. Indeed, Connswater Community Greenway has proved to be the inspirational living landmark its designers envisaged.

WEST SOLE GAS FIELD

THE NORTH SEA'S FIRST GAS FIELD

LOCATION SOUTHERN NORTH SEA, UK
DATES 1967–

DISCOVERED IN DECEMBER 1965, some 42 miles east of the Humber, the West Sole gas field was the first to be developed in the North Sea, with gas being produced since March 1967. It originally had three platforms: the WA manned rig and the unmanned WB and WC rigs. These set the standard for North Sea platform design and construction. Steel space frame jackets were lifted into position and steel piles were driven through the legs. The decks were then installed on top of the jackets.

The North Sea is a notoriously extreme environment, and the Holderness Coast, where the gas terminal sits, is the fastest eroding coast in Europe. Ensuring the safety of structures and maintaining the natural ecosystem requires innovative, sympathetic engineering. The rigs are monitored to analyse the effects of extreme wind and wave forces. The opportunity to inspect the degradation of a rig when dismantled adds to the knowledge to influence future offshore developments.

Cliff erosion and the longshore drift means that the pipeline and gas terminal are under constant threat because the land is not stable. Permanent defences are not appropriate as they interfere with the natural processes creating adverse effects. Enhancing the natural defences – soft engineering – is used to ensure that the natural processes are maintained whilst protecting this key energy supply.

GLASGOW WATER SUPPLY

BRINGING CLEAN WATER TO SCOTLAND'S BIGGEST CITY

LOCATION LOCH KATRINE TO GLASGOW, SCOTLAND, UK
CONSTRUCTION DATES 1855–59 (UPGRADE 2004–08)

ONE COULD ARGUE that even more than developments such as X-rays or penicillin, the greatest breakthroughs in medicine have been the supply of clean drinking water and the removal of waste water. In 1820, cholera was rife in Glasgow and life expectancy was just 35 years and falling. Water supplied from the River Clyde was polluted with sewage and had become inadequate for the rapidly expanding city. In 1848–49, a cholera epidemic killed 4,000 people in the city and the Glasgow Corporation asked the civil engineer John Frederick La Trobe Bateman to advise a long-term solution.

Bateman had already devised a scheme for Manchester, which was under construction, and confirmed that Loch Katrine would be the best source of clean water – an idea that had been suggested in 1846 but not acted upon. He advised raising the water level in the loch by 1.2 metres by building a small dam to allow a daily supply of 227 million litres of water to the city. The work was carried out between 1855 and 1859.

From Loch Katrine the water was transported to two reservoirs at Milngavie, just north of Glasgow, through a 41-km-long pipe or aqueduct, half of which was tunnelled by hand through hills. The aqueduct used 25 bridges to cross valleys, passing the water through a rectangular cast iron tube supported on masonry pillars up to 24 metres above the valley floor. The entire aqueduct drops just under 7 metres throughout its length (16 cm per 1 km), just enough for the water to travel by gravity.

When Queen Victoria opened the scheme on 14 October 1859, it was one of the largest water supply schemes ever created and had employed 3,000 people. "It is a work which will bear comparison with the most extensive aqueducts in the world, not excluding those of ancient Rome," said resident engineer James Gale. "It is one of which any city may well be proud."

By the 1880s it had become clear that friction through the unlined aqueduct meant that the proposed daily supply of 227 million litres was actually 191 million. Gale designed and supervised construction of another dam to raise the water level by 1.5 metres and a new aqueduct using lessons learned from the original. Just over half of this aqueduct was lined with concrete to reduce friction and it took a more direct route through the hillside, taking advantage of pneumatic drills and more powerful explosives that were now available. The Loch Katrine scheme is still in use today, using dams and bridges that are now listed by Historic Environment Scotland. "I leave you a work," said Bateman, "which I believe is as indestructible as the hills through which it has been carried."

He was right, but by the beginning of the 21st century, it was clear that a new water-treatment works was needed to replace the old one in Milngavie. Scottish Water carried out a huge research project looking at 17 locations to identify the best site before settling on an embankment north of the old facility and near Mugdock and Craigmadde reservoirs, which serve the new one. The treatment works and buildings were built between 2004 and 2007 by MJ Gleeson. Some 7,000 tonnes of steel bars reinforced the structural concrete, enough to stretch all the way to Canada. Bankell Reservoir, which contains the treated water, is large enough to hold 1,200 double decker buses.

The area around the reservoirs close to the new site is a popular beauty spot. The treatment facility was built partly below ground, and Scottish Water invested £1 million on landscaping and tree planting to disguise the buildings and create a wetland area to attract wildlife.

ICE 200
BELFAST SEWERS PROJECT
NORTHERN IRELAND WATER'S "BIG DIG"

LOCATION BELFAST, NORTHERN IRELAND, UK
CONSTRUCTION DATES 2006–10

THE BELFAST SEWERS Stormwater Management Project is a major £160-million investment aimed at reducing pollution to the River Lagan, helping to prevent homes and shops from flooding, and permitting new development within the city.

The work included the upgrade and repair of old brick sewers, and the construction of a new stormwater tunnel that is 6 miles long, up to 4 metres in diameter and, in places, 30 metres below the ground. This even featured on the television programme *Top Gear*, when Jeremy Clarkson led an *Italian Job*-style race along the tunnel in a Renault Twingo, showcasing one of Europe's biggest engineering projects to an audience of millions.

Work on the project started in 2006 and took a team of up to 300 four years to complete. The tunnel terminates at Northern Ireland's largest pumping station, which has a capacity of 4 million gallons. The soil from the tunnelling process was re-used as a capping layer on a municipal waste site, which has now been developed into Giant's Park in the north of the city.

It was critical that the project was delivered efficiently, effectively and safely, with consideration to the specific challenges of Belfast and its highly variable geology. Crucially, the system had to ensure the city's famous buildings were unaffected by excavations and, most importantly, limit disruption to life and business in the city.

A wide range of local and international technical expertise was needed, including engineers from Northern Ireland Water, consultant firm Atkins as project managers, and Morgan Est and Farrans as contractors. Community "buy-in" was also vital, and help from Belfast City Council and the Northern Ireland Executive's Department for Infrastructure was essential to ensure that work was planned in a way that was sympathetic to the needs of the city and its people.

Belfast has been transformed in the last decade and this project brought many benefits to the city, including reducing the risk of flooding and improving water quality in the River Lagan. The complex system of sewers has played an important and largely unseen role in supporting world-class tourist attractions, new business and urban redevelopment.

DINORWIG POWER STATION

A HYDROELECTRIC PIONEER IN THE SNOWDONIA NATIONAL PARK

LOCATION DINORWIG, GWYNEDD, WALES, UK
CONSTRUCTION DATES 1970–84

WE ARE ALL creatures of habit and this can place demands on our basic infrastructure. During ad breaks or at the end of a major TV programme, for instance, many put on the kettle to make a cup of tea, which creates a surge in the demand for water and power.

Completed in 1984, Dinorwig Power Station was built to ensure that such surges do not lead to power cuts. It generates hydroelectric power by transferring water through tunnels and six turbines from a reservoir high in the mountains to a lower reservoir. It can generate 1,728 megawatts of power in just 16 seconds. At night, when there is low demand for power, energy from other power stations can be used to pump the water back uphill ready for further generation.

Built in 11 caverns, including the largest man-made cavern in Europe, hidden within Elidir Fawr mountain near Snowdon in North Wales, Dinorwig Power Station was the largest single construction project and pumped storage scheme in Europe at the time. Its largest cavern is 180 metres long, 23 metres wide and 51 metres high. Around 16 km of shafts and tunnels were excavated up to 11.5 metres in diameter, some to carry water, others to carry

traffic to service the station. A 35-metre-high dam was built to increase the capacity of Marchlyn Mawr to form the upper reservoir, 503 metres above Lynn Peris, an existing lake that was remodelled to form the lower reservoir.

The local road network and Bangor harbour were improved to provide access for materials and equipment for the station, and care was taken to protect the environment during construction. Extensive landscaping was undertaken, fish from Lynn Peris were moved to adjacent lakes, spores from local heather were collected to clad the dams and outgoing transmission lines were buried underground to connect the station to the national grid 9.5 km away.

Dinorwig Power Station was designed by James Williamson and Partners and the main contractor was the McAlpine Brand Zschokke joint venture. Gleeson constructed Marchlyn Dam, designed by Binnie & Partners. The client was the Central Electricity Generating Board and it is now (2018) operated by the First Hydro Company. Dinorwig has made a huge contribution to ensuring that power is always available, even at short notice, to customers in Britain.

ICE 200
ABERFAN DISASTER

THE CIVIL ENGINEERING LESSONS LEARNED

LOCATION ABERFAN, SOUTH WALES, UK
DATE 21 OCTOBER 1966

AT 9.20AM ON Friday 21 October 1966, the hooter at the Merthyr Vale Colliery – a mine that had not suffered a major disaster in nearly a century – broke its long silence. A huge pile of colliery waste that had been tipped onto a nearby mountainside had collapsed and engulfed the neighbouring village of Aberfan. In total, 144 lives were lost, 116 of them children. Fifty two years on, the lessons learned from this disaster continue to define the standards for the safe construction and management of spoil tips.

The sinking of the first shaft of the Merthyr Vale Colliery commenced in 1869 and the first coal was produced in 1875. By 1916, the colliery had run out of space to tip the waste on the valley floor and began tipping on the mountainside above the village of Aberfan. Tipping continued until 1966, by which time seven tips had been constructed containing 2.7 million cubic yards of colliery spoil. There was no legislation on the safety of tips anywhere in the world at this time, except in parts of West Germany and South Africa. The National Coal Board had no tipping policy, later found to be the basic cause of the disaster.

The steep hillside above Aberfan was riddled with recorded springs in a high rainfall area and no effort was made to enclose the streams that would eventually become buried beneath the tips. A large failure of Tip 4 in 1944 was not even a reportable incident because nobody from the colliery was injured. Those in charge were inappropriately qualified and inexperienced in civil engineering soil mechanics and hydrogeology and lacked direction from above.

Tip 7 covered material that had previously slipped in 1944, as well as the very same watercourse that had caused earlier failures.

Its catastrophic failure on 21 October 1966 was, geotechnically, the result of a build-up of water in the tip. When a small rotational slip occurred, the disturbance caused the saturated fine material of the tip to liquefy and flow down the mountain. Around 140,000 cubic yards of black slurry avalanched down the mountainside wiping out everything in its path and continuing down to the village. It destroyed a farmhouse, cottages, 18 houses, Pant Glas Junior School and part of the neighbouring County Secondary School, before finally coming to rest. The dead included half of the youth of Aberfan.

A tribunal of three, including ICE Past President Sir Harold Harding, was appointed to inquire into the disaster. It recommended new safety legislation, wider powers of inspection, the strengthening of the Mines Inspectorate by the addition of qualified civil engineers experienced in tip stability and control, and the need for tips to be regularly inspected. This was enshrined in legislation, but Aberfan residents still had to campaign for the removal of the remaining tips.

Disasters are tragic but – if the root causes are thoroughly researched and implications are considered wisely and thoughtfully – the likelihood of repeat events becomes vanishingly small. New legislation and codes of practice set higher standards. The competency of design, construction, management, inspection and regulatory professionals are reviewed and, if necessary, upgraded.

Most importantly, Aberfan has taught us that all lessons learned must be effectively communicated and embedded in current practice. Civil engineers have always learnt from the past, turning hindsight into insight. Disasters are opportunities to safeguard the future.

CARDIFF BAY BARRAGE

A WATERFRONT LAKE TO REGENERATE THE WELSH CAPITAL

LOCATION CARDIFF, WALES, UK
CONSTRUCTION DATES 1994–99

CARDIFF ROSE TO prominence during the Industrial Revolution as a port for exporting iron, coal and steel. By the 1880s, the port was handling more coal than any other in the world, reaching its peak just before the First World War. However, by the 1980s, with industry in decline, the area had become run down and in need of a new purpose. The Cardiff Bay Development Corporation was set up in 1987 to consider how to regenerate and attract business and investment to the area. The mission statement was "to put Cardiff on the international map as a superlative maritime city... thereby enhancing the image and the economic well-being of Cardiff and Wales as a whole."

Cardiff has the second-highest tidal range in the world (14.5 metres), meaning that boats could only access the bay for several hours each side of high tide. In addition, the bay area exposed mudflats twice each day. The solution put forward was to build a 1.1-km-long concrete barrage, or low dam, across the mouth of the bay from Cardiff Docks to Penarth. This would trap water from the rivers Ely and Taff to create a 200-hectare freshwater lake with 10 km of waterfront ripe for development.

There were major objections to the scheme. The mudflats were a winter-feeding area for wading birds, and migratory fish needed to be able to return to the rivers. There were also historic rights of navigation to and from the bay area, and fears that the lake could raise the water table and cause low-level flooding. The Cardiff Bay Barrage Act 1993 set strict operating requirements on the construction and subsequent operating process.

The barrage was designed by Sir Alexander Gibb and Partners with three locks protected by breakwaters, allowing boats to leave and enter the bay. Five sluice gates are used to control water levels in the bay and provide flood defence. It also incorporates one of the largest and most advanced fish passes in the UK, with an underwater camera that allows fish species to be identified and numbers monitored.

The barrage was the largest civil engineering project in Europe at the time and was constructed by Balfour Beatty and Costain. It has been the catalyst for a £2 billion regeneration, transforming Cardiff Bay into a residential and commercial centre, as well as a popular tourist attraction.

LIFTING THE BRENT DELTA

THE WORLD'S HEAVIEST OFFSHORE LIFT

LOCATION UK SECTOR OF THE NORTH SEA
PROJECT DATE 2017

ON FRIDAY 28 April 2017, *Pioneering Spirit*, a colossal lifting vessel operated by offshore contractor Allseas, removed the Brent Delta platform in a single lift, and commenced the 700 km journey from Shell's iconic Brent oil and gas field, 186 km north east of the Shetland Islands, to Able UK's decommissioning yard in Hartlepool. At 382 metres in length, *Pioneering Spirit* is the largest construction vessel ever built, equating to over six jumbo jets set nose to tail. The entire process marked the culmination of five years' study and engineering work. This involved strengthening the platform underdeck, installing lifting points and cutting the platform's massive legs. All of this was required to prepare for the world's heaviest offshore lift, breaking 10 seconds for the fast lift of the Delta's 24,200 tonnes topside.

After arriving close to Hartlepool four days later, the Delta was transferred onto the 200 metre *Iron Lady* barge, and carefully guided up the channel to the quayside. This feat put the lift in the record books, cementing the credibility of the new innovative lifting technology employed.

Shell's Brent Decommissioning team began work on the project with Allseas in 2013, with teams of engineers from both companies working tirelessly together to ensure that the platform and vessel were ready. Additionally, Able UK's decommissioning and recycling yard quayside facilities were strengthened to receive and recycle over 97 per cent of the Delta platform.

FIMISTON OPEN PIT

ONE OF THE WORLD'S LARGEST OPEN PIT GOLD MINES

LOCATION KALGOORLIE, WESTERN AUSTRALIA
CONSTRUCTION DATE 1989

AT 3.5 KM long, 1.5 km wide and more than 700 metres deep, the Fimiston Open Pit or Super Pit at Kalgoorlie can be seen from space. It was the largest open-pit gold mine in Australia until 2016, when it was surpassed by the Newmont Boddington gold mine, 600 km away on the Western Australia coast.

The Golden Mile Dolerite around Kalgoorlie has been mined since 1893 and has produced more than 608 million ounces of gold. It plays a major part in Australia's position as the second-largest gold producer in the world, behind China. The brainchild of Alan Bond, the Super Pit was created in 1989 by combining many small underground mines.

The pit faces unique challenges: it is on top of a network of more than 3,500 km of historical mine workings that stretch 1,200 metres below the surface. No other open pit in the world has this many open spaces or voids to avoid. Engineers have to use historical plans and drilling data, as well as laser technology, to check for voids below the surface.

Owned jointly by Barrick Australia Pacific and Newmont Australia, Fimiston Open Pit makes a major contribution to the local economy, attracting thousands of tourists each year. It produces up to 800,000 ounces of gold a year and employs more than 1,100 employees and contractors, with approximately 30 per cent of the mine's suppliers based locally in Kalgoorlie-Boulder.

ICE 200
DAU TIENG WATER RESOURCES SYSTEM
THE DEVELOPMENT OF THE PHUOC HOA BARRAGE IN POSTWAR VIETNAM

LOCATION TAY NINH PROVINCE, VIETNAM
PROJECT DATES 2000–07

DURING THE 1980s, the Vietnam reunification government completed one of its priorities: the development of agriculture in Tay Ninh Province, involving the building of the Dau Tieng Dam and a 64,000-hectare irrigation project. The motivation was to show appreciation to the many farmers who had supported the Vietcong during the war. However, by 1998, Ho Chi Minh City and the five surrounding provinces still faced major challenges in meeting their future water-supply demands, as the Dau Tieng irrigation scheme had not fulfilled expectations in terms of area supplied or reliability.

An additional project to support the population of Binh Duong Province through the construction of the 26-metre-high Phuoc Hoa Barrage, a 40-km transfer canal and a 30,000-hectare extension to the Dau Tieng irrigation scheme by 2014 was funded by the Asian Development Bank. The project was planned, designed and constructed under the supervision of Black & Veatch, who also prepared sustainable management plans for the operation. The scheme increases water availability to the Dau Tieng scheme, as well as providing 38 cubic metres per second

for domestic, municipal and industrial water supply, including 10 cubic metres per second for Ho Chi Minh City and other uses. The project was complemented by the modernisation of the Dau Tieng irrigation system under a World Bank assistance scheme.

Black & Veatch became involved when they showed that an original concept was unworkable and helped the Vietnamese to re-plan the project in its current configuration. Along the way, the canal alignment had to cope with unexploded ordinances and groundwater problems, while the impounding reservoir had to be tested for dioxins from Agent Orange.

"As a civil engineer and water resources planner, I had the pleasure of involvement in planning the project concept in 2000, the two-year design phase, four years of construction and a year preparing a participatory management plan for the combined projects," says David Meigh. "My colleagues included Vic Hobcroft, Harry King, Martin Donaldson, David Stopher and Lance Gore. Such long involvement from concept to operation in such an interesting and dynamic country is unusual and highly rewarding for a civil engineer."

ICE 200
MAUREEN PLATFORM REFLOAT AND DECOMMISSIONING
THE RAISING OF A NORTH SEA GIANT

LOCATION UK SECTOR OF THE NORTH SEA
PROJECT DATES 2001–03

THE MAUREEN OIL Field in the UK North Sea ceased production in 1999, having been in operation for 16 years. As part of the decommissioning programme, the Maureen platform had to be removed from the offshore site and then fully decommissioned (at a cost of around £200 million).

The first phase of the removal involved the hydraulic jacking of the Maureen platform (which, at the time of refloat, weighed 112,000 tonnes) from the seabed. This process commenced with the deballasting of the structure to leave a minimum on-bottom weight.

With the platform free from the seabed, the next major issue related to the overall hydrodynamic stability of the structure as it floated upwards. The structure had to move upwards by around 21.6 metres before the three upper domes broke the surface of the sea to dramatically increase the overall floating stability of the unit. The platform was then towed to Stord Island in Norway to be broken up.

Additional offshore works continued, including the removal of all the remaining facilities at the Maureen location. The field's concrete loading column was reused as a breakwater, also at Stord Island. At the time, this was the largest decommissioning project of any offshore installation in the world. Dr Peter Broughton was a project engineer during many phases of the original design and construction work for Maureen (1979–83) and was project manager for Phillips Petroleum for the whole of the removal and decommissioning of the Maureen field (1998–2003).

ICE 200
AKOSOMBO DAM
THE DAM THAT CREATED THE WORLD'S LARGEST MAN-MADE LAKE

LOCATION VOLTA RIVER AT AKOSOMBO, GHANA
CONSTRUCTION DATES 1961–65

AKOSOMBO IS A 660-metre-long, 124-metre-high rock-fill dam and hydroelectric power station on the Volta River in Ghana. It was originally designed by Sir William Halcrow & Partners in 1949 and was eventually built after the country gained independence in 1957. The Italian contractor Impregilo, which had just completed the Kariba Dam, won the contract in 1961.

The dam demonstrated Ghana's ability to commission and carry out huge infrastructure projects. It was part of a larger scheme that included the construction of an aluminium smelter and deep port at Tema. The aluminium plant initially used the majority of the electricity produced by Akosombo but, by 2018, the 1,020 megawatt power station provided 85 per cent of Ghana's electricity.

The dam created Lake Volta: at 8,500 sq km, the world's largest man-made lake by surface area. As well as the huge benefit of electric power, it has prevented flooding in the Lower Volta flood plain, allowing increased fishing and commercial farming activities and attracting tourism.

Fifty years ago, the social and environmental impact of large dams was not considered as carefully as it is today. The dam required 80,000 people to be resettled and the lake provided a habitat for disease-carrying creatures such as black-fly, mosquitoes and snails. However, it encouraged Ghana to be the first African country to establish an environmental governing body, the Environmental Protection Council, in 1974.

ASWAN DAM

THE LARGEST MASONRY DAM OF ITS DAY

LOCATION ASWAN, EGYPT
CONSTRUCTION DATES 1898–1902 (HEIGHTENED 1910–12, 1930-33)

AT MORE THAN 4,000 miles in length, the Nile is the longest river in the world. For millennia, it has provided those living along its banks with water for drinking and irrigation. In Egypt, at its downstream end, the traditional flood season was from June to September, the sowing season from October to mid-February, and the harvest from February to May.

By the mid-1800s, improved irrigation practices were required to meet worldwide demand for Egyptian cotton. As a result, the Delta Barrages at Cairo were completed in 1861 to facilitate better water control in the fertile Delta region of Egypt. They were only partially successful, and it became clear that what the country really needed was a massive dam to store the Nile floodwaters for use later in the year.

Sir Samuel Baker wrote to *The Times* in 1866 suggesting that the best location for the dam was at Aswan, on the first Nile cataract. However, it was 30 years later when William Willcocks completed his design for what was then the largest masonry dam in the world.

Built of Aswan granite, the dam was constructed with a random stone hearting, encased in an elegant dressed ashlar facing. It was built between 1898 and 1902 by John Aird & Co under the supervision of Sir Benjamin Baker. It stood 22 metres high, 1,950 metres long and incorporated a navigation lock on the western bank to facilitate the passage of shipping upstream as far as the second cataract. The dam wall contained 180 two-metre-wide undersluices along its base, which allowed the Nile flood and associated silt to pass freely through the structure. The gates were designed to be closed on the falling flood to store one billion cubic metres of

irrigation water. This cleverly prevented the silting up of the reservoir.

The success of the dam was immediate, but the need for cotton was insatiable and so it was raised twice: by five metres between 1910 and 1912, increasing the storage to 2.5 billion cubic metres; and then by eight metres between 1930 and 1933 to bring the total dam height to 36 metres and its storage to five billion cubic metres. The first raising was commissioned by the Egyptian Public Works Department (headed by Sir Murdoch MacDonald) and was designed by Baker. The second raising was designed and supervised by MacDonald's new consulting firm, Sir M MacDonald & Partners.

In the late 1960s, Egypt commissioned the massive Aswan High Dam designed by the Moscow-based Hydroproject Institute: a 111-metre-high earthfill dam impounding 132 billion cubic metres of water with 592 megawatts of installed capacity hydropower plants. The associated reservoir (Lake Nasser) can easily contain the entire annual Nile flow and, as a result, water is now only released downstream on the basis of demand. There has been no Nile flood since the new dam's construction and, as the Aswan High Dam has no undersluices, no discharge of silt downstream. The dam powered Egypt's industrialisation programme but the loss of the silt has meant that Egyptians have had to use nitrogen-based fertilisers on their fields for the first time, which has in turn caused the river's water quality to deteriorate.

The Ethiopian government is currently building the huge 155-metre-high Renaissance Dam further upstream. The story of capturing the waters of the Nile for irrigation, water supply and power has chapters yet to be written.

ICE 200
EKOFISK PROTECTIVE BARRIER

PROTECTING A NORTH SEA OIL PLATFORM FROM THE EFFECTS OF SUBSIDENCE

LOCATION NORWEGIAN SECTOR OF THE NORTH SEA
CONSTRUCTION DATE 1989

THE EKOFISK COMPLEX is a series of interconnecting oil and gas platforms, built in the early 1970s. At its centre is the Ekofisk Oil Storage Tank, the world's first offshore concrete gravity platform, installed in 1973. By peak production in 1980, the complex – in block 2/4 of the Norwegian sector of the North Sea – was extracting 624,000 barrels of oil per day from the chalk reservoir located around 3,000 metres below the seabed. This oil is continuously exported by pipeline to the Teesside Refinery in the north-east of England, while the gas is exported by pipeline to the Emden terminal in Germany.

In 1984, Phillips Petroleum Company discovered that the platforms, including the Ekofisk Tank – its largest North Sea oil and gas field – had sunk by around 6 metres. This subsidence was due to the partial collapse of the chalk reservoir from which the hydrocarbons were being extracted, and it meant that Phillips's entire Ekofisk central complex – all around 220 miles from land – were in danger. No equipment existed that could possibly lift this enormous, million-barrel oil storage-tank out from the seabed, which is why the US oil company commissioned the ingenious Protective Barrier project to protect the offshore structure from the effects of ocean-floor subsidence.

"Installation of the concrete barrier is the safest and most economical way to protect the tank and related processing facilities," said MH McConnell, the then President of Phillips Norway.

In May 1986, Dr Peter Broughton commenced full time as lead project engineer on all work related to subsidence on the Ekofisk Tank. Under his supervision, Phillips engineers designed an enormous cellular sea wall: a cellular circular concrete structure more than 140 metres in diameter and 106 metres in height. The lower 12 metres in height of the Protective Barrier was cast in two half units, near Rotterdam, Holland. Once floated out of the dry-dock, a submersible lift ship transported each half unit to a second construction area in Alfjorden, Norway, closer to the installation site of the Protective Barrier. Weighing 27,000 tonnes apiece, both 12-metre-high semi-circular components represented one of the greatest dry-weight shipments of a single object ever made. At Alfjorden, the two half units were completed to the full height of 106 metres.

Installed, the total weight of the completed structure is equal to 315,000 tonnes of reinforced and pre-stressed concrete, with around 672,000 tonnes of gravel ballast placed in the 48 cells offshore, in order to provide an effective on-bottom weight of around 500,000 tonnes for purposes of seabed stability.

It was a truly gargantuan engineering project. Each half unit had a shape and mass that was unique from anything constructed previously. The two half units were installed to very close tolerances around the Ekofisk Tank and connected together offshore, and the entire Protective Barrier was subsequently subjected to wave impact and severe wave loading. What is particularly impressive about the installation of the Protective Barrier is that the entire offshore works took place in the space of around 6 weeks – in June and July 1989 – with no production shut-down in the field. Some fields in the Greater Ekofisk area (including Cod and Albuskjell) have since been decommissioned, but others are still producing oil and gas, and the Ekofisk complex is planned to continue until at least 2050.

Dr Broughton has since produced several technical papers on the Protective Barrier, and received several awards for his work on the project, including the George Stephenson Medal from the Institution of Civil Engineers.

ICE 200
KAINJI DAM
NIGERIA'S LARGEST RESERVOIR

KAINJI DAM IS a 7.2-km-long gravity dam on the River Niger, one of longest dams in the world. It created Lake Kainji which, at 135 km in length and 30 km in width, is Nigeria's largest man-made lake, and the power source for Kainji's eight turbines generating 800 megawatts of electricity. Until it was commissioned in 1968, Nigeria's electricity was inefficient and unreliable, relying on small diesel generators in cities with the larger part of the country in darkness.

The dam was designed by Balfour Beatty and Nedeco, and constructed by Italian contractor Impregilo. Two new townships and 128 villages were built for resettlement. Transport links were improved with 1,000 km of road repaired between the site and the port of Lagos to allow heavy machinery and the turbines to be delivered. During the five years of construction, half a million tons of material and equipment were transported to the site by road and rail.

A road was built across the dam, and two locks in the dam enable boats to pass. A team of highly skilled divers are on call 24/7 in case repairs are needed. The dam was intended to reduce flooding through regulating the flow, but management is difficult. The lake supports fishing and irrigation for farming. Hydro power remains relatively reliable and the power station has outlasted thermal stations built more recently.

ICE 200
KIRI DAM
A PROJECT TO IRRIGATE THE SAVANNAH SUGARCANE PLANTATION

LOCATION ADAMAWA STATE, NIGERIA
CONSTRUCTION DATE 1982

THE KIRI DAM on the Gongola River in north-east Nigeria is part of a larger irrigation scheme comprising the dam, a series of canals, a pumping station and storage reservoirs. It was originally commissioned to irrigate 15,000 hectares of the sugarcane plantation of the Savannah Sugar Company, a company originally set up as a joint venture between the Nigerian Federal Government and the Commonwealth Development Corporation (CDC) of London.

The company is now part of a privately owned conglomerate and the dam is controlled by the Upper Benue River Basin Development Authority (UBRBDA). The sugar company remains a major local employer, with 700 permanent staff increasing to 5,000 during the harvest. It is Nigeria's only sugar producer with 50,000 tons distributed annually.

Designed by Sir Alexander Gibb & Partners, the Kiri earth-fill dam is 20 metres high and 1.25 km long with an internal clay blanket. It created a 615 million cubic metre reservoir, Lake Kiri, which has become popular with hippos, not welcomed by local farmers despite the potential for tourism. Below the dam, the river has become narrower and flow during the dry season has increased, which has improved farming potential.

The Kiri Dam is located in a remote area prone to power cuts. A study has concluded that it has potential for a 35-megawatt hydropower to be installed.

LONDON ARRAY

THE WORLD'S LARGEST OFFSHORE WINDFARM

LOCATION KENT, UK
CONSTRUCTION DATES 2011–13

"THIS IS A great day for Kent and a great day for Britain," said David Cameron at the inauguration of London Array in July 2013. "London Array has been built by some of the bravest seamen, the most talented engineers and hardest workers."

Completion of the world's largest operational offshore wind farm was a landmark event for the world's renewable energy industry. Much further out to sea and – at 630 megawatts – with more than twice the generating capacity of the previous record holder, it paved the way for a new generation of substantially bigger wind farms. Nothing on this scale had been attempted before and construction of the £2 billion project posed formidable engineering challenges that required innovative solutions.

London Array's 175 turbines are a minimum of 20 km from the Kent coast in the outer Thames Estuary. It's a windy location, susceptible to changing weather and with sea depths varying from intertidal to 25 metres. The tide and the weather had to be just right when lifting large items such as the turbines, blades and the monopile foundations into place.

The single heaviest lifts were the installation of the two offshore substation topsides, which each weighed around 1,250 tonnes.

Despite poor weather, construction was completed as planned in December 2012, with three of the four 50-km export cables, over 200 km of array cables, 90 remaining foundations and all 175 turbines installed in the final 10 months. It was an effort that required up to 60 vessels and 1,000 people working on site at any one time. It took only 95 working days to energise and commission all the wind farm's turbines, setting a new industry benchmark.

Five years on, London Array's performance is exceeding expectations and providing enough clean electricity to power well over 500,000 UK homes. "Every year we prevent the emission of some 900,000 tonnes of carbon dioxide and are continually finding ways to boost our output," says General Manager Jonathan Duffy. "It won't be long until we lose our crown as the world's largest offshore wind farm but I am proud that we have helped the UK – and the world – transition to a lower-carbon economy."

ICE 200
KARIBA DAM

ONE OF THE WORLD'S LARGEST DAMS, ENERGISING SOUTHERN AFRICA

LOCATION ZAMBEZI RIVER, ZAMBIA AND ZIMBABWE
CONSTRUCTION DATES 1955–59; 1971–77

KARIBA DAM, AT 579 metres long and 128 metres high, is one of the world's largest. The double curvature concrete arch dam was designed by Gibb Coyne Sogei (Kariba), a joint venture of Sir Alexander Gibb & Partners and the French firms Coyne & Bellier and SoGEI. The dam and the Kariba South power cavern were constructed between 1955 and 1959 by the Italian contractor Impresit. The Kariba North power cavern was awarded to Mitchell Construction in 1971, but financial and political difficulties brought down the company, and it was completed by a Yugoslavian contractor in 1977.

The dam spans the Kariba Gorge between Zambia and Zimbabwe, and its hydroelectric turbines have provided cost-effective electricity to both countries, enabling industrial development and providing electricity where there was none. It has increased regional energy security by connecting the electricity grids of many countries, reduced reliance on fossil fuels, and reduced power and development costs. It has also developed tourism, wildlife sanctuaries, fisheries and improved crop irrigation in the area.

But damming the Zambezi created Lake Kariba, the largest man-made lake in the world, and 57,000 people had to be resettled – a huge social upheaval. As the waters rose, over 6,000 animals had to be rescued and relocated to the mainland in "Operation Noah". These social and environmental impacts had to be borne before the benefits of plentiful electricity could be realised – always a difficult judgement.

ICE 200
GHAZI-BAROTHA
HYDROPOWER PROJECT

ONE OF THE WORLD'S LARGEST HYDROELECTRIC POWER PLANTS

LOCATION RIVER INDUS, PAKISTAN
CONSTRUCTION DATES 1996–2004

THE PLANNING AND construction of Ghazi-Barotha in Pakistan was one of the largest hydropower projects in the world and involved engineering companies from Asia, Europe and the USA.

The 2.5-km-long barrage on the Indus River is situated at Ghazi, 7 km below the Tarbela Dam, which is mainly used for irrigation. The primary purpose of the project is to provide constant peak power, even at the Tarbela's driest times.

It is a run-of-the-river hydroelectric project, meaning it does not store water in a reservoir. Instead, the barrage diverts water from the Indus River into a 100-metre-wide, 52-km-long, concrete-lined open channel, one of the largest canals in the world. This transports the water to the powerhouse at Barotha, where it passes through five generators before being returned to the river. The plant produces 10 per cent of Pakistan's power: a major contribution to its energy expansion programme.

This socially responsible project focused on the social and economic needs of village communities. The barrage site and the route of the channel were chosen to avoid villages where possible; and, for the first time in Pakistan, the spoil banks made up of excavated material were covered with fertile topsoil, so generated farmland space.

The project won the Energy Institute's Platinum Award in 2006 for its innovative and responsible approach to providing clean, sustainable, low-cost energy.

ICE 200
FORTIES FIELD
ONE OF EUROPE'S BIGGEST OIL FIELDS, STILL GOING STRONG

————————

LOCATION UK SECTOR OF THE NORTH SEA
DATES 1964–

THE FORTIES FIELD has a proud history, both under the 27-year tenure of British Petroleum (BP) and with the Apache Corporation since 2003. In 1965 BP was awarded UK North Sea exploration licence number 001. In October 1970 the field, covering 93 sq km, was discovered by the semi-submersible drilling vessel Sea Quest 110 miles north-east of Aberdeen in a water depth of 110 metres. It contained more than 4.4 billion barrels of oil.

BP engaged Brown & Root Inc to help develop the design for the exploitation of the field. The chosen design included four platforms, a 32-inch outside diameter (OD) subsea pipeline to Cruden Bay, 105 miles long, and a 130-mile-long 36-inch OD pipeline from Cruden Bay to BP's Grangemouth refinery.

The four substructure designs were similar 20,000 tonne self-floating steel tubular space frame towers secured to the sea floor by tubular steel piles driven through grouted sleeves. The towers were built in graving docks on top of 10,000-tonne reusable rafts that included complex ballasting systems which allowed the towers to be rotated to the vertical and placed on the seabed once in the field. The modular topside facilities with a maximum module weight of 2,000 tonnes were designed to be lifted into position by crane vessels in the field and then hooked up and commissioned.

To allow rapid progress of the project two graving docks were used; one at Graythorp, Teesside and a second, newly constructed, at Nigg Bay on the Cromarty Firth. The first tower was installed in July 1974 and the second in August 1974. The rafts returned to their graving docks and the remaining towers were installed in June 1975.

Forties production peaked in 1979 at 500,000 barrels of oil per day (BOPD). In the 1980s the more conventional Forties Echo platform joined the four original platforms. In 2013 the Forties Alpha Satellite Platform was installed. On acquisition of the field Apache immediately implemented an ambitious upgrade programme, beginning with an intensive re-evaluation. Production had declined to 40,000 BOPD. Apache revived production to over 60,000 BOPD by year-end 2004. Prior to Apache's acquisition, the field was expected to cease production by 2013 but Apache's investments have extended the field's life by more than 20 years. It is still one of the single largest oil-producing assets within the UK's continental shelf.

ICE 200
THAMES TIDEWAY
ADDING CAPACITY TO LONDON'S VICTORIAN SEWERS

LOCATION LONDON AND THE THAMES ESTUARY, UK
CONSTRUCTION DATES 2017–

LONDON'S SEWERAGE SYSTEM was designed by Sir Joseph Bazalgette in the 1860s for a population of four million people. Although the sewers remain in excellent condition and major extensions were made around 1910 and again between the wars and in the 1950s, the system cannot cope with a growing population, now about 10 million, and sewage regularly overflows into the Thames when rainfall is high.

The London Tideway Improvements are a three-part solution to tackle this pollution. The first step was upgrading Thames Water's major sewage treatment works in London – Mogden, Crossness, Beckton, Riverside and Long Reach – to increase the amount of sewage that can be treated at each. The second part of the plan was the construction of the Lee Tunnel, a 6.9-km long, 7.2-metre-diameter tunnel running from Abbey Mills Pumping Station to Beckton Sewage Treatment Works. The tunnel, completed in 2015, is drastically decreasing sewage overflows into the River Lee.

The third part of the solution is the £4.2 billion Thames Tideway Tunnel, which will stretch for 25 km from Acton in West London to Abbey Mills Pumping Station in Newham, where it will connect to the Lee Tunnel. The tunnel will intercept 34 of the most polluting sewer overflow points along the river, collecting sewage that would otherwise pour into the River Thames and transferring it to Beckton for treatment. The project is being financed by a consortium of investors, including Allianz, and includes pension funds covering 1.7 million savers.

The tunnel has been divided into three sections, each being constructed by a different main works contractor. The tunnelling conditions vary from section to section, and include clay in the west, mixed sands and gravels in the centre, and chalk in the east.

A joint venture of Balfour Beatty, Morgan Sindall and BAM Nuttall is constructing the west section, from Acton to Fulham. This also includes the Frogmore Connection Tunnel, linking the main tunnel in Fulham to Wandsworth. Ferrovial and Laing O'Rourke are building the central section, using two tunnelling machines – one boring from Battersea to Fulham, the other tunnelling east to Bermondsey. Costain, Vinci Construction Grands Projets and Bachy Soletanche are constructing the east section, from Bermondsey to Newham, and a connecting tunnel from Greenwich.

The Thames Tideway Tunnel is the biggest infrastructure project ever undertaken in the United Kingdom water industry and its ultimate vision is to realise the potential of a cleaner river for the environment, recreation and employment. Construction will create three new acres of public realm along the Thames, including areas at Blackfriars and Victoria Embankment, allowing people to get closer to the river.

Tideway is also aiming to inspire a future generation of engineers and construction workers. At the peak of construction, the project will create 4,000 direct, sustainable jobs and one in 50 site jobs will be an apprenticeship. Tideway and its contractors are also offering opportunities for ex-offenders to get back into work, and recently launched programmes to help people from the work-site boroughs to find employment.

Health, safety and well-being are also a priority. More than 10,000 people have now gone through the organisation's interactive health and safety training day, EPIC. This year, Tideway also became one of the first organisations in the construction industry to pilot the new Mates in Mind scheme, which helps tackle mental health problems in the industry.

ICE 200
EUROPEAN MARINE ENERGY CENTRE

TESTING TIDAL ENERGY OF THE COAST OF SCOTLAND

LOCATION ORKNEY, SCOTLAND, UK
CONSTRUCTION DATE 2003

WAVE AND TIDAL energy technologies are still in their infancy, and testing is essential to develop devices to a point where they can be deployed on a large scale. The European Marine Energy Centre (EMEC) was established in 2003, and is the world's first and leading facility for demonstrating, testing and verifying such devices. EMEC has now hosted 20 companies, testing 31 prototypes so far – more than at any other site in the world.

Orkney has a wide range of tide and wave conditions, as well as sheltered harbours, and EMEC's location enables developers to explore how equipment can be installed, operated and maintained in rough conditions while producing electricity efficiently. The centre provides purpose-built, accredited open-sea testing facilities that reduce the time, cost and risk in developing innovative renewable energy technologies. It has test sites linked to the national grid that offer independently verified performance assessments of devices, as well as confirming efficiency, reliability and ability to survive.

EMEC has also worked on more than 100 research and development projects across the sector, looking at marine energy sub-systems, components and infrastructure. It attracts developers from around the world, testing some of the most innovative technology, and has been central in developing international standards for the industry. Marine energy supports around 200 jobs in Orkney and local companies benefit from each device tested.

ICE 200
BECKTON SEWAGE TREATMENT WORKS

AN ENDURING SOLUTION TO A LIFE-THREATENING PROBLEM

LOCATION LONDON, UK
DATES 1887–89 AND TO PRESENT DAY

JOSEPH BAZALGETTE'S 1866 sewage system that rescued London (see London Sewerage System pages 204–5) delivered sewage directly into the Thames estuary on a retreating tide. London's rapid expansion increased the volume of raw sewage, and health concerns led to Bazalgette being commissioned in 1887 to devise a means of treating the sewage before it was released from the reservoirs at Beckton and Crossness. His solution was to separate the "solids", consolidate them into sludge for dumping at sea, and construct a new jetty.

Progressive upgrades to sewage treatment at Beckton, the larger catchment of the two outfalls, were built in the 1930s and the 1950s and again by Greater London Council in the early 1970s. In 2010–14, Beckton Sewage Treatment Works had another major upgrade by Thames Water, enabling the plant to treat 60 per cent more sewage, augmenting the link to Bazalgette's Abbey Mills "Northern Outfall" through the Lee Tunnel.

Water quality has improved in the vicinity so much that in 2010 a desalination plant was built to treat Thames water to drinking-water standard. Although more expensive than traditional clean water treatment, the plant is a crucial component for adding resilience to water supply during drought conditions.

Europe's largest sewage treatment works can now treat the waste of 3.9 million people, delivered there through London's oldest and its newest infrastructure-led improvements to its proud heritage of public health engineering.

ICE 200
IRRIGATION IN INDIA
HOW INDIA HAS MANAGED ITS WATER FOR CENTURIES

LOCATION INDIA
DATES TO THE PRESENT

IRRIGATION DEVELOPMENT IN India can be traced back to prehistoric times. Ancient Indian scriptures referred to the construction and maintenance of wells, canals, tanks and dams, while traces of irrigation structures dating back 3,700 years have been found in Maharashtra. During the Mauryan era (2,600–2,200 years ago) farmers had to pay taxes for irrigation water from neighbouring rivers. The Grand Anicut, which runs across the Cauvery River in Tamil Nadu, was begun in the 2nd century AD and is still used today.

The careful deployment of water in India has always been crucial. "One day's flow in the Godavari river during high floods is equal to one whole year's flow of the Thames in London," said the British engineer Sir Arthur Cotton, who built several key dams and canals in that area from 1825–1860. British interest in irrigation in South Asia dated from around 1800, and by the early 20th century they were undertaking increasingly ambitious schemes, with Indian engineers like Mokshagundam Visvesvaraya playing a prominent role.

Since independence, high priority has been given to irrigation, with nearly 10 per cent of all government expenditure being invested in irrigated agriculture. This has resulted in the development of, on average, 0.6–0.7 million hectares of new irrigated schemes every year. While major basin schemes have been undertaken, private groundwater irrigation, with shallow wells that serve 3–5 hectares each, is often considered to be more cost-effective. Around 16.43 million wells are in use (7.85 million dug wells, 8.10 million shallow tubewells and the rest deep tubewells).

In many states, especially in the north, the conjunctive use of surface water and groundwater has been practised using canal systems and wells to increase the yield and general efficiency of the system. Water from tubewells installed alongside existing canals is added for use in the canal command areas. This practice helps prevent waterlogging, but requires that farmers adopt good management techniques.

Many of India's rivers are shared with bordering countries, leading to international agreements. The 1960 Indus Water Treaty with Pakistan helped to resolve some issues; the building of the Farakka Barrage in 1974 led to a 1996 treaty ensuring that Bangladesh got a fair share of the flow during the dry season; and similar arrangements were drawn up with Nepal for the exploitation of the Kosi and Gandak rivers between 1954 and 1966.

REDR

LEADING THE WAY IN HUMANITARIAN CRISIS MANAGEMENT

HEADQUARTERS LONDON, UK
ESTABLISHED 1980

IN APRIL 1980, a 28-year-old civil engineer called Peter Guthrie stood up at an Institution of Civil Engineers symposium and announced the start of a new organisation: the Register of Engineers for Disaster Relief, or RedR. His vision for RedR was borne out of his experience volunteering in a camp for Vietnamese boat people the previous year. As the only engineer present – helping to provide water, sanitation and shelter for 40,000 people – it was clear to him that this kind of technical expertise was vital in emergencies.

Nearly 40 years on, RedR is a non-profit non-governmental organisation (NGO) with 1,800 members based in 43 different countries. It has offices in Kenya, Sudan and Jordan. In 2017 it trained 7,450 people in 55 countries, and it runs 448 training courses worldwide. Engineering heritage remains at the heart of what it does, but instead of being a register of engineers for disaster relief, it now focuses on training relief organisations and their staff all over the world.

In any humanitarian crisis – whether human-made through conflict or climate change, or caused by natural phenomena such as volcanoes and earthquakes – the immediate life-saving needs are the same. They are shelter, water and sanitation, together with the project-management skills to get things done. It means that civil engineers are always needed.

RedR helps to relieve the suffering associated with disasters by training humanitarian relief personnel and providing technical expertise. Its registered members offer their skills to help direct the efforts of United Nations and NGOs in times of crises. In 2016, 80 of its members responded directly to disasters. The work they did included helping to coordinate the frontline response in Mosul, Iraq, where many thousands were fleeing from military operations, and setting up water, hygiene and sanitation programmes for refugees escaping from South Sudan into northern Uganda.

RedR offers training to NGOs, aid workers and communities around the world to help them respond better to emergencies. Courses cover a range of subjects including water, hygiene and sanitation (WASH), shelter, safety, logistics, project management and the training of trainers. RedR does this in several different ways: face to face in the classroom, out in the field and online. In 2016, the company trained more than 7,400 people in 55 countries.

RedR runs a free online technical support, called KnowledgePoint, to people working in the field, so that they receive expert answers to technical questions quickly and easily. In 2017, the United Nations made KnowledgePoint the go-to site for Hurricane Irma technical support, as it did had done for the Haiti earthquake in 2010.

RedR's UK programme delivers a range of training courses, from a basic introduction to the sector to specialist courses for professional aid workers. RedR offers credit-rated master's degree courses in partnership with Oxford Brookes University in pursuit of its goal to further professionalise the humanitarian sector. RedR is also leading the way in preparing for future challenges. To deal with the demands posed by population growth in urban centres, the organisation has developed a programme geared specifically to urban disasters and encouraging engineers to get involved. Civil engineering is a career that gives you the opportunity to change lives: to help communities in their hour of need and make them more resilient for the future. The world, and RedR, needs more civil engineers.

ICE 200

ENGINEERS WITHOUT BORDERS UK

ENGINEERING A BETTER WAY FORWARD

LOCATION LONDON, UK
ESTABLISHED 2004

CIVIL ENGINEERS MAKE a difference to people's lives, providing them with shelter from the elements, clean water for their health and environmental design for their safe existence. People's lives today would be very different if it weren't for civil engineers. But access to this infrastructure is not equal throughout the world, and for the past 15 years, Engineers Without Borders UK has worked hard to make sure that the benefits it brings are available to communities across the globe.

For example, Engineers Without Borders UK has been working with its Kenyan partner for the last six years to improve the living conditions of the people of Kibera. Kibera is a large informal settlement on the southern side of Nairobi that is home to a population of between 250,000 to 1 million people. But it is challenged by poor waste management, open sewers and limited access to clean water. The seasonal rains can also affect the people living in Kibera more adversely than their wealthier Nairobi counterparts. The lack of good drainage systems and consequent build-up of waste combines with the proximity to the Nairobi River to cause the flooding of homes and access routes. These floods reduce mobility, damage property and increase the risk of disease. By supporting the community of Kibera with civil engineering capacity, Engineers Without Borders UK has helped improve drainage and flood protection in some of its worst affected areas, mitigating the impact of flooding on some of Kibera's poorest inhabitants.

As humanity looks forward, it sees itself on the precipice of the Anthropocene – an era some are calling the sixth mass extinction. In it, the decisions people make are on such a massive scale they have a momentous impact on the global environment and on the future of our planet. Civil engineers are at the heart of environmental changes relating to the movement of resources and materials, and play a key part in adapting landscapes and waterways to meet the demands of society. The decisions they make in designing today's increasingly urbanised environments will impact the world's well-being and influence how inclusive, healthy and prosperous its societies are. With increased awareness of that impact comes greater responsibility.

"Engineers Without Borders UK is leading a movement to place global responsibility at the heart of engineering," says Jon Prichard, Chair. "We know that engineers are pivotal to how humanity responds to the challenges it faces; and we know that the work of engineers is impacting both locally and globally, now and in the future. We are asking that engineers choose to make a difference, and that they adopt a globally responsible mindset, so that their skills are invested in engineering that benefits the global community.

"Civil engineers create the fabric that underpins humanity's well-being," says Prichard. "It is imperative that our efforts are delivered with respect for the environment, so that we guarantee healthy and thriving living conditions throughout the planet for both current and future generations." He points out that this sentiment is the same today as when it was expressed by the ICE's founding fathers; and in Thomas Tredgold's introduction to the Royal Charter. "I am proud to be a part of the Engineers Without Borders UK movement," Prichard says. "It's an inspiring organisation challenging all engineers to take responsibility for their global impact."

ICE 200
WATER INFRASTRUCTURE IN THE MIDDLE EAST
BRINGING WATER TO AN ARID AND DEVELOPING REGION

_____

LOCATION THROUGHOUT THE MIDDLE EAST
DATES TO PRESENT DAY

WATER IS FUNDAMENTAL to human life and access to water underpinned the ancient civilisations of the Middle East. Techniques developed there over millennia underpinned Islamic societies from Spain to South Asia. Most spectacular were the irrigation and drainage works of Mesopotamia, relying on the twin rivers of the Tigris and the Euphrates, where evidence of some of the earliest civil engineering in the world survives from thousands of years ago.

Less spectacular are the smaller scale but sustainable water storage and management techniques developed in arid areas. Since the 19th century civil engineers have studied the works of the ancients and sought to bring modern engineering techniques to help governments to manage the water resources of the region.

A combination of growing populations and an increase in industry by the 19th and early 20th centuries meant that governments needed to take greater control of water supplies to ensure their countries' economic future. The Kut barrage on the River Tigris in Iraq is one such example. Built by Balfour Beatty near what is now Kut City between 1934 and 1939, this 519 metre long by 10 metre high structure was designed by irrigation engineer William Willcocks (who also proposed the first Aswan Dam across the Nile in the 1890s). The Kut barrage was the first of five barrages across the Tigris and was designed to keep water levels high enough to feed water to the Gharraf River. This allowed the river to irrigate about 320,000 hectares of land used for farming. Before the structure was built, the Gharraf only flowed during floods.

Kuwait was traditionally a place where water was either brackish or imported by dhow from the Shatt al-Arab River and distributed in goatskins on the backs of donkeys. In the 1950s John Taylor & Sons designed a water distillation plant at Shuwaikh, with five British contractors engaged to build it with the associated electricity and water distribution systems – infrastructure that helped to transform Kuwait town from a small fishing port into a modern city.

Some idea of the scale of the challenge in the Middle East is given by the World Bank-funded study to tackle Iran's water and energy needs. This would see the construction of 177 dams. Iran, like most other states in the region has been affected by political change and regional conflict and the resultant postponement of work and damage to existing infrastructure. Thus, Alexander Gibb & Partners were involved in planning Tehran's water supply from 1946 until 1983, initially abstracting from the Karaj River, with a new treatment works commissioned in 1955.

Today, a state such as the United Arab Emirates is both an example of civil engineering success, and a caution for the future. Despite being one of the most water-scarce countries in the world it now has one of the highest water consumption rates. Emiratis use more than 500 litres per day per capita. Achieving a balanced sustainable future is a challenge for society.

More recent conflicts have exposed the interrelationship of all elements of modern infrastructure, thus damage to power supply also impacts water distribution systems. The public health impact of such damage has been a constant element of news bulletins over the past 30 years and serves to underline the significance of the work of the civil engineer and of the vulnerability of water infrastructure in the region.

ICE 200
GANGES CANAL
A GIANT PROJECT THAT IRRIGATED THE INDIAN PUNJAB

LOCATION DOABA, PUNJAB, INDIA
CONSTRUCTION DATES 1842–54

CONSTRUCTED BETWEEN 1842 and 1854, the Ganges Canal system is located between the River Ganges and the Yamuna River. It was designed by Proby Thomas Cautley and a team of young engineers employed by the British East India Company. It was built primarily as an irrigation system for the Doaba region, although it also has a navigation channel and locks. The canal was a response to the disastrous Agra famine of 1837/8 when around 800,000 people lost their lives. Ten districts benefit from the 437-km-long canal, which has 6,000 km of distribution channels. A 300-ft aqueduct was also built to carry the canal over the Solani River.

To deal with the lack of local technological skills, workshops were established at Roorkee and an engineering school to train technicians to work on the canal. This is now part of the Indian Institute of Technology, Roorkee.

The canal was opened by Lord Dalhousie on 8 April 1854, and was visited by engineers around the world, who came both to admire the project and conduct research. In 1887, one observer described it as "the most stupendous monument of that kind yet constructed".

The canal has since been expanded and several small hydroelectric power stations built. Along with Cotton's work in Madras this was one of the first irrigation projects undertaken by British Engineers in India and was followed by increasingly ambitious schemes over the next century.

ICE 200
BRIGHTON SEWERS
THE VICTORIAN WALK-THROUGH SEWER SYSTEM

LOCATION BRIGHTON, UK
CONSTRUCTION DATES 1860s

AT THE BEGINNING of the 19th century, Brighthelmstone was a small fishing village where the sewage drained into cesspits behind people's homes. By 1849, the population had grown from 7,000 to 60,000 and the renamed seaside resort of Brighton was one of the fastest-growing towns in the country. By this time, however, there had been several outbreaks of cholera. In 1860, the town council resolved to build a system that would drain the sewage into the sea.

Over the next decade, 44 miles of sewers were built 12 metres below ground. With no hydraulic tools, manual labour built a system that is still in use today. Seven million bricks were used in a subterranean network of tunnels. The cement was made from sand taken from the beach and shells are still visible in the mortar. It's said that this is why Brighton has a pebble beach. Later improvements included Sir John Hawkshaw's interceptor sewer in 1874. Today, more than 300 miles of sewers carry 22 million gallons of wastewater daily, rising to 90 million after heavy rain, and Southern Water runs popular walking tours of the sewers. However, to meet bathing-water quality requirements, a three-mile long storm-water storage tunnel was built under Brighton in the 1990s, and a modern wastewater treatment works was opened in Peacehaven in 2013 with a long sea outfall.

ICE 200
STORMWATER MANAGEMENT AND ROAD TUNNEL (SMART)

THE WORLD'S LONGEST MULTIPURPOSE TUNNEL

LOCATION KUALA LUMPUR, MALAYSIA
CONSTRUCTION DATES 2003–07

FLOODS HAVE SEVERELY affected Kuala Lumpur for several decades, a problem that has been exacerbated by the city's rapid expansion. But it was only once the idea of a drainage tunnel was proposed that it became clear such a project might also address the city's other problem: that of traffic congestion.

At more than six miles, SMART is the longest stormwater tunnel in Southeast Asia. It is unique in that the central section includes two road decks above the drainage channel. The structure is designed to cope with major and minor flooding. Normally the roadway portion is protected against floodwater by a pair of gates at each end; but during major and prolonged flooding, the gates can be opened and the roadways evacuated and used to divert water. The water is redirected from a holding pond on the Klang River, north of the city, to a reservoir on the Kerayong River, downstream on the south side.

To avoid incurring charges for tunnelling under private property, construction consultants Mott MacDonald followed the route of several highways. The tunnels had to be bored through the ground rather than by the "cut and cover" method, which would have caused disruption and road closures. The task was hampered by the presence of limestone covered with a layer of alluvium or sediment. Water had dissolved the limestone in places and the alluvium had filled these holes, making the ground crumble easily. As well as factoring in this unpredictability, the tunnelling process had to avoid the remnants of old tin mines. Tunnelling just 20 metres below street level meant the ground had to be monitored carefully to ensure the buildings above remained stable.

Two of the world's largest tunnel-boring machines at the time were brought in from Germany. At 13 metres wide and 71 metres long, they were bigger than a Boeing 747 and weighed almost as much as 12 jumbo jets. The spoil produced by the cutting heads was mixed with water and bentonite (a soft powdered clay) to allow it to be pumped out. The waste removed would have filled 500 Olympic-sized swimming pools.

SMART has won many plaudits – including the UN-Habitat Scroll of Honour Award in 2011 – for its innovative and unique management of both stormwater and peak-hour traffic.

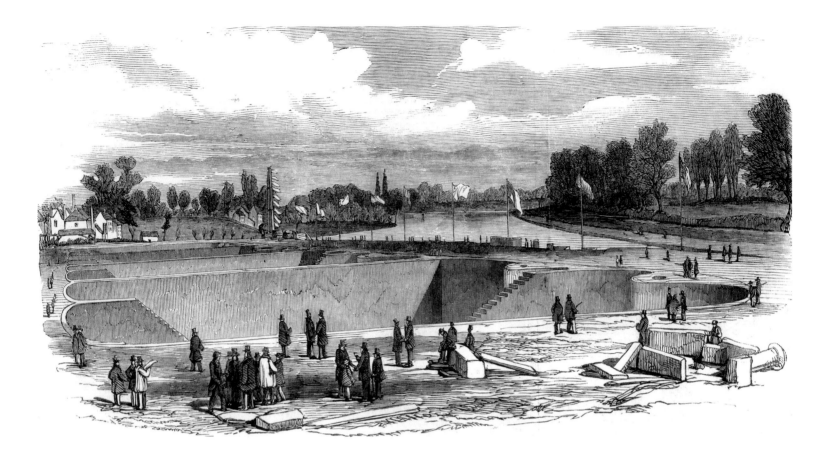

LONDON WATER SUPPLY FILTRATION SYSTEM

THE FIRST SAND FILTRATION SYSTEM IN BRITAIN

LOCATION LONDON, UK
CONSTRUCTION DATE 1829

UNTIL THE BEGINNING of the 20th century, London's water was supplied by private companies, each in charge of a specific area. One of the earliest was the Chelsea Waterworks Company, established in 1723 to provide Central London with water. It converted two ponds in Green Park, built a reservoir in Hyde Park and drew water from the River Thames to these reservoirs using a system of small canals. The company's expansion was initially assisted by its ability to serve the royal palaces, a responsibility that also forced it to introduce an atmospheric pumping engine after London suffered severe water shortages during the winter of 1739–40. But the river was often polluted with sewage, waste from slaughterhouses and toxins from factories making dyes, soap and lead.

By the 19th century, Londoners were complaining about the quality of the water coming from the Thames. Chief civil engineer James Simpson designed a filter bed at the Chelsea works in 1829. Measuring one acre, it consisted of beds of loose brick, gravel and sand. It was the first successful attempt in Britain to use slow sand filtration to purify river water. The system was slow but had the advantage of not requiring chemicals.

Simpson was also Chief Engineer to the Lambeth Water Company, which in 1849 tasked him to find a suitable site for a waterworks outside London. This was Seething Wells, near Surbiton, which opened in 1852. In the same year the Metropolitan Water Act banned the use for household purposes of any water taken from below Teddington Lock, so the Chelsea Water Company asked Simpson to construct a new waterworks next to Lambeth's at Seething Wells.

Seething Wells was still not an ideal water source: the Rivers Mole, Ember and Rythe entered the Thames nearby and stirred up the mud, which was then sucked up with the water. As a result, both waterworks moved again in the 1870s to Molesey, where they pumped water from the Thames into the Molesey reservoirs. The Metropolitan Water Board was created by the Metropolis Water Act 1902 and compulsorily acquired 11 water companies including the Lambeth Water Company. The filter beds at Seething Wells are now a conservation area and a haven for wildlife, while the remaining buildings are used as a fitness centre and as part of the campus at Kingston University.

SHAJIAO B POWER STATION

LOCATION GUANGDONG PROVINCE, CHINA
CONSTRUCTION DATES 1985–87

CHINA'S FIRST PRIVATELY BUILT AND OWNED POWER STATION

CHINA EMBARKED ON its "Four Modernisations" programme in 1978 in a bid to revive the flagging economy. Industry developed rapidly in Guangdong province, which resulted in an electricity shortage. Like most areas in China, the Guangdong electricity grid was not linked to other regions, so it had to produce its own power.

The Shajiao coal-fired power station was constructed in three phases beginning with Shajiao B. Ove Arup and Partners led the design team and Costain took on the construction. Slipform Engineering, Hong Kong, carried out the architectural and engineering work.

The site was located on a steeply sloping hillside, which had to be levelled before construction could begin. The building was made of reinforced concrete, with granite for aggregate. There was plenty of clean water available.

Construction involved excavating 1.5 million square metres of rock, reclaiming 23 hectares of land and building 1,500 metres of seawall. To complete a project of this scale in a remote part of China was a major achievement, but to do so in 22 months was almost a miracle.

A traditional "Bai-Sun" ceremony – featuring a 30-metre-long firecracker – marked the start of the chimney's construction, and although it rained at the end of the day, the weather didn't spoil the event. Indeed, in China this is considered an auspicious portent of a successful project.

MAJES IRRIGATION PROJECT

IRRIGATING AN ARID PART OF SOUTHERN PERU

LOCATION AREQUIPA REGION, PERU
PROJECT DATES 1978–

THE MAJES IRRIGATION Project is one of three irrigation schemes being carried out in Peru's southern coastal region by the Peruvian Ministry of Agriculture. Located in the Arequipa region, the Majes scheme is in two phases.

The first comprised the construction of the Condoroma Dam, 93 km of tunnels and 10 km of canals to capture water from high in the Andes and channel it westward through the mountainous region of the cordillera, to irrigate the coastal desert plains. Mitchell Construction, later Tarmac, was the UK member of Macon, a five-country consortium of major contractors that constructed it in the 1970s and early 1980s. The project transformed 150 sq km of desert into fertile land. The engineering was on a heroic scale, with no shortage of challenges – not least the access to finance in a time of dramatic currency fluctuations.

A second phase is planned, with a new 105-metre-high dam at Angostura, 48 km of canals and 20 km of tunnels. There will also be at least two hydroelectric power plants, with the capacity to store 1.1 billion cubic metres of water, to be distributed to the Pampas de Siguas. This will irrigate a further 385 sq km.

Around 38,500 hectares of farming land will be tendered to both large companies and small-scale farmers, and the lands will be divided into 200-hectare plots.

ICE 200
OIL INFRASTRUCTURE IN THE MIDDLE EAST

CREATING THE INFRASTRUCTURE TO EXPLOIT OIL RESERVES

————

LOCATION VARIOUS COUNTRIES, MIDDLE EAST
DATES 1905–

THE FIRST LARGE deposits of oil were discovered in Persia (now Iran), in the early part of the 20th century, when the motor vehicle was still in its infancy, power stations and many ships still ran on coal, and commercial flights had yet to start.

At that time, transport systems in the Middle East were almost non-existent or largely inadequate for the demands placed upon them. As a result of the lack of deep-water ports, lighters – flat-bottomed barges – were often needed to unload goods to and from moored ships, and thus totally unsuited to the movement of bulk liquids such as crude oil or refined petrochemicals. It was not until the 1920s that larger scale oil production was developed by Anglo-Persian (later BP) and others, Arthur Hartley being a pioneering oil pipeline engineer.

The growing demand for oil from the 1950s onwards meant that many Middle Eastern countries could now pay for a more effective infrastructure. Hundreds of engineering projects in the 1950s and 1960s transformed the lives of entire populations as a result. Engineers – many of them British – designed and built transport, water and sewer systems as well as the pipelines and jetties required to export hydrocarbon products. Cities grew and health and life expectancy in the region improved. The results were similar to those achieved by Victorian engineers in Britain and elsewhere in the 19th century.

Today, the Middle East has some of the largest and oldest oil refineries in the world and an equally expansive network for the distribution of oil and natural gas. However, any engineering work has a design life, after which it has to be renewed or replaced.

Engineers in the region are now also having to deal with other issues. Jetties and onshore facilities need to be upgraded to cater for increased demand, and better and more stringent environmental protection protocols. In many Middle Eastern countries, including Iran, Iraq, Kuwait and Syria, engineers have to deal with the explosive remnants of war from recent regional conflicts. Siltation and sedimentation has reduced the depths of key waterways limiting access for bulk carriers. Upgrading the infrastructure to cope with these challenges has created a demand for the next generation of engineers to implement innovative techniques to enhance and extend the life of the existing infrastructure.

As the oil wells in the region come to the end of their life, and with indications that "peak oil" has been reached, some countries – the United Arab Emirates in particular – are preparing for a post-oil economy, developing their infrastructure to expand sectors such as finance, transport, telecommunications, manufacturing, hospitality and tourism. While the 19th century was built on coal, the 20th century on oil and gas, the 21st century will be built on renewable energy. This is the case in the Middle East, where oil and gas revenues are being invested in sustainable cities such as Masdar in Abu Dhabi.

The Middle East was transformed in the 20th century by oil and gas leading to substantial population end economic growth. The challenge for engineers in the 21st century is to provide the infrastructure for a sustainable future through investment in transport, water and sanitation, renewable energy and housing.

ICE 200
HAMPSTEAD HEATH PONDS PROJECT
THE DESIGN SUCCESS PREVENTING DAM FAILURE

LOCATION LONDON, UK
PROJECT DATES 2015–16

FED BY THE headwater springs of the River Fleet, there are 30 large freshwater reservoirs on Hampstead Heath, three of which have been used for swimming since the 17th or 18th century. The Hampstead Heath Ponds Project was an environmentally led engineering solution to ensure that the Heath's dams could withstand extreme rainfall and to virtually eliminate the risk of dam failure.

The City of London Corporation, as custodians of the Heath under the 1871 Hampstead Heath Act, undertook to ensure that the design complied with reservoir legislation and was in keeping with the natural landscape. More than seven million people visit Hampstead Heath ever year, many to use the swimming ponds, and it was recognised that access to swimming needed to be maintained during the two-year construction programme.

Due to the constraints of working in a busy open space, the materials to build the raised dams were found on site, including 30,000 cubic metres of London clay. Five of the ponds were de-silted using a suction technique that avoided lengthy excavations or the requirement to drain down the ponds and minimised the disturbance to wildlife and visitors. A centrifuge was then used to remove the water from the silt and the clean water was pumped back into the ponds. The dried silt was then used to backfill the borrow pits. This sustainable solution reduced the amount of vehicle movement during the project and is an example of the sensitive approach taken.

Many environmental enhancements have been achieved as a result of the project, including improved water quality, enhanced wetland habitats and increased biodiversity. The new habitats have already benefited birds, amphibians and insects with higher numbers and more varied species noted since the works took place. Over a thousand wild flower bulbs and plants, 40 native trees and 140 shrubs were planted during the reinstatement phase of the project. In addition, log piles and amphibian and grass snake hibernacula have been created, and 20 bat boxes were installed.

The project has provided a passive design solution to the risk of dam failure. The landscaping works have enhanced the ponds in both appearance and in ecological terms, and the project has been recognised with several awards, including the Community Benefit Award at the ICE London Awards 2017. BAM Nuttall was designer and contractor.

JUBILEE POOL RESTORATION

REVIVING BRITAIN'S LARGEST LIDO

LOCATION PENZANCE, CORNWALL, UK
PROJECT DATES 2014–16

JUBILEE POOL IS Britain's largest lido and one of only a handful of surviving saltwater pools. It was built on Penzance's promenade to celebrate George V's silver jubilee and opened to great fanfare in 1935. Built to a design by borough engineer Captain F Latham, its triangular shape was determined by the surrounding rocks. A high sea wall protected the pool during storms and provided terraces for spectators.

As holidays abroad became more popular toward the end of the last century, the pool became less so. By 1992 its future looked uncertain. Local supporters formed a committee, the Friends of Jubilee Pool, and helped to source grant funding to refurbish and reopen the lido in 1994. But a severe storm in February 2014 left it badly damaged, and an initial survey uncovered serious structural problems. The Friends of Jubilee Pool began a campaign for the pool to be renovated, and in due course Cornwall Council led a successful bid for nearly £2 million from the Coastal Communities Fund toward a £3 million renovation programme.

The challenge was to repair the pool and modernise its structure and facilities while retaining its period style. The other test the engineers faced was working with concrete in a tough location and in foul weather. Cormac Solutions Ltd carried out the complex repairs to the outer sea wall to protect the lido. Water had begun to seep between the floor of the pool and the rocks below it. The engineers had to instal a pump to drain the area before fitting an astonishing 155 rock anchors to secure the pool to the bed beneath.

The pool reopened to the public in May 2016 and Prince Charles attended its grand opening two months later. Since then it has attracted over 100,000 visitors supporting local tourism. One was *The New York Times* journalist David Shaftel, who wrote, "Perhaps the best thing to see in Penzance – aside from the scenery – is the Art Deco-inspired Jubilee Pool, one of Europe's last saltwater lidos."

The renovation project won the ICE South West People's Choice Award in 2017, going on to win the overall award in 2018. The council recently passed the ownership and operation of Jubilee Pool to the friends' aptly named Community Benefit Society.

WIND OF CHANGE

NAME ØRSTED
HEADQUARTERS FREDERICIA, DENMARK
WEBSITE WWW.ORSTED.CO.UK

"BRITAIN LEADS THE world in decarbonisation. That is something to be really proud of," says Matthew Wright, Managing Director (UK) of renewable energy giant Ørsted. Wright believes that the key to the company's progress on green energy on these shores lies in governmental support for change. "The public-private relationship is the real success story of offshore wind in the UK," he says.

"The UK's leadership is down to the partnership between successive governments," says Wright, "and the developers in the industry. It makes Britain a place where we can invest with certainty, drive down the costs, and experience the curve effects and the economy of scale benefits. It's an approach that really works."

As a global leader in offshore wind power, Ørsted is a driving force behind Britain's pioneering position in the field of decarbonisation and green energy. The company has cultivated the world's first and largest offshore wind farms. It has 11 offshore wind farms already operational in Britain, two more under construction and a further two in development. It already produces enough electricity to power more than two million British homes; but this figure is set to rise to 4.4 million by 2020. Globally, the company has a 25 per cent market share of all offshore wind energy, having built enough farms to provide power to 9.5 million people. It aims to increase to 30 million people by 2020.

The benefits from Britain's commitment to renewable energy were highlighted again in 2017, during the latest round of Contracts for Difference (CFD) auctions for green energy schemes. Three offshore wind farms dominated, two of which – including Ørsted's Hornsea Two project – were awarded CFDs at a record low "strike price" of £57.50 per megawatt hour (MWh).

"We really saw a breakthrough in terms of costs," explains Wright. "People were staggered at how quickly these came down, and how competitive offshore wind now is, and I think people now appreciate the ability to deploy it on a massive scale. Hornsea Two is 1.4 gigawatts (GW); the last nuclear plant built in the UK before Hinkley was 1.2 GW. Offshore wind truly is utility scale, with huge potential power generation."

FROM BLACK TO GREEN ENERGY

Wright believes the cost argument in favour of offshore wind is "on the way to being won", with the focus now moving to energy storage and conversion. He also believes that developers should match the commitment shown by government: an area where Ørsted leads the way.

Founded in 1972, Ørsted was originally known as DONG (Danish Oil and Natural Gas) Energy. In November 2017 it was renamed after the Danish scientist Hans Christian Ørsted, who discovered electro-magnetism in 1820. This rebranding was the final transition from a coal-dominated, northern European state-owned utility to a listed company.

By this stage, it had divested itself of its "black energy" assets to focus entirely on renewables.

"With the sale of the upstream oil and natural gas business," says Wright, "we're nailing our colours firmly to the renewables mast. Our vision is to help create a world that runs entirely on green energy. We feel very liberated, unencumbered by a fossil fuel legacy, and the transformation of the company is almost complete. Renewable energy has moved into the mainstream, so it's excellent timing."

Although Ørsted won't be entirely coal-free in Denmark until 2023, a big part of the transformation involves converting all its coal power stations in Denmark to biomass. And while 80 per cent of the company's focus is on the offshore wind business, it's investing in other areas of renewable energy. The company has subsidiaries in energy storage and energy sales and is exploring flexibility products and how best to integrate with the grid.

Ørsted has also developed a patented biotechnology called Renescience that uses enzymes to treat residual household waste while also producing green energy. The company recently built the first Renescience plant at Northwich, Cheshire. The plant will enable a significantly higher proportion of household waste to be recycled while simultaneously producing renewable biogas.

BRITISH INTERESTS

This is the latest example of Ørsted's commitment to development in Britain. Around 1,000 of its 5,800 global staff are based in the UK. It is currently constructing two large offshore wind-farm projects in the North Sea: Hornsea Project One and Hornsea Project Two. The company's operations in areas such as Grimsby, Merseyside and Barrow-in-Furness also boost the wider economy and create much-needed jobs locally; not just at Ørsted but also at associated and supply-chain businesses such as Siemens-Gamesa.

"The 'place' aspect of our industrial strategy is really important," says Wright. "UK governments are always keen to rebalance the economy north to south, and regenerate coastal communities. Some regions of Britain have had a tough time in recent years because of the decline of traditional industries. Offshore wind and the broader renewable technology sector can counter that, providing a new source of growth."

Looking forward, Wright is optimistic about the outlook in terms of the company, the British economy and the future of green energy.

"The industry has a good relationship with the UK government," he says. "It's not just about the government making good on its commitment to continue auctions and CFDs. It's also about what the sector can do to improve the competitiveness of the British supply chain and its content of projects. It will enable start-ups and new businesses to develop and export manufactured goods, services, knowledge and experience right around the world. That's the vision we share with government. It's a really exciting time for the industry."

ALLIANCE FOR CHANGE

NAME ANGLIAN WATER
HEADQUARTERS PETERBOROUGH, CAMBRIDGESHIRE, UK
WEBSITE WWW.ANGLIANWATER.CO.UK

"IT'S LIKE CLIMBING a mountain," says Chris Newsome, Director of Asset Management at Anglian Water and a Fellow of the ICE. "You stand at the bottom and think you can see the highest point, but when you get there it's only the top of the foothill. New ambitions emerge. So you focus on the next highest point you can see and work towards the new goal. When we began this alliancing journey in 2004, we couldn't define everything we needed, but by the time we got to the first foothill we were able to fill in the gaps. We're still on that journey, still challenging ourselves to go further. We've not put the flag down yet."

Anglian Water is geographically the largest water company in England and Wales, serving six million customers and employing 4,200 workers. It provides drainage and sewerage to an area stretching from the Humber to the Thames. But it did not want to be complacent about its influence.

ALLIED FORCES

In 2004, the directors decided to fundamentally change the way Anglian operated on infrastructure projects. The traditional client-contractor relationship, based around single short-term projects, was replaced by something more collaborative and long-term. Anglian Water together with Barhale, Balfour Beatty, Mott MacDonald Bentley, Skanska, Stantec and Sweco were invited as a group of construction and infrastructure specialists, to work together to deliver common objectives linked directly to customer outcomes.

This collaborative organisation was called @one Alliance, a revolutionary idea in construction and engineering but one that borrowed ideas from best practice outside the sector. What makes it unique is its approach to incentive. "The Alliance don't get a return for work, they get returns for delivering customer outcomes," explains Dale Evans, Director, @one Alliance. "We challenge the Alliance to deliver a set of outcomes for a given affordability. If they reduce cost, they generate a return. That incentivises innovation."

This approach has brought results. Anglian Water has achieved efficiency savings that considerably outperform the sector, while improving its quality of service and its health and safety record. It has also cut carbon use by more than 50 per cent. Where other companies attain carbon-neutral status by offsetting or switching to renewables, Anglian recognised that carbon – in the form of steel and concrete – is one of the biggest costs. Cutting carbon brought several benefits: it was an identifiable challenge for engineers, it appealed to residents and local authorities who had to agree to new infrastructure schemes, and it saved money.

"Anglian Water is in the east of England, suffering from hot, dry summers, flash floods and rising sea levels," says Newsome. "It means we need to take seriously the impact of climate change. So how do you link a desire to lead on mitigating the effects of climate change with something that still demands cost reduction? In 2009, we were still digging trenches for pipes, still building new assets with concrete and steel. We wanted to know what the world would be like if we used no-dig technology and reused assets that already have the carbon burned in them. Our answer was to take 54 per cent carbon out, and that led to a 23 per cent cost reduction."

CARBON CONTROL

To make the Alliance work, mindsets needed to be challenged. "After years of driving efficiency after efficiency, engineers were a little battle weary, and wary of increasing risks or challenging traditions," says Newsome. "Now we have witnessed previously isolated groups including engineers, water-quality scientists and regional planning authorities work together with carbon as a common goal, and all contribute to fantastic sustainable solutions created at a lower cost."

Anglian's Peterborough HQ is now filled with integrated teams of workers from every company in the Alliance. Firms that are rivals elsewhere now share information, because they have been incentivised not to compete but collaborate. "All incentives are collective," says Evans. "So if you are in Skanska, the return you generate depends on everybody else. You need to help them. We created the conditions for collaboration through incentives."

ENGINEERING WITH TECHNOLOGY

When it came to infrastructure, Anglian tried another new approach. Instead of building bespoke facilities for each individual project, it designed low-carbon components that meant plants could be assembled as if in a factory, cutting time and costs, simplifying maintenance and operation, and driving out carbon.

Engineers can don a VR headset and explore a plant before a spade enters the ground, and use data to get a picture of a site before construction begins. If a new housing development is planned, @one Alliance can look at existing water needs,

sewerage and flood areas, then zero in on a specific site to see how construction will physically take place, examining everything from access and worker safety to impact on local residents. These are the tools the Alliance will wield when tackling their next big targets – commitments to deliver new schemes in half the time and reduce carbon use by 60 per cent.

It all came together on the Grafham Water Treatment Works resilience project, spanning 15 sites near Huntingdon. The new solution was built for £32 million less than the original design and using 62 per cent less carbon, while cutting delivery time; one pipe that would have taken three days to install was installed in nine hours, thanks to 3D modelling and comprehensive data. This single project saved a CO_2 emission of 26,845 tonnes – that's more than some engineering firms manage in an entire year.

Anglian Water now wants to get the message out. The company believes its model offers sustainability and innovation, while addressing climate change, and can improve productivity and reliability. Evans is chair of ICE's Infrastructure Client Group, while Newsome is a member of the government's Green Construction Board and Chair of its Infrastructure Working Group which has produced the Infrastructure Carbon Review and Publicly Available Specification (PAS) 2080, published by the British Standards Institution. "This is the first international standard for measurement and management of carbon in infrastructure," says Newsome. "We want it to go national and then international, so the UK is seen as leading the agenda."

WHEN HULL
BREAKS LOOSE

NAME GREEN PORT HULL
LOCATION HULL, EAST YORKSHIRE, UK
WEBSITE GREENPORTHULL.CO.UK

KINGSTON UPON HULL has long been a hub for fish and Nordic timber, but recent developments have focused on a more easily renewable resource: wind. Green Port Hull is an ambitious scheme to make the port area – and the wider East Riding of Yorkshire – a global centre for renewable energy.

Geography plays a key role. Hull is close to several huge North Sea wind farm developments which are planned to offer a combined maximum capacity in excess of 17 gigawatts and supply energy to more than 14 million homes and businesses.

"These are game-changing numbers for the UK market in renewables," says Tim Rix, Chairman of the Hull City Leadership Board and Chair of the Green Port Growth Programme, which manages funding to support residents and businesses to access opportunities realised from the emerging renewables sector. "Significant investments in the renewables sector have already created thousands of new jobs in the local area and in the future are set to create thousands more jobs and a wealth of opportunity for local people and business."

The catalyst for Green Port Hull was Siemens, now operating in Hull as Siemens Gamesa Renewable Energy. In 2011 Hull's Alexandra Dock was chosen by the German firm and Associated British Ports as the site for a £310 million offshore wind turbine blade factory. Further inward investment in the Green Port Hull scheme is expected to top £1 billion in the next few years.

In July 2015 VolkerFitzpatrick was selected to deliver the turbine-blade factory. The single-stage design-and-build project involved creating a new 430,000 sq ft state-of-the-art facility for manufacturing and servicing 75-metre-long turbine blades, the world's largest fibreglass components

cast in one piece. Plans are already underway to manufacture 81-metre blades at the factory.

The factory is the centrepiece of a multi-million-pound investment which also involved the construction of new offices and welfare facilities. It has delivered more than 1,000 new permanent jobs and a further 500 during the construction phase. VolkerFitzpatrick maximised local labour by achieving targets for employing 40 per cent of its workforce from residents within 50 miles of site and at least 25 per cent within 20 miles.

The 600-metre quay was reclaimed and developed to accommodate three jack-up vessels at any one time. The substructure used 4,650 driven precast concrete piles and in-situ pile caps. The superstructure is steel frame with steel roof trusses to accommodate the large postal spans. The envelope is a combination of precast concrete panels up to 2.4 metres for low-level protection and Eurobond composite cladding to roof level.

The project is VolkerFitzpatrick's first contract with Siemens in the renewable energy sector, and was completed ahead of schedule in autumn 2016. The blade factory has been in operation 24 hours a day since completion and is seen as a critical factor of the Humber's role as the UK's energy estuary. In addition to offshore wind the area boasts developments in biofuels, solar, wave, tidal and waste-to-energy power generation. Local businesses have also won supply-chain contracts in excess of £260 million

Having enjoyed the spotlight as UK City of Culture in 2017, Hull now stands on the threshold of a new purpose – as guardian and supplier of an increasing share of Britain's energy needs for cleaner, greener generations to come.

POWER TO
THE PEOPLE

_____

NAME INNOGY RENEWABLES UK LTD
LOCATION SWINDON, WILTSHIRE, UK
WEBSITE WWW.INNOGY.COM/RENEWABLESUK

IN THE SPACE of just 15 years, the UK offshore wind industry has gone from being non-existent to generating enough energy to make a double-digit percentage contribution to the UK's electricity supply. And while today there are a number of companies operating within this flourishing sector of the renewable energy market, there had to be a first – innogy Renewables UK. "The UK has come a long way in 15 years," says Paul Cowling, innogy Renewables' Managing Director in the UK. "The pace and the transformation has been staggering. And we started it. We were there at the beginning."

Indeed it was. In 2003, North Hoyle Offshore Wind Farm was built in Liverpool Bay, off the coast of North Wales, becoming the UK's first commercial scale offshore wind farm. Today, the UK is a world leader in offshore wind. And what innogy Renewables (a part of the German energy company, innogy SE) is cleverly doing is taking the knowledge and experience accrued over the last 15 years to a global market. "We are very much on a growth path," says Cowling, "and we are looking at new and emerging markets, like Asia and America. These markets, new to the offshore wind industry, are keen to tap into our experience and expertise."

The renewable market in this country is a great asset for UK PLC. In the last five years alone, innogy Renewables has delivered, either on its own or with partners, new renewable energy projects in the UK with a total investment of nearly £4 billion. Projects in the pipeline of more than 2 gigawatts have the potential for another £4 billion of investment.

"Wherever possible we try to invest in the UK and, importantly, local companies," says Cowling. "In Wales we're currently building three onshore wind farms with a total investment of £270 million, so there's a huge amount of investment at stake in UK PLC and more and more UK companies are benefitting as our industry grows."

While offshore wind represents innogy Renewables' largest investment, it also operates 17 onshore wind farms and 24 hydroelectric power stations. "We develop, construct and maintain renewable energy assets," says Cowling. "At the heart of our desire to expand the use of renewables and transform the European energy sector are our engineers of all disciplines. They passionately believe in renewable energy and its benefits and have chosen to make a career in its evolution."

The knowledge these engineers have gained over the past 15 years enables innogy to work quicker and smarter, completing more and more renewable projects. Just 11 years after North Hoyle, innogy built Gwynt y Môr (pictured, left), the world's second-largest offshore wind farm, and almost 10 times more powerful than North Hoyle.

And while the traditional utility companies are still coming to grips with the changes taking place in the energy market by pioneers like innogy, the public have been much quicker to embrace the greener and more sustainable energy they offer.

"Renewable energy is no longer a niche industry," says Cowling. "It's mainstream and it's here to stay. Just look at the contribution to the UK's energy mix as an example – renewable energy accounted for just over 29 per cent of electricity generation in 2017, up from 25 per cent in 2016. The latest figures from the Department of Business, Energy and Industrial Strategy indicate that 85 per cent of the public support renewable electricity generation. The public has clearly recognised it as a key part of the energy mix."

POWER AND RESPONSIBILITY

NAME ITAIPU BINACIONAL
LOCATION PARAGUAY & BRAZIL
WEBSITE WWW.ITAIPU.GOV.PY

THE ITAIPU DAM, which straddles the Paraná river on the border of Paraguay and Brazil, has been described as one of the seven modern engineering wonders of the world. Constructed between 1974 and 1982, the dam is 7.7 km long and 196 metres high, equal to a 65-storey building and containing 12.3 million cubic metres of concrete. The iron and steel used could build 380 Eiffel Towers.

Construction required the diversion of one of the great rivers of the world, the Paraná, and the relocation of 36,450 animals. "At the time when it was designed and built, it was a proposal which was totally innovative and challenging for the knowledge and technology of the time," says James Spalding, General Director of Itaipu Binacional.

And it didn't stop there. When the Treaty of Itaipu was signed in 1973 between Brazil and Paraguay, it coincided with the outbreak of the global oil crisis. The use of renewable energy sources was seen as a way to ensure a vigorous development for both countries. The Itaipu hydroelectric power plant began to generate electricity in 1984, and this has since become the largest generator of clean and renewable energy on the planet, having produced more than 2.5 billion MWh (megawatt hours) since it began operation.

The commitment to the environment goes even further. The area around the dam in the Atlantic Forest of Alto Paraná, Paraguay, is recognised as an important international biosphere, sheltering diverse species including harpy eagles, jaguars, pumas, tapirs, birds and insects. This Itaipu protected area provides sufficient oxygen for 22 million people.

"It is the first time in the history of UNESCO that a hydroelectric plant has been incorporated into the World Network of Biosphere Reserves,

which highlights the commitment to the environment we hold," says Spalding.

The principle consideration remains energy production. In 2016, Itaipu Binacional was the first hydroelectric power plant in the world to surpass 100 million MWh (megawatt hours) of global energy generation. The installed capacity is 14,000 megawatts provided by 20 generating units of 700 megawatts each. A single generating unit can supply a city with a population of 1 to 1.5 million. The vastness of the enterprise presents both opportunities and challenges.

"The challenges include maintaining our global leadership in clean and renewable energy production in order to fulfil Itaipu's strategic objectives," says Spalding. "Also, we need to maintain and improve our excellence in the production and supply of energy, to perfect the energy supply and minimise operational costs. At the same time, this presents the opening of countless opportunities to modernise the power plant through the replacement of equipment that is considered obsolete or at the end of its useful life with equipment of more advanced technology, as well as the incorporation of new systems and the latest technology with new features."

With this, Spalding believes Itaipu can continue to serve those around it – both the humans who rely upon it for power and the animals that can thank it for the protection of their habitat. "We have a responsibility to fulfil the mission and vision of Itaipu Binacional, as well as its corporate structure, and address the challenges in three areas – finances, social responsibility and the environment," he says. "This way, you can continue to have a company dedicated to transparent management, with excellence, and in favour of the people."

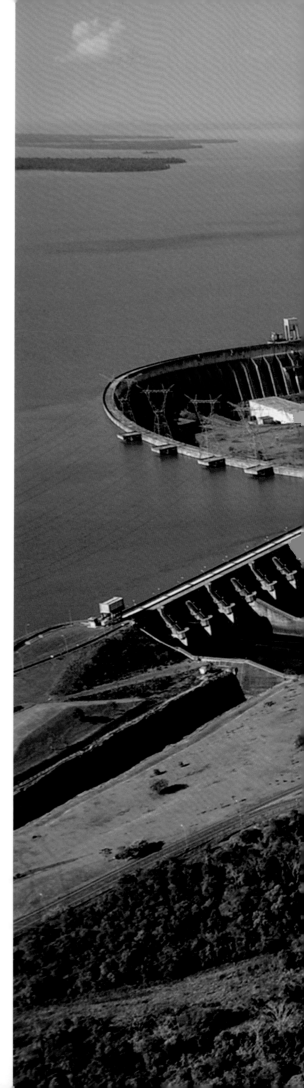

ENVIRONMENTAL INTEGRITY

NAME RPS GROUP
HEADQUARTERS ABINGDON, OXFORDSHIRE, UK
WEBSITE WWW.RPSGROUP.COM

"MANAGING THE ENVIRONMENTAL aspects of infrastructure is key to unlocking the success of a major project," says Andy Young, Commercial Director for RPS Europe, part of the RPS Group. He has seen RPS grow since its inception in the 1970s from a few staff in Oxford to a multi-disciplinary consultancy with more than 5,000 staff. It now has a global reach yet retains the agility to respond to complex, localised environmental concerns.

Infrastructure projects are an area of growth for RPS, particularly in transport and energy. It is the lead environmental consultant on the largest highways scheme to be commissioned by the Welsh Assembly since devolution in 1998, with the M4 corridor around Newport requiring a coordinated and far-reaching Environmental Statement to support the scheme's application.

"We provided no fewer than eight expert witnesses at the public enquiry," says Young, "who covered environmental coordination, cultural heritage, land contamination, noise, impacts on the community, the local ecology, bird life and water quality. This level of scrutiny and expertise sets us apart." In the built environment, RPS is involved in every stage of a development, from masterplanning, consenting and environmental impacts to engineering, architectural design and decommissioning. "Our client groups are as diverse as the business itself," says Young. RPS also provided services for a major gas pipeline across some of Ireland's most sensitive terrain (pictured, above).

The decommissioning of North Sea oil rigs is a fledgling industry, but RPS comes to it with a track record of decommissioning nuclear sites for 20 years. "It is part of our agile nature not to offer disparate services, but to meet industry demands," says Young. "The waters around oil rigs are rich in marine life and that has to be protected." With offices in the UK, Ireland, Norway and the Netherlands, RPS coordinates services that embrace onshore and offshore environmental teams, health and safety experts, and port infrastructure services in order, as Young explains, "to deliver a service that adds value".

From major transport and energy projects in Europe, North America, Australia and Asia to local ecology and archaeology consultancy work, the RPS Group has evolved a comprehensive, forward-looking portfolio of professional disciplines that deliver projects with environmental integrity.

FLOATING POINTS

NAME INTERNATIONAL JACK-UP BARGE
OPERATORS ASSOCIATION
HEADQUARTERS YEOVIL, UK
WEBSITE WWW.IJUBOA.COM

TEN YEARS AGO, there were no specific regulations for the
operation of jack-up barges (JUBs) or self-elevating platforms
(SEPs). That's when John Howard held the first meeting of the
International Jack-up Barge Operators Association (IJUBOA),
"to set, sustain and promote standards for the safe and effective
operation of self-elevating platforms throughout the world".

"I felt there should be some qualification, so people could be
sure that barge operators knew what they were doing," he says.
"I wanted to train them to operate the vessels properly and to be
able to talk knowledgeably about their barges to their clients and
relevant authorities. There were around 40 issues, including
hydraulics, mechanics and man-management that I felt needed
clarification. Following on from that initial meeting, we've now
evolved into an accredited training association, recognised by the
Health & Safety Executive and the Maritime & Coastguard Agency."

Howard has now handed over chairmanship of the IJUBOA
to Benny De Sutter but will remain as honorary president. "The
certificated training courses that the IJUBOA has introduced and
manages through the Scottish Qualification Authority (SQA) are
not mandatory," explains De Sutter, "but the view is that these
will be seen as the global standard in the training of operators
and managers, from self-elevating support vessels and lift ships
through to non-propelled construction jack-up barges. Over time,
we hope it will become an industry requirement. If a barge has
an accident but hasn't operated to best practice standards, people
should and will ask questions. We want barges universally to
operate and comply with these standards, that's our objective."

The IJUBOA also wants to create a recognised career path
for barge operators, to improve safety and training. It wants to
continue to build the association to ensure it encompasses barges
worldwide in many different legislative authorities. "The recent
SQA accreditation of the IJUBOA course for Barge Masters is a very
positive step for our industry," says De Sutter. "The course is run
in conjunction with STC BV. Nautical Training College in Rotterdam,
while the Managers Course takes place at DNV GL offices in
London. For too long there has been no qualifications for the highly
skilled and complex operation of jack-up barges and lift ships."

DELIVERING EXCELLENCE

NAME NORTH MIDLAND CONSTRUCTION PLC
LOCATION NOTTINGHAMSHIRE, UK
WEBSITE WWW.NORTHMID.CO.UK

NORTH MIDLAND CONSTRUCTION plc (NM Group) is headquartered in Nottinghamshire but reaches far beyond its heartland, with 12 regional offices from Leeds to Cornwall and Kent to Warrington. That physical expansion dovetails with the growth of the firm, which since the millennium has seen a six-fold increase in staff to 1,600 and a fivefold growth in turnover to £300 million.

The company has high ambitions for the future. "We have an action plan to get us to 3 per cent margin in the next two years," says Chief Executive John Homer, who joined the firm from Morgan Sindall in mid 2016. "But I'm a great believer in having ambitious goals to aim for, so I want five and five – a 5 per cent margin and a £500 million turnover – within my term as chief executive."

It's a long way from NM Group's origins as a family firm in 1946, laying ducts for the Post Office under the command of demobbed Major Terence Moyle, the company's founder. Despite the firm's expansion, the sense of a family business is vital to the whole employee experience. "We make sure our people are aligned with where the business is going, and vice versa, listening and taking their thoughts on board," says Homer. "That's leadership – making sure the 1,600 people in the group are all doing the right things and pulling in the same direction while enjoying their jobs."

That means keeping in close contact with his workforce. "This morning I've been with 30 guys in our utilities gangs, digging the road up to maintain and expand our national infrastructure, and they really appreciate the chance to talk to the chief executive," he says. "I heard stories of the mistreatment they receive: verbal abuse from motorists, rotten eggs and other things thrown at them. They bite their tongues and say, 'We're just here to do a job to help the nation prosper.' And they do a great job. They deliver good service to our customers and in turn we're looking after the community in which we operate – that's the circle of respect and service we're looking to promote."

It's an approach that's paying dividends, with 20 per cent year on year growth across the group's sectors of water, highways, construction, power and telecoms. Water management now underpins the business, accounting for 60 per cent of turnover since NM Group signed a management, design and construction deal with Severn Trent Water in 2006. That single deal delivered £750 million of work over ten years, and continues in NM's new joint-venture to deliver the Birmingham Resilience Project. This major piece of work will ensure the reliability of the city's water supply and includes tunnelling on the Elan Valley Aqueduct, which draws water from the Welsh hills, and the wholesale refitting of a treatment plant en route at Longbridge.

There's strong growth in the telecoms sector with the project to build Virgin Media's nationwide superfast broadband network. Construction projects include student accommodation in Sheffield, Manchester, Birmingham and Lincoln, and a £20 million highways contract will deliver infrastructure for a new potash mine in Yorkshire.

Executive chairman Robert Moyle won an Institution of Civil Engineers Lifetime Achievement Award in 2017, while Nomenca, NM Group's water division, won Best Use of Technology at the British Construction Engineering Awards. "We were delighted for Robert," says Homer. "And pleased about Nomenca because lots of the entries were ethereal – virtual in their application. Ours was grounded in reality, and knowing that while we're not perfect, we're always striving to get better."

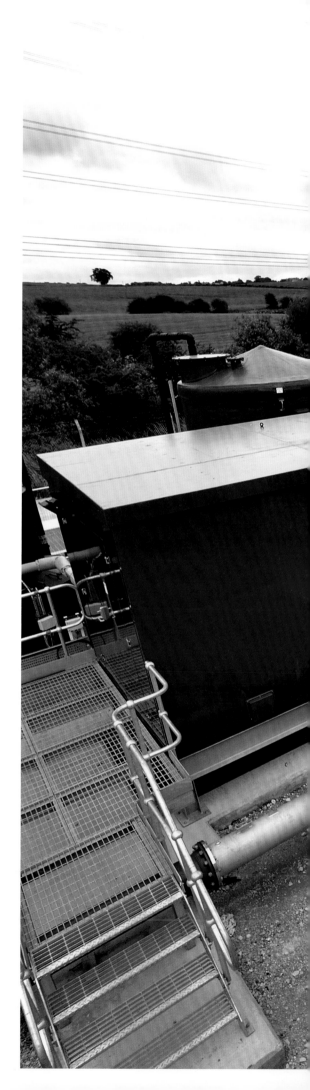

SUSTAINABLE FLOODING

NAME FLOODLINE CONSULTING
HEADQUARTERS WOKING, SURREY, UK
WEBSITE WWW.FLOODLINECONSULTING.CO.UK

AS THE RISK of flooding increases across many parts of Britain, Woking-based firm Floodline Consulting has positioned itself at the forefront of those tackling the challenge through active flood management. Managing these risks through sound engineered solutions, Floodline is able to offer community-wide protection and has introduced a new asset class of flood-resilient "can-float" homes to the UK housing market.

"Our mantra is 'Building With Nature'," says Justin Meredith, a chartered surveyor who founded Floodline in 2010. "It means we fully understand the environmental considerations for a site at risk of flooding through the benefits of active water management." Floodline's aim is to create viable and sustainable development proposals, built to cope with climate change. With each project, it hopes to enhance the natural surroundings which bring tangible benefits to the wider community, all at no cost to the public purse.

"We have a very different approach to development than the traditional builders," says Meredith. "For them, much of the cost is tied up in the land. We consider land that has a very low value. This enables us to provide flood-management solutions that offer new protection to the community as well as making the development proposal safe. As a consequence we are able to promote schemes that offer 100 per cent affordable housing and other community benefits, making these truly sustainable solutions."

Floodline has been recognised for two years running in *New Civil Engineer*'s list of Top 100 companies. Its landmark developments have been acclaimed for technical excellence. In Berkshire it proposed a flood alleviation and mitigation scheme to offer relief to the surrounding community and road network; in Christchurch, Dorset it had to provide safe buildings that accounted for a rise in sea level of more than a metre.

"We have remained true to our core values – 'nature, lifestyle and community' – which are at the heart of any sustainable development proposal," says Meredith. "Our unique offer is to provide engineered benefits to the wider community which are paid for solely through the development. These are solutions that otherwise could not be funded through the state system. It's something that should be a standard requirement in the UK."

TRIED AND TESTED

NAME SOCOTEC
UK HEADQUARTERS BURTON-ON-TRENT, STAFFORDSHIRE
WEBSITE WWW.SOCOTEC.CO.UK

SOCOTEC IS THE UK leader in testing, inspection and compliance services, with a range of involvements from major construction projects, such as London's Shard and Crossrail developments, to chemical and microbiological analysis. Each year, the firm undertakes some seven million tests for over 5,000 clients.

"We're by far the largest supplier of support services to infrastructure, in terms of testing and compliance," says Philip Ball, Group Technical Director of Socotec in the UK. "But the main thing that characterises us is our breadth of service – you can come to us for just about anything to do with testing and inspection in both the environment and safety sector, and the infrastructure and energy sector. We represent a single point of contact."

Socotec's list of activities includes materials testing – on site as well as in laboratories – structural investigations and a wealth of geotechnical expertise. The company's services are called upon by almost every sector, including healthcare, recycling, waste management, retail, leisure and manufacturing.

In March 2017, Socotec acquired ESG (Environmental Scientifics Group), with its solid reputation for stringent internal quality control, endorsed by a comprehensive array of accreditations that have made it the gold standard for technical expertise and service.

Socotec now has more than 20 testing facilities certified by UKAS (United Kingdom Accreditation Service), including site-based laboratories across the country. "UKAS accreditation is effectively a top-end quality control," says Ball. "It governs almost everything we do in many parts of the business."

When a developer works with Socotec, the firm's experts advise on local planning rules and ground conditions, and provide help in fulfilling the specified terms. They can also take care of compliance matters – such as landfill permitting and discharge controls – and address any complications. "If, for example, a contractor finds signs of contamination on a site, we will deploy scientists to take samples and undertake the necessary remedies to prevent delays," says Ball. Socotec can also help contractors to reduce costs and environmental impact by reusing materials on site that might otherwise be dumped.

"We aim to make our clients' lives as simple as possible," says Ball. "In the end it's about peace of mind."

TAPPING INTO TECHNOLOGY

NAME BLACK & VEATCH
UK HEADQUARTERS REDHILL, SURREY
WEBSITE WWW.BV.COM

IT MAY BE skyscrapers and megastructures that grab the headlines, but for international engineering specialist Black & Veatch, the focus is on a much more elemental resource. "Throughout history, safe drinking water and sanitation have been the cornerstones of well-being and prosperity," explains Scott Aitken, Managing Director of Black & Veatch's European water business. "Every civilisation has started with those things as core attributes. Our mission of 'building a world of difference' means that we try to give something back to the communities in which we work. It's not just about putting up the tallest towers – a society with safe drinking water is a precondition to the higher-profile projects."

The firm has emphasised the importance of what it terms "critical human infrastructure" since it was founded in 1915 in Kansas City, Missouri. Since then, the employee-owned business has grown into a global concern, with more than 10,000 staff and over 100 offices worldwide.

Black & Veatch's UK development has focused on water and waste-water engineering, and the company has been in the vanguard of using new technologies and technical expertise for the benefit of clients. "Technical innovation has been essential to us for the past century," says Aitken. "We are a technology-led company and our extensive grasp of water and wastewater-treatment technologies enables us to deliver the engineering and technical solution best suited to our clients' needs."

These solutions include a number of groundbreaking projects. Black & Veatch was responsible for a study that determined "preferred architecture", to demonstrate that tidal energy in the UK can be cost-competitive with other low-carbon energy by 2020. It also developed a tool to analyse multiple data points from wastewater pumping stations in order to accurately predict the risk of pollution incidents. Black & Veatch's teams created the world's first "piano key" inlet, at Black Esk Reservoir in Scotland, providing a safer, cheaper solution that manages water flow without moving structures.

The company now uses a similar approach to address 21st-century challenges such as climate change, sustainability, water scarcity and the greater use of renewable energy. It constructed the UK's largest urban water reuse facility at London's Olympic Park and, at wastewater-treatment plants in Manchester, Milton Keynes and London, it uses thermal hydrolysis and advanced digestion to generate renewable electricity from biogas.

Black & Veatch is also pioneering the use of digital technology in water engineering. This includes digitising asset data through intelligent piping and instrumentation diagrams (P&IDs) which enables an iterative design process through which the most efficient blend of construction cost and asset performance can be realised. The intelligent P&IDs form the building blocks of a digital data model, covering all aspects of an asset, which remains live and interactive through the asset's lifecycle – from tender through to decommissioning.

"We have transformed our approach to technology as our water clients move from the analogue to the digital age," says Aitken. "It is vitally important for us to integrate operational technology, work with a common data environment and to harness the benefits of digital engineering. Enabling different technologies to work properly with each other is crucial. For us, it's about continuing to be at the forefront of what technologies are out there, and looking at new, innovative ways to utilise them and integrate them to meet our clients' needs."

WATER WAYS

NAME WAITINGS
LOCATION PENRITH, UK
WEBSITE WWW.WAITINGS.CO.UK

INNOVATORS IN BUSINESS are often people who think differently to most; and who find a niche uniquely suited to their talents. This was the case with David Waiting, whose offbeat approach as an apprentice revealed the enterprising spirit with which he started his own company. He came away from his apprenticeship with little formal training – but he'd spent his lunch breaks designing and building a digger.

In 1970 he set up Waitings Drainage, a Penrith-based engineering firm that specialises in working with water. Although David died in 2004, his daughter Victoria and latterly son Robert have maintained the firm's close-knit character – and its reputation for honesty and plain dealing.

"It's important to us that it's a family-owned business," says Robert Waiting. "You live on your reputation and that's been very hard-earned."

There's plenty of demand for water-management expertise in Cumbria, and Waitings has a broad remit. The company manages the flow from Ennerdale Water into the River Ehen to maintain levels for wildlife living in the river. It fixes and prevents flood damage, something that provided a demanding challenge after Storm Desmond in 2015. It also has a hand in preserving wildlife, cutting a channel – or "fish pass" – to encourage spawning in the River Lowther. Meanwhile, it needs to balance the impact of engineering in the Lake District, England's favourite national park. "You have to be kind to the environment," says Waiting. "Some disruption is unavoidable but we try to keep it to a minimum."

Today the company has spread its reach to Yorkshire and Humberside; and further south, with a contract for specialist plant hire at London's Docklands. But its roots are firmly in Cumbria. "Our growth has been organic," says Waiting. "We now employ 75 people – a near fourfold increase since 2000. And we have a very low staff turnover. Most people who come to us stay for years!"

He explains that the company has diversified from where it first started in agricultural contracting and drainage. "We're now a multi-discipline civil engineering company," says Waiting. "But we still have the values the company was originally founded on. We're problem solvers. We're proactive and we make things happen." His father David would doubtless have approved.

THE AGE OF AQUARIUS

NAME AQUARIUS MARINE GROUP
HEADQUARTERS GLASTONBURY, SOMERSET, UK
WEBSITE WWW.AERATION.UK.COM

"RESERVOIRS AND LAKES are rather like ladies," says Tony Wynes, Managing Director of Aquarius Marine Group. "No two are the same." For more than 40 years, Aquarius has specialised in improving the water quality of reservoirs, lakes and fish farms. It does this with a system called the Aquaerator.

"In any lake or reservoir, the sun enters the surface layer, reducing water density, allowing plants and algae to grow," says Wynes, "and the bed water has got a very low dissolved-oxygen level. The Aquaerator sends tiny air bubbles in a powerful circulating plume, propelling water from the bed, which is a higher density, and reduces its density by mixing it with air. It sends that up towards the surface, so that you achieve a more equal quality of air in the water right the way up the depth. And equally, the density is the same."

This improves the quality of the water and allows the ecosystem to flourish. The process also reduces the running costs of the treatment plant and the need for purification chemicals. "It causes destratification of the lake, which means the fish have got water to breathe in from top to bottom of the lake," says Wynes. "They don't have to come up to feed."

His company has worked in the UK for almost 50 years, with clients including Anglian Water, Bristol Water, Thames Water and Scottish Water. The company's Environmental Consultancy Division provides water-quality analysis, initial design and specification. It has also expanded globally, working with Marine Harvest in Norway, the Yangtze River Fishery Research Institute, and is preparing for its greatest challenge: the 370-mile-long Lake Volta in Ghana. "Working in the world's biggest reservoir presents a different challenge," says Wynes. "We use the same equipment, just more of it."

The company now faces a new era. "Because of what's required abroad, we're changing the name to Aquaeration Ltd," says Wynes. "That means that people are much more easily aware of what we're trying to achieve."

Water is central to life, so a company that improves water quality is providing an essential service. Aqueration Ltd is an active member of the British Water forum and the Environmental Industries Commission, which it co-founded. Wynes believes that sharing information and promoting best practice is essential. "There's still an awful lot to learn," he says.

HARNESSING THE WIND

NAME THE CROWN ESTATE
HEADQUARTERS LONDON, UK
WEBSITE WWW.THECROWNESTATE.CO.UK

THE UK NOW generates more electricity from offshore wind energy than any other country in the world; a national success story in which The Crown Estate, as managers of the seabed around England, Wales and Northern Ireland, has had a key role to play.

"The Crown Estate negotiated the UK's first ever lease for offshore wind in 2000, off the coast of Blyth in Northumberland," says Huub den Rooijen, Director of The Crown Estate's Energy, Minerals and Infrastructure portfolio. "It soon became apparent that this was a potential growth business for the UK. In less than 20 years, the sector has made huge strides on technology, capacity, delivery time and most importantly price, with costs halving since 2015."

Den Rooijen describes the natural resources of the UK seabed as world class. "Its sheer size, the wind speeds, the infrastructure – whether in terms of ports or skilled labour – it's all here. We now have over 2,000 turbines operating in UK waters, and from a standing start, the sector now meets 6 per cent of the nation's electricity demand. That figure is set to reach 10 per cent by 2020, and is likely to more than double again by 2030."

Adrian Fox, Head of Energy Assets at The Crown Estate adds: "The industry is now delivering huge offshore turbines, far more powerful than anything on land. They truly are giants of the sea. You won't see 9-MegaWatt turbines onshore."

Established by Act of Parliament in 1961, The Crown Estate is a commercial real-estate business, which, aside from the seabed, manages a portfolio of commercial property in Central London and prime regional retail. It also has significant rural and coastal assets. The profit it makes, some £328 million in 2017, is returned to Treasury for the benefit of the nation's finances. "The Crown Estate's purpose is about creating brilliant places,"

says Fox, "whether by delivering prime office and retail space in London's West End, or helping to create the right environment for development on the seabed – now one of the best places globally to invest in offshore wind."

To do this, it has taken an active, long-term approach, helping to bring industry and partners together, identify common challenges and encourage information sharing, which together have helped attract investment and bring down costs. Projects like SPARTA for example, in collaboration with the industry body ORE Catapult, are helping the sector boost its performance, by enabling windfarm operators to benchmark their data against other sites.

"The seabed needs careful, organised development," says den Rooijen. "The demand for space has made our role in managing spatial conflicts and enabling sustainable development, even more important." Indeed, beyond offshore wind, The Crown Estate also provides rights for thousands of kilometres of seabed telecoms, power cables and oil and gas pipelines, as well as licensing the dredging of marine sand and gravel, a key component of construction concrete in projects across the country.

With the government now backing further UK offshore wind within the Clean Growth Strategy, The Crown Estate has announced plans to work with the offshore wind sector to consider making new seabed rights available to developers. With costs decreasing, and with the turbines becoming larger, more reliable and more efficient, there is an opportunity to supply half of the UK's electricity by 2050. "What we've done in the UK," says den Rooijen, "is create a mainstream source of low-cost, low-carbon, homemade electricity."

FIT FOR REPURPOSE

NAME HARSCO METALS & MINERALS
LOCATION LEATHERHEAD, SURREY, UK
WEBSITE WWW.HARSCO-M.COM

THE STEEL INDUSTRY produces a vital product, but is also one of the world's major pollutants. This is where Harsco Metals & Minerals comes in. It takes by-products from the manufacture of iron and steel and recycles them in a range of ways that are economically, socially and environmentally beneficial. The result is a sustainable supply of products to the steel, agricultural and construction industries that help clients meet their sustainability targets.

"We aim to become 100 per cent sustainable, and part of that vision is to ensure that the by-products do not go into landfill," says Director of Technology and Engineering, Chris Byrne. "We recover the valuable metal and give it back to the steel industry, but we also take the slag and convert it into products for fertiliser, cement and road construction. We provide solutions that reduce the carbon footprint and we repurpose a large volume of dust and fine particles to safeguard local communities against potential environmental issues."

According to the World Steel Association, every tonne of steel produced results in at least 200 kg of by-products. Harsco makes annual sales of over 7 million tonnes of processed slag in more than 25 countries, while developing solutions to reduce waste. Road surfaces that use steelmaking by-products are safer and longer lasting than traditional asphalt. Through its asphalt production facility at SteelPhalt, Harsco built a car park for a hospice in Rotherham, assisting with fundraising and managing the project, as well as providing the raw material. Harsco's commitment to reducing environmental impact even extends to its own facilities. "We are developing new technology that will create a more modular solution rather than the typical fixed structures with concrete foundations," says Byrne. "This will reduce the impact on the environment and will ensure that we become more mobile and flexible."

Harsco recycles and repurposes throughout its chain wherever possible, always adding value. "This is engineering that affects people every day," says Byrne. "It is an approach to making life better for people while reducing the environmental impact. Some of the best engineering advancements are things you don't even notice. We have been the pioneers in this space and developed many innovations currently in use within the market. It has been a very positive journey for everyone involved."

POWER ENGINEERING

NAME CLUGSTON CONSTRUCTION
LOCATION SCUNTHORPE, LINCOLNSHIRE, UK
WEBSITE WWW.CLUGSTON.CO.UK

WHEN CLUGSTON WAS founded 80 years ago, one of its earliest ventures was recycling blast furnace slag, the waste produced by steelmaking. Today it operates in something surprisingly close to this sphere, by providing the civil engineering for energy from the waste plants that turn household waste into power.

"We began working with waste in 1937 and now build plants that use household waste to generate electricity, heat and steam," says Steve Radcliffe, the company's Managing Director. Clugston originally recycled waste from Scunthorpe's iron and steel plants, using it to provide concrete, cement and other building products for road surfaces, including RAF runways in the Second World War. Postwar, the company expanded to become contractors themselves, delivering roads and infrastructure while maintaining relationships with the waste recovery and energy sectors.

Clugston has already built around a dozen waste incinerators, making it the leader in the field. A new incinerator under construction in North Wales will process up to 200,000 tonnes of non-recyclable waste per year, which

would have otherwise have gone to landfill. The plant will generate up to 19 megawatts of sustainable electricity annually for the National Grid, enough to power 300,000 UK homes and businesses, and will provide steam or heat to local industry and housing. The company also works on water facilities, power stations and chemical plants and provides the infrastructure for offshore wind turbines. In addition, Clugston's building capabilities have included supermarkets, schools, public buildings, universities and health centres. "These can be either refurbishments or major projects," says Radcliffe. "Responding to our customers' needs demands that we provide flexibility."

Clugston remains a family firm, allowing it to respond quickly to changes in the market. "There are no shareholder pressures, so we are more flexible and can reinvest into the business more easily," says Radcliffe. "It also affects culture and values and makes us more user-friendly." Although Clugston operates in many different fields, the company's history is a unifying factor. "We've always had an ability to build long-term relationships," says Radcliffe, "as we look back on 80 years of exceptional and innovative civil engineering."

SEA CHANGE

NAME NEWWAVES SOLUTIONS
UK HEADQUARTERS CANARY WHARF, LONDON
WEBSITE WWW.DEME-GROUP.COM

KNOWN AS THE Pentland Firth, the Scottish strait separating the Orkney Islands from Caithness features breathtakingly fast currents – making it the ideal location for the MeyGen tidal energy project, the largest power scheme of its kind in the world.

Enter NewWaves Solutions, a London-based subsidiary of the Belgian DEME group (Dredging, Environmental and Marine Engineering), and a company – alongside its sister companies GeoSea and Tideway – experienced in dealing with marine environments. Its task was to carry out this installation work and, as Managing Director Ian Taylor recalls, the current speeds of up to 5 metres per second presented a tough challenge even for him and his expert colleagues.

"We had to create a platform stable enough to maintain precise positioning in this extreme environment," says Taylor. "This is so each of the 300-tonne turbine support structures and ballast blocks – six for each support structure – could be optimally positioned. You have to deal with the effect of the powerful vibrations from those currents, and no one had ever done this scale of project before. Proving the impossible is possible is what we do."

NewWaves undertook extensive sea trials at the Raz Blanchard site, considered one of the most energetic tidal sites in the world, successfully demonstrating the company's jack-ups could be positioned accurately and operated safely in tidal sites. To complete the task at MeyGen, the company deployed Neptune – a special barge-like platform with long supporting legs that can be raised or lowered in the water.

Such innovations keep the company ahead of the competition, and enable NewWaves to provide specialist solutions to modern problems.

"We understand what it takes to define and deliver a project cost-effectively, safely and on time," says Taylor. "We're very specialised – much of our business is in global, marine-related construction projects. We have extensive knowledge and skills in installing all types of foundations, cabling and port facilities, as well as in repair and maintenance."

NewWaves' dredgers were used in constructing the London Gateway container terminal, a £1.5 billion mega-scheme covering an area twice the size of the City of London. One of the biggest privately funded infrastructure projects the UK has ever seen, this highly complex undertaking demanded that 150,000 tonnes of special rock be placed between the sea and sand to prevent erosion.

Mattresses made of asphalt were also used, as protection for the support that keeps everything in place. "The scale was different from other projects," says Taylor. "It was a huge undertaking, and a busy waterway like the Thames is used by vessels all the time. But nothing is too big for us to manage – we've done projects globally, like the Suez Canal."

For Taylor, the company's vision is to constantly improve and refine its techniques. This includes developing and building new vessels, as well as creating innovative solutions: the team devised a special lock system, enabling wind turbines to be installed offshore in severe weather conditions.

Predicting where the market is going to be in the coming decades is crucial. "We have to ensure we have the right equipment for meeting future demand," says Taylor. "We have to future-proof because the market is about driving down the cost of energy, and weaning the industry off subsidies."

As NewWaves' success proves, it is already on course to deliver what its clients need whatever the environment. For them, no mission is impossible.

OUT OF THE ASHES

***

NAME BALLAST PHOENIX
LOCATION BOURNE, LINCOLNSHIRE, UK
WEBSITE WWW.BALLASTPHOENIX.CO.UK

IF YOU SPOKE to someone in the construction industry over 20 years ago about the use of Incinerator Bottom Ash (IBA) as an aggregate, you'd have been met with a blank face. No companies were processing and recycling the ash produced at energy from waste (EfW) plants across Britain and converting them into a sustainable Incinerator Bottom Ash Aggregate (IBAA).

Until the advent of Ballast Phoenix that is. Founded in Lincolnshire by David York in 1996 to produce a cost-effective alternative to traditional aggregates in the construction industry, the business now employs 160 people working across 11 production sites in England. In a growing sector, Ballast Phoenix is clearly the market leader. "We process around 1.5 million tonnes of IBA in the UK," says Financial and Business Director Matthew Turner. "We're probably handling around 70 per cent of the British market."

IBAA is produced from the residual ash produced from burning black bin waste and a small percentage of commercial and industrial waste in an EfW plant. Metals are recovered and reused, the remaining ash is processed to make IBAA: a true demonstration of the circular economy.

This highly regulated business is governed by the Environment Agency. "It wouldn't be wrong to say that, as an aggregate supplier in the UK we are more highly regulated than any other supplier," he says. "This is primarily because the source of our material comes from waste."

In addition to operational staff, Ballast Phoenix has an extensive technical team of geologists, hydrogeologists, chemists and a whole range of other specialists to support business activity throughout the country. It's a sophisticated operation.

Successes include the supply of IBAA as a constituent in a cement-bound material at the Olympic Park in London and IBAA for the "smart motorway" sections of the M25. "Depending on the project and on the local geology and water courses, our material is the most cost-effective option," says Turner.

It's also the green option, and Turner is proud of that. "We continue to work with our industry," he says, "to drive this aggregate's availability and use within the UK market because it is part of sustainability and the green circular economy."

CREATING BETTER PLACES

NAME ENVIRONMENT AGENCY
HEADQUARTERS BRISTOL AND LONDON, UK
WEBSITE WWW.GOV.UK/ENVIRONMENT-AGENCY

"ENGINEERING IS SUCH an exciting and rewarding career, particularly with the environment," says Alison Baptiste, the Environment Agency's Director of Flood and Coastal Risk Management. "It's about creating beautiful places for people to live and work – and that requires our young people."

The Environment Agency fulfils a vital role in creating those beautiful places. "We are looking to reduce the negative impact on the environment through regulation, pollution control," says Baptiste. "And to improve the environment, and make better places for people to live, work and play."

Climate change affects all aspects of the agency's work. "We plan for it in everything we do," says Baptiste. "Our thinking has to change faster than the climate." Most of the agency's 10,000 staff – including more than 400 engineers – work with local communities. It is funded by the government, particularly for reducing flood and coastal risk to the country, and also by charging those industries it regulates.

"We have £2.6 billion of government funding up to 2021 to reduce the risk to around 300,000 houses," says Baptiste. "We have £1 billion between 2015 and 2020 on maintaining assets. We don't just want to build things like the Thames Barrier – we need to maintain and operate them."
The Environment Agency backs big infrastructure schemes such as the new Boston Barrier in Lincolnshire; new flood defences in Leeds, and the River Thames Scheme (which protects England's largest undefended flood plain, from Windsor to Richmond).

"Our smaller-scale projects are just as important," says Baptiste. "Particularly with rural communities, the obvious infrastructure – concrete walls, big barriers – aren't appropriate there. And the most effective solutions need not be the most hi-tech. People often say concreting over your driveway is 'death by a thousand cuts', because lots of little measures cause problems of flooding in urban areas. I think of natural flood management as life by a thousand interventions. By doing lots of little things – planting trees, storing water in mini reservoirs, putting in these little woody dams to slow the flow – we're creating beautiful places, but also we're reducing the flood risk for those rural communities."

PERFECT BALANCE

NAME RED7MARINE
HEADQUARTERS IPSWICH, SUFFOLK, UK
WEBSITE WWW.RED7MARINE.CO.UK

"WORKING ON THE water can be challenging," says Kristen Branford, Managing Director of Red7Marine. "Respecting the environment you're working in is crucial, so we make sure we have safe working systems in place and our specialist teams are trained to the highest standards to ensure that everyone goes home safe."

Red7Marine is a specialist marine services company that works on and around the water in the construction, civil engineering and renewable sectors. With a global turnover of £20 million a year, Red7Marine operates mainly in the UK and Europe and employs a team of 100 people.

Its impressive track record includes constructing the foundations for the Thames-spanning service known as the Emirates cable car; performing maintenance on the marine side of the LondonEye; and currently working on the Thames Tideway Tunnel, "London's super sewer". It also works on renewable energy projects supporting companies that lay the export cables from the wind farms to the shore. "Working in the near shore and inter-tidal zones makes it very difficult for normal construction companies to operate," says Branford, "So we support them on these projects to provide the safest access solutions."

Red7Marine has a specialist marine workforce to operate workboats, cranes and jackup barges as well as turnkey project teams. Its in-house engineers assess the complex challenges involved when working on and around water. "When operating equipment on the water, there are a lot of things to take into consideration," says Branford. "We do all the stability and engineering calculations for our clients to make sure they don't have such issues."

Red7Marine's fleet largely consists of jackup barges, including the latest hi-tech EuroJack that is currently being used in the construction of a marine jetty at Hinkley Point C nuclear power station. With accommodation onboard for all the personnel, the jackup barge can keep operating 24 hours a day. "They have kitchens and a gymnasium on board so projects can keep moving," says Branford, "They don't have to stop, which is vitally important on large infrastructure projects such as Hinkley."

The company has a full maintenance team that ensures its equipment is kept operating to the highest standards. Red7Marine also provides training for everyone involved with its business because of the demanding environment in which they operate. "With us, it begins with the culture," says Branford. "We get people into the right mentality by bringing them along on the journey so they understand why we're doing it, and so that we can get feedback. Then, that message goes out to our clients, to show that we're working at a high standard."

As ICE marks its 200th anniversary, Red7Marine finds new ways of embracing digital technology. "Our barge masters use iPads and smartphones on a daily basis," says Branford. "They can be working in quite remote conditions but can be connected to us in the office as if they were just over the desk."

Red7Marine is making every effort to share its specialist knowledge, expanding its apprentice scheme in the hope of bringing new people into the industry. "It's very much about giving something back to the next generation," says Branford. "We need to help train and educate people to work in the marine sector to ensure that we don't have the skills shortage in the future."

UTILITY SPECIALISTS

NAME GATTICA ASSOCIATES
HEAD OFFICE SOUTHSEA, HAMPSHIRE, UK
WEBSITE WWW.GATTICAASSOCIATES.CO.UK

"IT'S ALWAYS ABOUT the client," says Mark Temple, Managing Director of Gattica Associates. "If the client understands what we do, then the client will keep giving us the work."

Specialist utility infrastructure consultant Gattica Associates offers peace of mind for clients, contractors and designers on major highways and regeneration schemes. By project-managing arrangements for alterations to utility infrastructure, the company provides an end-to-end solution for diversions and alterations to electric, gas, communication, drainage and water infrastructure, from consultation right through to delivery.

"A lot of consultancies and contractors are realising that utility infrastructure works offer unique challenges that they do not want to have to manage," says Temple. "We can take away a major headache from them and offer guidance and solutions throughout the project."

At project-design stage the company advises clients of the feasibility and risk that relates to the diversion of existing utilities. "Contractors often engage in projects without fully understanding the implications of utility infrastructure," says Temple. "For instance, if you imagine moving a set of pylons, you're talking millions of pounds, and it could take two years to move. So without early engagement, the project is in the mire from day one. The earlier we are engaged in a project, the less stress there will be by the time the project commences on site."

The company also provides design facilities, procurement solutions and handles commercial management and legal issues throughout the delivery process. Since being formed in 2004, Gattica Associates has become a UK-wide consultancy with a strong presence on the country's major highways and smart motorway projects. It has a strong working relationship with many of the UK's leading clients, contractors and consultants, working with the likes of Highways England, Jacobs, AECOM, Costain and BAM Nuttall.

"We are highly specialised in what we do and have a dedicated and experienced team," says Temple. "Our commitment to our clients, their projects and their delivery has led to excellent collaborative working relationships and a great reputation within the industry.

ON THE WATER FRONT

NAME SOUTHERN WATER
LOCATION WORTHING, WEST SUSSEX, UK
WEBSITE WWW.SOUTHERNWATER.CO.UK

BECAUSE CUSTOMERS AND regulators rightly expect water companies to continually improve their services, the water industry is constantly having to challenge itself. Southern Water, based in Worthing, West Sussex, faces a range of very particular challenges. As well as increasing regulatory and political scrutiny, it is having to deal with the pressure of population growth in the south-east of England, climate change, and the limited options for supplying water in a sustainable, environmentally friendly way.

"The key to delivering solutions lies in innovation," says Elin Williamson, Research and Development (R&D) Manager at Southern Water. "Central to this is working in collaboration, which is why we spend £5 million annually on R&D. We sponsor PhD students, build innovation ecosystems, conduct experiments and develop and test new technologies and techniques."

One example is DataWell. This project, co-created with Google, enables water companies to seamlessly share key operating data with regulators and scientists. It remotely monitors many of the key drivers – from water usage at the abstraction and customer ends, to water quality and more – enabling easier integration with network-management functions. Eventually the network itself will detect and resolve problems.

Southern Water is also trialling the "Smartball" (pictured, above), which is equipped with an acoustic sensor that can detect tiny variations in the flow along a pipe. It can "hear" a leak of as little as 0.11 litres per minute, while other detectors inside the ball can spot unevenness in pipes and pockets of air. "Finding the exact location of a leak without digging up an entire street has been very tricky until now," says Williamson. "With technologies such as Smartball, we can carry out repairs more quickly and with less inconvenience."

In another example of innovative working, academics from the University of Portsmouth are carrying out groundbreaking research to remove phosphorus compounds from waste water at Southern Water's Petersfield treatment plant. Whether it's the major infrastructure investment of constructing desalination plants or reservoirs, or using innovative technologies such as DataWell and Smartball, Southern Water is harnessing research, development, collaboration and exploration to deliver a better water future for the region.

THE ART OF TAKING APART

NAME WESTLAKES ENGINEERING LIMITED
HEADQUARTERS WHITEHAVEN, CUMBRIA, UK
WEBSITE WWW.WESTLAKES.CO.UK

CONVENTION DICTATES THAT, when a building or structure is no longer fit for purpose and needs to be removed, it either gets blown up or knocked down. There are, of course, safety implications associated with these exercises on a small scale, but nothing compared to the dismantling and decommissioning of a nuclear power station.

"It's not just about taking something to pieces," says Andy Hooper, Managing Director at Westlakes Engineering Limited, an engineering consultancy that specialises in nuclear decommissioning work. "We can't do that to buildings with a radiological inventory that have been contaminated."

Hooper founded Westlakes in 2004, when he recognised the need for a smaller task-focused company that would concentrate on decommissioning. Westlakes has since become a key player in the sector, tackling certain issues that need to be solved for the first time.

"These sorts of things were never thought about when the sites were originally built," he says. "They weren't built with the intention of taking them down, which is why the liability is so high. You need to have a good understanding of the problem to come up with a solution."

One of Westlakes' current projects is the decommissioning of Calder Hall, the world's first industrial-scale nuclear power station, which was opened by the Queen in 1956 at Sellafield in Cumbria. Prior to Calder Hall, Westlakes worked on a variety of schemes at Sellafield, including decommissioning its Pile One Chimney, work in one of its reprocessing plants and, in collaboration with the University of Dundee, developing a lightweight concrete that could fill a 12-storey cell in a building to stabilise vessels before decommissioning them.

"That was a unique and creative solution," says Hooper. "It might sound obvious now, but no one had developed the material to do it before. So we had to solve all these little problems to come up with a solution for the big problem."

Dismantling all the ancillary items surrounding Calder's main reactor cores has involved taking down the four heat exchanges around the building, followed by the turbine halls. By 2023, everything bar the reactor cores will have been cleared.

This portfolio of problem solving has provided the 50-strong team at Westlakes with a singular skillset, and the knowledge gleaned from its work has enabled the company to counsel those designing and building the next generation of power stations. "We can advise people on how to design features into these new power stations," says Hooper, "so that when they come to decommission them in 60 years it's going to be a lot easier to execute."

The UK has always been a pioneer in this sphere, so this information is an invaluable attribute in the global marketplace – a market Hooper says has been valued at around £300 billion. "Calder Hall is one of the most complex environmental clean-up projects in the world," he says. "Therefore it's potentially a huge asset for the UK PLC, because it's an opportunity for us to develop our skills and then sell them on to the rest of the world."

It's no wonder, then, that Westlakes' civil and structural engineers have been recognised by their peers. Last year, the team came seventh in *New Civil Engineer* magazine's Top 100 Companies and was named SME of the Year. "We might not have the resources some of the bigger guys have – we're 50 people and a regional business," says Hooper. "So it was nice to have our work recognised."

WATER WONDERFUL WORLD

———————

NAME ALBION WATER
HEADQUARTERS HARPENDEN, HERTFORDSHIRE, UK
WEBSITE WWW.ALBIONWATER.CO.UK

BRITAIN NEEDS MORE homes, and homes need water. The problem is that we, as consumers, already use too much water – approximately 150 litres per person per day – and supply is hugely inefficient. Recent studies suggest that 20-30 per cent of water is lost through leaking pipes before it even reaches the customer.

The solution, according to Gareth King, is to keep water services local. King is Chief Operating Officer of Albion Water, a company that competes with the "geographical monopoly" water companies in England and Wales (such as Thames Water and Severn Trent) to supply new housing developments. "We're unique in providing a full service," says King. "We add value to sites environmentally and lower costs for developers and consumers."

In practice, this means Albion builds infrastructure not only to supply drinkable water, but also to treat effluent on-site and recycle it, for example as "green water", to be used for flushing toilets, hosepipes and garden irrigation systems. The benefit is two-fold: per capita water consumption is reduced and energy is saved in not having to pump waste water miles away to the nearest treatment works. "We believe we can reduce individual consumption by up to 30 per cent," says King. "And developers benefit from modular treatment systems that reflect the build programme, saving capital expenditure."

One such programme is Oaklands Hamlet in Essex – 425 homes in an area unconnected to mains drainage. King estimates the saving to developer Countryside Homes to be around £2 million, compared to the cost of an off-site pipeline and pumping station required to connect to Thames Water.

Great for customers, then, but how do the incumbent water companies feel about Albion muscling in with new-fangled ideas about saving water? "There's been some resistance," says King. "But there's never been proper competition in the water industry before. Now the government is applying pressure to improve water services as part of a 25-year environmental plan, which means incumbents have to be more innovative. There's been a move towards more collaboration: other companies are looking over the fence and seeing how our solutions can help them." Wishing to protect their futures, the water companies might understandably have viewed Albion as a competitor to be seen off. But the penny seems to have dropped that the future is already here.

DELVING DEEPER

NAME SUBSEA 7
OFFICE SUTTON, SURREY, UK
WEBSITE WWW.SUBSEA7.COM

EVEN BY SUBSEA 7's high standards, the Enochdhu Pipeline Bundle was an incredible feat of engineering. At 7.7 km long and weighing 3,900 tonnes, it's believed to be the longest man-made movable structure made to date. Connecting the Enochdhu oilfield with the North Sea's existing Britannia platforms, it was fabricated at the company's Wick site, then towed 220 km out to the sea at 50 metres below the surface, before being positioned on the seabed.

As a global leader in seabed-to-surface engineering, construction and services, Subsea 7 is accustomed to pushing the boundaries of technology and scale and operating in challenging environments. For field engineer Edward Hac, working on the Enochdhu project was also an important step towards achieving chartered engineer status. Ed joined the company's graduate training programme after studying civil and coastal engineering at Plymouth University, and believes his first two years with Subsea 7 were crucial to his development. "I had four six-month placements in different areas and roles within the business over that time, which is a great starting point for acquiring a diverse skill set very quickly," he says. "That structured approach certainly helps, because you can easily find yourself working in one discipline without having seen the bigger picture."

After a placement rotation in Aberdeen, Ed moved to the firm's Sutton office, from where he was involved in the offshore completion of the Enochdhu project. "I also wanted to get more deep-water experience and was interested in some of the projects out in West Africa," he says. He has since worked on projects as far afield as Ghana, Ivory Coast and Egypt, gaining knowledge of a wide range of engineering fields and becoming an accomplished cameraman for some of Subsea 7's internal communications videos.

Ed achieved chartered status only five years into his career. Senior Engineering Manager Paul Steward, his supervising civil engineer, believes Subsea 7's graduate and professional development programmes are crucial to the success of the company. "Ed joined us as a graduate engineer and there is potential for him to become one of our future managers," he says. "If you want to attract and retain the best people, you have to give them the best opportunities."

A NATURAL SANDSCAPE

NAME ROYAL HASKONINGDHV
LOCATION NORFOLK, UK
WEBSITE WWW.ROYALHASKONINGDHV.CO.UK

COASTAL EROSION IS such an enduring and growing difficulty in some places that combating the problem has become a part of daily life. In 2011, the Dutch spent €70 million on a new scheme called the "sand engine".

"The Netherlands is, of course, very vulnerable to flooding and climate change," says Jaap Flikweert. "For the nation to survive the next few centuries, it has to find ways of doing things differently." Flikweert is the Leading Professional for Flood Resilience at Royal HaskoningDHV, which is joining forces with The Crown Estate – owners of the sea bed and part of the UK coast – to introduce a similar approach in Britain under the name "sandscaping". Work should begin in summer 2019, and since eastern England is especially prone to coastal erosion, it will first be used within a North Norfolk District Council project on the north-eastern coast of Norfolk, at the Bacton Gas Terminal and two nearby villages.

"Sandscaping is essentially a mega beach nourishment," says Flikweert. "You place the sand on the beach in the right location, designed so that nature moves it over time to benefit neighbouring beaches. Sometime after

– 15, 20, even 40 years – you come back and can do the same thing again. Nature does some of the work you'd otherwise have to do yourself. For instance, rather than place the material along 10 km of beach, sandscaping uses a bigger, more efficient vessel to place it in one location and let nature do the rest. And there is a lot of potential for creating habitats and improving amenities for tourism."

This area of Norfolk was affected by fierce weather in December 2013. "That storm induced a sense of urgency to protect the terminal, which supplies up to a third of the UK's gas," says Flikweert. "The villages nearby are protected by a sea wall built after the 1953 floods. If and when that sea wall fails, replacing it just won't be affordable. A combined sandscaping scheme is much more cost-effective, and this makes it possible to justify national and regional public funding to give the communities an extra 20 years or so of life." Sandscaping, says Flikweert, can be an innovative and effective approach to flood defences, if designed well and in the right place. "Bacton shows that it can be affordable and benefits the local community."

CHAPTER THREE

SMART INFRASTRUCTURE

Civil engineers are using smart technology to meet the needs of an ever-growing, urbanising population. Cities around the world must become more energy efficient, and forward-looking engineers are vital for sustainable growth. Despite smart technology seeming to be a modern concept, the journey towards its inception began 200 years ago. The rise of communications has been indomitable, from increasingly sophisticated methods of disseminating news and information to the global spread of education, technology and innovative thinking. Engineers now look to the opportunities that the digital world provides to shape our planet's future – and the training and education of engineering students is having to become ever more complex to deal with this.

ICE200

ICE 200
BELL ROCK LIGHTHOUSE

THE WORLD'S OLDEST-SURVIVING SEA-WASHED LIGHTHOUSE

───────────

LOCATION OFF THE COAST OF ANGUS, SCOTLAND, UK
CONSTRUCTION DATES 1807–11

SITUATED 11 MILES from Arbroath off the east coast of Scotland, the Bell Rock is a treacherous reef in the North Sea, covered by 14 feet of water at high tide. Before the construction of the lighthouse it was a notorious site for shipwrecks.

By the end of the 18th century, the Northern Lighthouse Board had built several lighthouses around Scotland. The First Engineer to the Commissioners of Northern Lighthouses was Thomas Smith, and his stepson and assistant, Robert Stevenson, proposed building a stone lighthouse on the reef in 1799.

Initially, there were doubts about the practicality of a young engineer's proposal to build on a reef that was only above water for two hours a day. But in 1804 the warship HMS *York* struck the Bell Rock with the loss of all on board. The Northern Lighthouse Board Commissioners presented Stevenson's design to the eminent engineer John Rennie, who improved the plans, updated the costs and managed the process of parliamentary approval. In 1806, Parliament passed legislation for construction to begin. Rennie was put in charge of the project with Stevenson as assistant engineer with responsibility for supervising the exceptionally difficult execution of the works.

Stevenson used interlocking stones and based his design for the Bell Rock Lighthouse on John Smeaton's earlier Eddystone Lighthouse, which was lit in 1759. The Eddystone, located nine miles from the Cornwall/Devon border, was the only lighthouse to have been built on an offshore

reef at that point. Given that the sea would allow so little time on site, Stevenson had a work-yard set up in Arbroath where each course of stone was prepared, cut to shape and assembled on a platform before being shipped out to the rock.

In August 1807, Stevenson hired 60 men, including a blacksmith to sharpen tools onsite, to build the lighthouse under his direction. One of the biggest problems during the initial stages of construction was that the men had to return to shore at night or remain on board the supply boat. This was overcome by the construction of a beacon barrack to allow the men to stay on the rock.

There were numerous stops and starts during the construction and the lighthouse was not completed until February 1811. It is 115 feet high and 42 feet in diameter at the base, tapering to 15 feet at the top. It was built with four different types of stone, which were transported and set in position with little or no damage. This was achieved with the first ever iron counter-balance tower crane and a narrow gauge cast iron railway, both dreamed up by the ingenious millwright Francis Watts.

The Bell Rock Lighthouse is such an important landmark that it was targeted by enemy aircraft during the Second World War. Luckily, it survived. The signal station at Arbroath, which acted as the shore base for the building crew and the living quarters for the keepers and their families, is now a museum dedicated to the history of the lighthouse.

ICE 200
WILLIAM LINDLEY AND HAMBURG
THE REBUILDING OF A GERMAN CITY

LOCATION HAMBURG, GERMANY
DATES FROM 1837

IN THE 19TH century, Hamburg developed rapidly from a modest trading town on the River Elbe into a world-class harbour. One of the most influential men in the development was the British civil engineer William Lindley (1808–1900), who was elected a member of the Institution of Civil Engineers in 1842.

Lindley travelled to Italy and German between 1837 and 1838, and was commissioned to construct the Hamburg to Bergedorf railway, opened in 1842. Lindley developed an increasing interest in urban planning and, in 1840, he was commissioned to drain the marshes east of Hamburg. This drainage system, which was implemented through the construction of a grid of canals connected by locks with the River Elbe (1842–47), provided the basis for Hamburg's first industrial suburbs.

In May 1842, a devastating fire destroyed much of Hamburg's central Altstadt district. Lindley, who had already been commissioned to design Hamburg's new sewer system, was appointed as a member of the city's technical commission and presented the first fundamental plan for the reconstruction of the city. For the engineer, this was an opportunity to modernise the city.

Lindley went on to introduce revolutionary new public baths, gas distribution, dry docks, harbour works and many other projects. He also proposed and commissioned a central water supply and a waste-water system. Gravity sewers were planned and dimensioned, not only for storm and surface water, but also for human waste. Resistance to the radical reconstruction was considerable, but a compromise was reached within the commission and work started in 1843.

Following reorganisation of the Hamburg building authorities, he gave up his position as a consultant. Nevertheless, his main interest remained in water supply and waste-water disposal and treatment and he went on to design systems around Europe, in cities such as Amsterdam, Agram, Bad Homburg, Baku, Basle, Belgrade, Berlin, Bremen, Budapest, Bucharest, Chemnitz, Leipzig, Lódz, Mannheim, Prague, St Petersburg, Vienna, Warsaw and Würzburg.

Lindley saw that it was necessary to tackle sewerage and water supply holistically, anticipating the recommendations of Edwin Chadwick and the British Sanitary Movement. Lindley's work was far in advance of what civil engineers were doing in most British cities. A memorial to him is located in Hamburg near the Baumwall underground station at the entrance to the sewer.

ICE 200

ONE GREAT GEORGE STREET

THE INSTITUTION OF CIVIL ENGINEERS' NEOCLASSICAL HQ

LOCATION LONDON, UK
CONSTRUCTION DATES 1910–13

ICE HAS HAD its headquarters in Great George Street since 1838, although not on the current site. It originally leased number 25 before acquiring the neighbouring properties at numbers 24 and 26. Later ICE commissioned architect Charles Barry to design a new building, which was opened in 1895.

Government redevelopment of Whitehall in the early 20th century led to an agreement with ICE to move again to its current location. Inspired by high-rise buildings in New York and Chicago, ICE decided to commission a new steel-framed structure, inviting entries from six eminent architects. The winner was James Miller, a Scottish architect who had designed buildings for the Glasgow International Exhibition (1901) and extensions to Glasgow Central Station and its neighbouring hotel (1905).

Miller's proposed steel-framed structure featured a brick exterior faced with Portland stone. The structural engineer for the steelwork was Ferdinand Hudleston and the contractor was John Mowlem & Co. The building's foundation stone was laid on 25 October 1910, and can be found on the west side of the entrance. Under the stone is a time capsule containing a copy of the ICE charters and by-laws, the membership list, and bronze impressions of the Telford, Watt and George Stephenson medals. The first event in the new building was the Annual Dinner in the Great Hall on 22 October 1913. The demolition of the corner building in the 1930s permitted the north-east façade to be extended, thereby completing Miller's design.

The rooms on the ground and first floors serve as elegant function rooms. The reading rooms – named after prominent engineers Smeaton, Brunel and Stephenson – are lined with walnut-wood panelling, while the council room is lined with oak. Much of this panelling, several of the fireplaces, and the library shelving for its unparalleled archive and library of civil engineer, was saved and reused from the 1895 building. There is also a lecture theatre, seating around 240 people, named after Thomas Telford, ICE's first president. The second floor has a glass barrel roof and there are several glass domes throughout the building that make the most of the natural light.

This grand, neoclassical building has appeared in many films including *Gandhi* (1982), *Eyes Wide Shut* (1999), *Bridget Jones: The Edge of Reason* (2004) and *Wonder Woman* (2017). It housed the media centre for the London 2012 Olympics and Paralympics.

ICE 200
HALLEY VI ANTARCTIC RESEARCH STATION

A SPACE-AGE BASE BUILT TO WITHSTAND THE WORLD'S HARSHEST CLIMATE

LOCATION BRUNT ICE SHELF, ANTARCTICA
DATES 2013–

HALLEY VI, THE British Antarctic Survey's new "space-age" research base, is one of the most challenging, technically complex buildings ever delivered, in the harshest climate on Earth. The world's first fully relocatable, permanently manned research station, Halley VI is designed to lift itself out of rising snow. Its successful delivery, the result of a uniquely collaborative process, is an outstanding example of British innovation, construction and procurement at its best.

The unspoilt landscape of Antarctica provides a unique environment for the study of crucial earth science. Operated by the British Antarctic Survey (BAS), Halley is its most southerly station, located on a floating ice shelf 150 metres thick, flowing off the continent at 400 metres a year. With snow levels increasing by 1.5 metres a year and temperatures dropping to minus 56 degrees Celsius in the depths of winter with wind speeds of 100 mph, it is an extreme environment.

Ever since the first base was constructed in 1956 (for a global scientific project called the International Geophysical Year, which was held in 1957–58), Britain has had a manned research station on the Brunt Ice Shelf, part of the British Antarctic Territory. The first four bases were buried and ultimately crushed by the ice. The fifth base, Halley V, was the first one designed to be above snow level. It was locked into the ice and unable to be moved, yet there was a growing risk of the ice shelf calving to form a giant iceberg, with the base cast adrift on the wrong side of the calving line.

Halley VI is a place where people actually live – throughout the winter in an extreme environment – so the base has to be aesthetically pleasing. It also has to be environmentally conscious, minimising the environmental footprint. But, above all, the base has to withstand extreme conditions.

UNIQUE DESIGN, UNIQUE ENVIRONMENT
In 2004, BAS launched an international competition for a new design. Engineers AECOM, in collaboration with Hugh Broughton Architects, produced the winning concept. The design's success rests on a comprehensive understanding of the station's scientific mission and the extreme conditions affecting the base. A transformational experience for all, the design team is now widely regarded as world experts in polar architecture and engineering.

Due to the unique environmental conditions on the Brunt Ice Shelf, the challenge was to design a building that would cope with the 1.5 metre accumulation of snow each year and have the ability for the whole base to be relocated during its lifetime.

The engineer, Michael Wright, was sent to Halley V to evaluate the conditions first hand and to undertake testing to prove the design concepts would work. The resulting design included hydraulically operated legs to lift the station out of the snow each year with relative ease. The legs are attached to giant skis that form the foundations of the building but, critically, allow each module to be relocated when the need arises.

Snow-modelling analysis and site testing using scale models defined the distinctive alignment of the modules perpendicular to the predominant wind, which minimised the impact of snow accumulation immediately beneath the building. All of these factors reduced further the maintenance effort to operate Halley VI.

PRECARIOUS CONSTRUCTION

Construction on the Brunt Ice Shelf was a further challenge that the project had to be designed to overcome. Restricted to just a couple of months in the Antarctic summer, delivery of components had to cross thin sea ice just one metre thick, which prevented anything heavier than six tonnes from being delivered from the cargo ship in one piece.

Components for the building were prefabricated as much as practicable to minimise assembly time, while being restricted to the six tonne limit. With the basic structural frame being mobile, a production line was formed to install services, flooring, podded rooms and the cladding. A great deal of design coordination work was carried out to ensure all the components from a variety of suppliers fitted together when they were assembled together on site.

At the heart of the Halley VI design was to make the base more efficient in use than its predecessors. The lifting operation, for example, can now be carried out by two people in a week, compared to requiring six steel-fixers for two months to prepare the structural frame ready to lift the old Halley V platforms. This and other innovative solutions mean that the number of people sent down to Halley to maintain the building has been drastically reduced. The ability to relocate the base has already been successfully tested. The modules, weighing up to 200 tonnes, have been pulled by bulldozers 15 km from their construction site at Halley V to the new Halley VI site. This had never been done before and was only thought possible following the site testing using the Dozers in the design competition phase.

Halley VI was formally opened in 2013 at a cost of £25.6 million.

ICE 200
MULBERRY HARBOURS AND PLUTO
TWO REMARKABLE ENGINEERING ACHIEVEMENTS THAT HELPED WIN THE WAR

LOCATION UK AND NORMANDY, FRANCE
DATES 1942–45

IN PREPARATION FOR landing in France during the Second World War, Allied troops needed to overcome the huge logistical difficulty of establishing temporary harbours that would work on the beaches of Normandy. "They must float up and down with the tides," wrote Winston Churchill in May 1942. "The anchor problem must be mastered. Let me have the best solution worked out. Don't argue the matter: the difficulties will argue for themselves."

The solution was one of the most remarkable engineering achievements to emerge from the war. Code name Mulberry, the brief was to design and construct two prefabricated harbours, transport them across the Channel and install them on the beaches of Normandy. Two separate harbours were agreed – one American and one British/Canadian. A sub-committee chaired by civil engineer Colin R White met at ICE on 4 August 1943 to organise the details.

The mammoth project involved around 45,000 people from 300 UK engineering and construction firms. Brigadier Bruce White had overall responsibility as the Royal Engineers' "Head of Ports". Each component, built in Britain, was given a code name. The concrete breakwater caissons (Phoenix) created a sheltered area for ships to load and offload. They were made up of blockships (Corn cob) and floating steel barriers (Bombardons). Floating pierheads and roadways (Whales), designed by Allan Beckett, were supported by floating pontoons (Beetles) made of steel or reinforced concrete.

Construction began in the summer of 1943 and on 4 June 1944 the move began. By 6 June 1944, both harbours were operational, but the American harbour was destroyed in a violent storm on 19 June. For 10 months, the Allies were supported solely by the British harbour at Arromanches. It was the gateway for two and a half million men, a half million vehicles and four million tons of supplies.

However, to advance, the Allies needed a source of fuel. An innovative scheme was developed by Arthur Hartley, chief engineer with the Anglo-Iranian Oil Company, to pump fuel through the world's first under-sea pipeline, using submarine cable technology. It was code-named Operation PLUTO (Pipe Line under the Ocean) and, between August 1944 and May 1945, it delivered over 172 million gallons of fuel to France. Together, Mulberry Harbour and PLUTO helped make D-Day successful, enabled the Allies to achieve a firm foothold in France and helped shorten the war.

ICE 200

SOCCER CITY

AFRICA'S LARGEST STADIUM

LOCATION JOHANNESBURG, SOUTH AFRICA
CONSTRUCTION DATES 1986–89, RENOVATED 2009

BEFORE IT WAS refurbished for the 2010 FIFA World Cup, the First National Bank Stadium had already hosted historic events such as Nelson Mandela's first speech in Johannesburg after his release from prison in 1990. Because of FIFA regulations on sponsorship, the stadium was renamed Soccer City for the duration of the World Cup, and it is still referred to as such locally. The basin-shaped new design, which would increase capacity from 80,000 to just under 95,000, was inspired by an African cooking pot and lent the stadium its third name, the Calabash.

Designed by HOK Sport and African designers Boogertman + Partners, the interior of the bowl featured earthy colours in a mosaic pattern. Lights decorating the lower section gave the impression of a huge flaming pot of food.

The 1.5 billion South African rand upgrade (£88 million) contract was undertaken by a joint venture between African contractor Grinaker LTA and BAM international, and employed as many as 4,700 local people. A commitment to sustainability meant these workers received special training that allowed them to be considered for other similar projects thereafter.

The construction consists of 90,000 cubic metres of concrete, 10,000 tonnes of reinforced steel, 13,000 tonnes of structural steel and 13 million bricks. The structure has a double layer fabric roof, and it took 32,400 fibre cement panels to complete the calabash design on the facade.

The stadium provides an unrestricted view of the pitch and the grounds from every seat, with the furthest seat situated 105 metres from the centre. After construction, there were 193 suites and nearly 3,000 seats for the media.

The stadium's location in the south west of the city already had convenient rail transport links to the major settlements of Johannesburg and the rest of the province of Gauteng. But the development installed a transport hub to the south of the stadium around the nearby Nasrec railway station, as well as providing 860 parking spaces. The hub provides facilities for rail, buses and taxis, and is linked to the stadium by a sweeping pedestrian bridge that leads to the promenade approaching the south entrance.

ICE 200
HIGH LINE
AN URBAN PARK ON A DISUSED RAILWAY

LOCATION NEW YORK CITY, USA
PROJECT DATES 2006–14

IN 1934, A section of elevated railway was built to carry goods trains to stores over New York's largest industrial district. This spur of the New York Central Railroad was designed to go through buildings on Manhattan's West Side, allowing trains to load and unload inside factories and warehouses.

With improved road transport in the 1950s, traffic on the railway decreased. Half the railway was demolished by 1960, and the remainder closed in 1980. After years of neglect, the railway was saved by the non-profit organisation Friends of the High Line who campaigned for a 1.5 mile section to become a park, inspired by the Promenade Plantée in Paris, which was completed in 1993.

The High Line transformation took place between 2006 and 2014, with engineering by Buro Happold and architecture and landscape architecture by DS+R and JCFO, respectively. Garden designer Piet Oudolf chose plants for their hardiness and sustainability as well as their appearance, using mainly native species.

Infrastructure corridors have a positive impact on the communities through which they pass. The High Line is a project that not only has led to regeneration of the area, improved mobility and increased property values but also created a public space for community-based activities. It has inspired similar initiatives in cities across the world.

ICE 200
MUSEUM OF TOMORROW
AN ECO-FRIENDLY TEMPLE TO INNOVATION

LOCATION RIO DE JANIERO, BRAZIL
CONSTRUCTION DATES 2011–15

LOCATED ON THE Maua Pier, the Museum of Tomorrow is part of a larger regeneration of Rio de Janeiro's port area, a project that began as part of the preparations for the 2016 Olympics. It sets new standards of sustainability using 40 per cent less energy than conventional buildings. Adjustable solar panels produce 9 per cent of its energy, and water from nearby Guanabara Bay is used to regulate temperatures inside the building. All the water used in the building is recycled, saving an estimated 9.6 million litres and enough electricity to power over 1,200 homes. The museum is also the first in Brazil to receive LEED (Leadership in Energy and Environmental Design) Gold certification.

The building has 5,000 square metres of exhibition space dedicated to issues that affect the future of mankind, such as population growth, increased life expectancy, consumption patterns, the distribution of wealth, technological advances and changes in biodiversity.

"Rio is setting an example to the world of how to recover quality urban spaces through drastic intervention," says the project's engineer/architect, Santiago Calatrava. His design, supported by engineers Arup, was inspired by the spiky bromeliads that grow in the Botanical Gardens. The museum is surrounded by a large plaza with reflecting pools, gardens, bike paths and recreational areas. In its first year the museum exceeded all expectations, receiving 1.4 million visitors.

STABILISING THE TOWER OF PISA

BRINGING STABILITY TO THE ICONIC TOWER

———

LOCATION PISA, ITALY
PROJECT DATES 1999–2001

COMPLETED IN ABOUT 1372, the Leaning Tower of Pisa is an architectural gem and would be one of the most important monuments of medieval Europe even if it were not leaning. In 1990 it was closed to the public because of fears for its safety following the collapse of a masonry tower in the nearby city of Pavia. Seeing the structure's huge importance, a multidisciplinary commission was established by the Italian government to implement stabilisation measures.

Its stabilisation proved to be a major civil engineering challenge. The tower is founded on very soft clay and its southward inclination has been accelerating over the years to the point at which it was about to fall over at 5.5 degrees. Any disturbance to the ground on the south side would have risked disaster, ruling out conventional civil engineering processes such as underpinning and grouting. Moreover, the masonry was highly stressed on the south side and at risk of failure. A further complication was that internationally accepted conventions for the conservation of valuable historic monuments ruled out any invasive or visible interventions.

A permanent solution was sought that involved reducing the inclination of the tower by about half a degree, which would not be enough to be visible but which would reduce the stresses in the masonry and stabilise the foundations. A novel method known as soil extraction was developed. This involved drilling a number of inclined holes just beneath the north side of the foundation and extracting small quantities of soil from them in a controlled manner. The method was studied over a number of years, first by means of physical models, then by computer modelling and finally by means of a large-scale trial.

Under the direction of Professor John Burland of Imperial College, London, soil extraction beneath the tower commenced in early 1999 and consisted of a preliminary phase to evaluate and prove the method, followed by full soil extraction using 41 extraction holes. The extraction work was completed in June 2001 when the tower's inclination had been reduced by about 0.5 degrees. On 16 June 2001 a formal ceremony handed the tower back to the civic authorities, and it was reopened to the public in December. Precise measurements continue, and, at present, the tower shows no signs of reverting to a southward movement.

GUJARAT INTERNATIONAL FINANCE TEC-CITY

INDIA'S FIRST HI-TECH BUSINESS DISTRICT

LOCATION GUJARAT, INDIA
DATES 2013–

GUJARAT INTERNATIONAL FINANCE Tec-City (GIFT City) is a new business district currently being built between Ahmedabad and Gandhinagar. It will be the first of its kind in India, designed to compete with financial centres worldwide. India's financial services sector has grown rapidly in the last decade and currently employs more than 3 million people with potential to grow to 11 million by 2020. GIFT aims to provide high-quality infrastructure, such as electricity, gas, transport, roads and broadband, and to attract companies from areas with inadequate or expensive infrastructure.

GIFT is planned to be more than just an area for business. This smart city will have zones for education, entertainment and shopping, as well as townships incorporating high-density high-rise housing.

Building a new city on a green-field site provides an opportunity to plan for future growth while retaining quality of life. Transport systems can be planned, including rapid-transit bus and rail, while encouraging walking and the use of public transport. Integrated district cooling and automated waste collection systems are also being provided.

GIFT is a collaboration between many service providers led by the Fairwood Group and supported by the East China Architectural Design & Research Institute (ECADI) and 41 other partners, including British Telecom, which is providing ICT advisory services. Market and talent demand assessment will be provided by McKinsey & Company and Hewitt Associates.

SHANGHAI TOWER

CHINA'S TALLEST SKYSCRAPER

LOCATION SHANGHAI, CHINA
CONSTRUCTION DATES 2008–13

AT 632 METRES in height, the Shanghai Tower is the second tallest in the world after Dubai's Burj Khalifa. Situated in Shanghai's financial district, its 121 floors house a hotel, offices, shops and leisure facilities. It boasts the world's highest restaurant and uncovered observation deck, and its fastest lift.

The challenge for the architect, the US firm Gensler, was to design an attractive building that could withstand both wind loading and seismic effects. This was accomplished by the structural engineer, Thornton Tomasetti, with a concrete core connected to a series of steel struts that support the outer curtain wall. Using computer modelling, engineers worked to reduce wind loading by 24 per cent, resulting in a lighter building and lower material costs. The weight was important: the building is built on soft ground requiring 1,079 concrete and steel bore piles to support it.

The tower's double layer of glass is unique. As well as helping with ventilation, the space between the outer and inner glass walls makes for a pleasant atrium. The building uses sustainable energy sources – including solar panels and 270 wind turbines – to reduce energy consumption. In 2015 the tower achieved Leadership in Energy and Environmental Design (LEED) platinum certification and won the Emporis Best Skyscraper award. In 2016 the Council on Tall Buildings and Urban Habitat (CTBUH) named it Best Tall Building.

SHANNON HYDRO-ELECTRIC SCHEME

THE SCHEME THAT POWERED THE NEWLY INDEPENDENT REPUBLIC

LOCATION SHANNON, IRELAND
CONSTRUCTION DATES 1925–29

ON 13 AUGUST 1925 one of the most important undertakings for the economic and social life of Ireland began when the first sod was cut at Ardnacrusha, in County Clare. It marked the beginning of the construction of the 90 megawatt Shannon Hydro-Electric Scheme.

The driving force behind the scheme was a young Irish engineer, Dr Thomas McLaughlin, an employee of the German firm Siemens-Schuckert. Together, Dr McLaughlin and Siemens convinced the Irish government of their plans to harness the River Shannon and create the first national integrated electricity system in the world. The scheme ultimately led to the establishment of the Electricity Supply Board (ESB) on 11 August 1927. Dr McLaughlin was the natural leader and became ESB's first managing director, with Professor Frank Sharman Rishworth from University College Galway serving as chief civil engineer.

The project cost £5.2 million, about 20 per cent of the Irish Free State's revenue budget in 1925. It was a huge undertaking, employing more than 5,000 people at its peak, including around 150 German workers and engineers. The logistics were astounding. Water was diverted to the station from the River Shannon downstream of Killaloe, via a dam and intake weir at Parteen, and diverted to the power station along a new 12 km head-race canal that was constructed using bucket excavators.

A dam and power station were built at Ardnacrusha. Siemens had to import large amounts of machinery from Bremen and Hamburg, and built a 96 km narrow-gauge railway from the docks in Limerick to bring in the supplies. A 2 km tail-race canal was blasted through the rock to route the diverted water back to the River Shannon in Limerick city. Two rivers were diverted, a double navigation lock was incorporated into Ardnacrusha dam and four new bridges were constructed where the intake canal and tail race cut across roads.

The scheme was officially opened on time and just slightly over budget on 29 July 1929 by President William Cosgrave. It was one of the largest engineering projects of its day and was a revolutionary infrastructural development bringing electricity to towns and cities, setting the foundation for rural electrification and paving the way towards a brighter future. In the early days Ardnacrusha supplied all the country's electricity needs. Nowadays, it contributes less than 2 per cent of the Irish Republic's total demand.

ICE 200

VENTURER PROJECT

ESSENTIAL RESEARCH INTO A MOTORING REVOLUTION

LOCATION BRISTOL AND SOUTH GLOUCESTERSHIRE, UK
PROJECT DATES 2015–18

VENTURER WAS A three-year, £5 million research and development project into connected and autonomous vehicles (CAVs). It was funded by government and industry, delivered by Innovate UK, managed by SNC-Lavalin's Atkins business and completed in June 2018. It investigated and predicted the effect of CAVs on the way we travel in Britain. In July 2018, the Venturer Alliance was formed to continue the collaborative work of the Venturer partners.

The technology involved in driverless car adoption is just one of many factors influencing CAV take-up. The project also explored how public acceptance of CAVs could be encouraged and what was needed to establish the legal, insurance and policy changes to support CAV technologies.

By 2018 the consortium behind Venturer comprised 10 organisations from across different sectors. From 2015, it trialled autonomous vehicles in the Bristol City and South Gloucestershire council areas to explore the feasibility of driverless cars. The vehicles used in these trials were required to respect all traffic laws and observe all speed limits and traffic signals. They could not tailgate other drivers or undertake any risky manoeuvres.

Autonomous vehicle technology offers opportunities to influence road safety, congestion, air quality, climate change and social inclusion in a positive way. Human error is currently a factor in 90 per cent of deaths and injuries on our roads. CAVs look set to reduce this significantly.

The impact of CAVs on insurance and other charges associated with car travel could be huge. Data will underpin every new insurance model and charging scheme that arises as part of this evolving marketplace. It is clear that if improved safety capability leads to reduced accidents then insurance costs should come down. However, intelligent data models and market awareness must also be factored in. Venturer is working to overcome any potential barriers there might be, so that it can safely work toward this driverless goal. It will use its extensive research to inform government and other public bodies about how best to go about achieving this.

The full impact associated with CAV will only be understood over time. Today, everyone has an opinion on driverless cars and many believe that the future could be driverless. The consortium is optimistic that Venturer will change people's lives for the better.

CENTRAL PLAZA
A TOWERING ACHIEVEMENT OF RAPID CONSTRUCTION

LOCATION HONG KONG
CONSTRUCTION DATES 1989–92

CENTRAL PLAZA IS a 78 storey, 374-metre-high office building in Hong Kong's business district. When completed in 1992, it was the tallest reinforced concrete building in the world and remained the tallest building in Asia until 1996. It was constructed on land that was reclaimed from the harbour in the 1970s and therefore had a high water table and had to be able to withstand typhoons. The floorplan is triangular, allowing for more offices with sea views.

The joint venture between Sanfield and Tat Lee was unusual in that only a general outline was ready when construction work began. Substantial changes were made to the original design to speed up construction. Design engineer Arup's initial plan was to use steel, the conventional material for tall buildings. However, this was changed to reinforced concrete to enable the lower floors to be completed with services and available for rent while the upper floors were still under construction. The architect was Ng Chun Man and Associates.

The building took just 44 months from land acquisition to completion – an average of four days per floor. The first temporary tenants moved in just 18 months after the land was acquired. The neon lights at the top of the tower are not only decorative but are also an unusual clock, indicating the time by a sequence of different colours.

BAHÁ'Í LOTUS TEMPLE
FAITH IN ENGINEERING

LOCATION BAHAPUR, NEW DELHI, INDIA
CONSTRUCTION DATES 1980–86

THE LOTUS TEMPLE in Delhi is one of nine temples of the Bahá'í faith in the world. It has become a prominent attraction, with more than 70 million visitors in its 30 years since opening, and has won numerous awards, including from the Institution of Structural Engineers, the Interfaith Forum and the GlobArt Academy. The civil and structural engineers were Flint & Neill.

Abdu'l-Bahá, the son of the religion's founder, decreed that each Bahá'í temple should be a nine-sided circular shape, and architect Fariborz Sahba's Delhi temple is formed of 27 free-standing marble-clad "petals" made of reinforced concrete. These "petals" are arranged in clusters of three to form a shape inspired by a lotus flower: a unifying symbol, and one recognised and used by all the Indian religions. The temple is surrounded by pools that help cool the air and give the impression that the building is floating. Testing of a model at Imperial College, London showed that openings in the basement and at the top of the building would draw the cool air through the building. The temple produces 20 per cent of the electricity it uses by solar panels, and is the first temple in Delhi to use solar power.

The faith welcomes anyone into its Houses of Worship, and scripts from other religions can be read or chanted. No pictures, statues or images are permitted inside the building and there is no permanent pulpit or altar.

CATHEDRAL CHURCH OF ST MICHAEL

REHABILITATION AND RECONCILIATION

LOCATION COVENTRY, UK
CONSTRUCTION DATES 14TH CENTURY; 1955–62

THE CURRENT COVENTRY Cathedral is the city's third. The first, St Mary's Priory and Cathedral, was built from 1095–1102 but fell into decay after the dissolution of the monasteries in 1539. The second, St Michael's Parish Church, was built in the late 14th century and elevated to cathedral status in 1918, but was heavily bombed in 1940 during a Luftwaffe raid. Only the outer walls, a 90-metre-high tower and a spire remained.

In 1951, architect Basil Spence was chosen to design a new cathedral with Ove Arup as structural engineer. John Laing, the main contractor, began work in 1955, and the cathedral was consecrated in 1962. Spence chose to keep the ruins of the old cathedral and link them to the new with a high porch.

The building, constructed of red Hollington sandstone, has a number of original features including the Great West Window, which is suspended from the roof, and the internal precast concrete columns supporting the ceiling, which were cast in sections and glued together. Projecting out on opposite corners are the Chapels of Unity and Christ the Servant. Zigzag walls with angled windows direct light down the nave towards the high altar.

The cathedral's Provost, Richard Howard, made a commitment of forgiveness for those responsible for the bombing, and this strikingly modernist building became a popular symbol of postwar reconciliation.

LIZARD LIFEBOAT STATION

A BUILDING INGENIOUSLY CONSTRUCTED FROM THE CLIFF ABOVE

LOCATION LIZARD PENINSULA, CORNWALL, UK
CONSTRUCTION DATES 2010–11

THE LIZARD PENINSULA is one of the most remote and treacherous coastlines in Britain and lifeboats have been stationed along it since 1859. The Lizard station has stood at the foot of a cliff at Kilcobben Cove since 1961. A funicular railway carries the lifeboat crew down to the boathouse; the only other access is by sea or down 200 steep steps.

In 2010 the old station was demolished to make way for a building that could accommodate the latest Tamar-class lifeboats. Construction took a speedy 19 months because while it was under way the lifeboats had to operate from an exposed mooring.

The new £7.4 million station, designed by Royal HaskoningDHV, is twice the size of its predecessor and based on an earlier design for a station at Padstow. It was built by BAM Nuttall to be as sustainable, energy efficient and low maintenance as possible. It sits on a reinforced concrete slab with a 72-metre slipway supported by 27 piles, which are driven up to 10 metres into the seabed.

An adjustable jack-up barge was chartered for constructing the foundations and slipway, so that all machinery and materials could be delivered by sea. Construction of the station was facilitated by a tower crane with a 75-metre reach sited on the cliff top.

ICE 200
PAVEMENTS OF THE FUTURE?
PROLONGING ROAD LIFE WITH SELF-REPAIRING ASPHALT

LOCATION WORLDWIDE
DATES PRESENT DAY

ENGINEERS USE THE word "pavement" to describe any man-made solid surface for clean and efficient travel. Road carriageways, airport runways, docksides and railway trackbeds are all types of pavement.

Road pavements are made of a sequence of layers. Vehicle wheels impose concentrated loads onto the road surface, so each layer in the pavement is designed to spread those loads over a larger area than the layer above until the stress on the underlying soil is small enough for it not to rut. The challenge is to select the most economical, yet effective, materials to achieve this. Asphalt (or "blacktop") is the most commonly used material, but it slowly deteriorates. Cracks and potholes appear as the asphalt can no longer cope with the stress applied by traffic, or when the cycles of hot, cold, wet and dry weather have aged it, loosening the crushed rock traditionally used as aggregate.

Amazingly, it was the Spanish version of *MasterChef* that inspired Dr Alvaro Garcia, of the University of Nottingham, to develop a recipe for self-repairing asphalt. A cook on the show used jellied liquid to form spheres that resembled caviar. Capsules containing sunflower oil can be placed into the surfacing and, when roads start to crack, the capsules break open and release the oil, softening the asphalt around it. This helps the asphalt and aggregate bind back together, effectively filling in the cracks.

Highways England has been helping to fund these developments. "We know road users want good quality road surfaces, with fewer potholes and not as many roadworks disrupting their journeys," says Highway England's senior pavements adviser Robin Griffiths. "This self-healing technology could give them that and offer real value for money."

Other innovations include low-noise asphaltic and concrete surfacing, lower-energy manufacturing and laying processes, the use of recycled aggregates (including glass, rubber and industrial by-products) and full-depth in-situ recycling of existing pavement materials. These ideas are indicative of the important role played by researchers working at the frontiers of the engineering materials of tomorrow.

TUNNEL-BORING MACHINES

HOW CIVIL ENGINEERING WENT UNDERGROUND

LOCATION WORLDWIDE
DATES 1818–

THE CONCEPT OF tunnelling is simple – provided the ground is stable and there is no seepage into the tunnel. Tunnelling for infrastructure developed from the techniques used by miners who had learnt to cope with a wide range of ground conditions, unstable rock and water ingress. While mining is usually in rock, at depth, and temporary, tunnelling for infrastructure can be softer ground, such as London Clay, near the surface and permanent. This requires a different approach to that used in mining in rock.

The decision to build a tunnel is normally only taken when some obstacle lies between you and your destination, which is why most early tunnelling technology was developed to cross beneath rivers in busy cities. To tunnel through unstable ground requires some means to prevent the soil and the water from inundating the tunnel. In the last two centuries the technology has evolved from piecemeal excavation by hand, through ground support by means of compressed air, up to the present day where huge tunnel-boring machines (TBMs) conquer and control uncooperative ground.

Engineering principles were first applied to tunnelling in the early part of the 19th century and, as with many other areas of engineering at that time, much of this development was in the United Kingdom. Indeed, the first tunnelling-related patent (filed in London by Marc Isambard Brunel) occurred in the same year as the formation of the Institution of Civil Engineers in 1818.

Between 1825 and 1841 Marc, together with his son Isambard, overcame many engineering, financial and political challenges to build the first tunnel using a tunnelling machine. Although the excavation was performed by hand, Brunel had

devised an ingenious shield device that enabled 18 miners to simultaneously excavate the ground while providing stability to the ground and protection for the workers.

The Thames Tunnel, between Rotherhithe and Wapping, was opened on 25 March 1843. It was followed by several tunnelling landmarks. In 1869, James Henry Greathead used a circular tunnel shield to construct the Tower Subway under the Thames between Tower Hill and Tooley Street. Ten years later came the first use of compressed air to construct tunnels in Antwerp and New York. In 1882, Colonel Frederick Beaumont and Captain Thomas English combined their patents to build the Beaumont-English tunnelling machine, the world's first mechanical excavation machine, used for trials for the first attempted Channel crossing.

In the 1960s, tunnelling technology was transformed by the invention of the slurry shield. In 1965 British tunnelling engineer John Bartlett patented the Bentonite Tunnelling Machine, which utilised a slurry shield to support the ground and to transport the excavated spoil to the surface. The method enabled tunnels to be built safely and efficiently in ground conditions that would previously have proved impossible.

In parallel with the development of the slurry shield, the Japanese introduced the earth pressure balance machine. This mechanised tunnelling method uses the excavated material to support the ground. The process normally requires the soil to be conditioned in some way by adding foams or polymers. In sand and gravel, polymers are added to glue the soil together and to prevent water running through the machine in an uncontrolled manner. In clay soils, foams are added to reduce the stickiness of the soil and preventing clogging of the head.

QUEEN ELIZABETH OLYMPIC PARK

21ST-CENTURY LONDON'S MOST STUNNING ACHIEVEMENT

LOCATION LONDON, UK
DATES 2005–12 AND BEYOND

BACK IN 2005, when London was chosen as the host city for the 2012 Olympics, Stratford was earmarked as the site for the Olympic hub. Until that point, it had been a disconnected and remote part of east London. Redeveloping wasteland there presented the opportunity to transform and regenerate one of the most deprived and underdeveloped areas of Britain.

Ken Livingstone, then the Mayor of London, was one of many individuals who seized the Olympic bid as an opportunity to entirely reimagine a whole swath of one of the world's greatest and most cosmopolitan cities. "I didn't bid for the Olympics because I wanted three weeks of sport," said Livingstone. "I bid for the Olympics because it's the only way to get the billions of pounds out of the government to develop the East End; to clean the soil, put in the infrastructure and build the housing."

This was more than just a civil engineering project. It was a megaproject, a once-in-a-generation scheme that involved an estimated 80,000 people to deliver the construction stage. The site itself was considerable: the Olympic Park spans 2.5 square km of land in east London, about the same size as Hyde Park. It was the biggest park to be built in London in 150 years and crossed four London boroughs: Hackney, Newham, Tower Hamlets and Waltham Forest.

With only seven years to transform the site into a gleaming 21st-century metropolis, the work of the Olympic Delivery Authority – led by John Armitt, later to become ICE president – swung into action. Civil engineers began the task of preparing the land for construction. They demolished old

structures and cleaned the contaminated soil, improved the many waterways that cross the park, buried the overhead power lines and ensured that any wildlife and plant species were protected.

During those seven years, 250 acres of new parklands were established, with 8.35 km of waterways in and around them and 10 rail lines. Five permanent venues, 30 new bridges, 11 residential blocks and 2,818 new homes were built in the Olympic Village.

MANAGING RISKS

Redeveloping such a complex site posed risks, however. Until the Second World War the land had been a rubbish dump for 150 years, and after the war there was the possibility of unexploded bombs. In addition, around 220 existing buildings and industrial facilities needed to be demolished.

The enabling works – demolition, excavation, soil treatment, landscaping and the protection of plant and wildlife species – were delivered, almost miraculously, on time. This was thanks to teams of people with different specialist skills working together. Engineers played a vital role in the success of the project, working in collaboration with project managers, archaeologists, ecologists, soil scientists and sustainability experts.

Working on such a site threw up some interesting finds, like a Roman coin from AD330–335, Roman river walls and an early 19th-century wooden boat. One of the most significant archaeological finds of all was evidence of an Iron Age settlement on the site that is now the Aquatics Centre, including an ancient burial site with four skeletons thought to be around 3,000 years old.

There were more obvious finds too. Over 30,000 tonnes of silt, gravel and rubbish were dredged from rivers and canals – including tyres, shopping trolleys and timber. But since sustainability was a key element of the scheme, 90 per cent of it was recycled or reused in the construction works.

Sustainability was also a critical consideration in transporting construction materials and waste in and out of the site. Moving materials by water instead of road is better for the environment as it uses less than a third of the fuel spent by road transportation and releases less than a sixth of the pollution. The large number of waterways linking the Olympic Park location to the Thames was the obvious choice.

TRANSPORT EXPANSION

While developing the site itself was important, failure to establish key transport links would have been a missed opportunity. ICE Fellow Sue Kershaw, as Deputy Director of Transport for the Olympic Delivery Authority, was entrusted with delivering a connected transport network. The East London Line was a central part of this network – London's largest transport infrastructure project since the opening of the Jubilee Line extension in 1999. The line now connects communities that had previously been poorly served by rail, and links 21 stations from Dalston Junction in east London to West Croydon and Crystal Palace in the south.

Timing is critical for any large-scale project, and the teams working across the multiple tasks on the Olympic Park got theirs absolutely right. They earned recognition and respect for delivering the completed Park in time for the launch of the 2012 London Olympic Games.

But the site wasn't simply about the glory of summer 2012. Once the Olympic Games had been delivered, the focus of the original plans and designs shifted toward carrying out long-term improvements for the people and communities living in the area. Work on the site soon started again with the construction of additional homes and facilities.

The legacy continued to roll out new schemes and investment in the area to this day, with new parks, homes, roads and sustainable energy systems being created. Alongside all this is the new International Quarter, which will be home to Transport for London and other leading British businesses and charities. And as long as the Olympics continue to be the gift that keeps on giving, the work of civil engineers will carry on helping to reshape this corner of London into the next decade.

ICE 200

SYMPHONY HALL, BIRMINGHAM

ENGINEERING PERFECT ACOUSTICS

LOCATION BIRMINGHAM, UK
CONSTRUCTION DATES 1986–91

———————

AS THE CONDUCTOR Simon Rattle raised his baton in front of a crowd that included Her Majesty The Queen on opening night – on 15 April 1991 – the design team were tense. Four years of efforts by more than 100 engineers to create "perfect silence" in the centre of a busy city was about to be tested. The trains that rumbled in a nearby tunnel posed a challenge of vibration suppression near the limit of what is possible. It was equalled by the accompanying target of maintaining a 2,200 audience in perfect but soundless air conditioning.

At the big moment, the audience was hushed; there was an exquisite silence followed by the magic sound of Ravel's *Daphnis et Chloé*. The audience loved it, and later the music critics hailed the new hall.

Birmingham City Council's ambition to build the best concert hall in the world for the City of Birmingham Symphony Orchestra (CBSO) required ambient sound in the hall below the level of human hearing. But the sole suitable location in the city centre presented huge engineering problems. A series of novel civil and mechanical engineering methods developed by the Arup team, which included supporting the entire Symphony Hall on replaceable rubber bearings, had proved successful.

ICE 200

WILLIS BUILDING

FOSTER'S SPACE-AGE GRAND PIANO

LOCATION IPSWICH, UK
CONSTRUCTION DATES 1971–75

———————

HOUSING AN INSURANCE firm, the Willis Building in Ipswich is one of the earliest buildings designed by architect Norman Foster's architectural practice Foster Associates. Designed by Foster and his wife Wendy Cheeseman, with Anthony Hunt serving as structural engineer, it is a unique shape, designed to make use of the whole plot of land available. It has been described by *The Architectural Review* as a "Spielbergian spaceship that has settled into the weave of the town" and is occasionally referred to as "the grand piano" because of its shape and dark smoked-glass curtain wall designed by Pilkington. The glass was designed to reflect the surrounding buildings by day but to show the lit interior at night.

The centre of the building is constructed from a grid of concrete pillars, supporting cantilevered concrete slab floors. It was designed with the future in mind and had pioneering raised office floors, anticipating the introduction of computers and need for cabling.

The building was also a leader in energy efficiency. The grass roof garden provides insulation as well as a place for staff to socialise. Originally there was also a swimming pool, which has since been covered to provide more office space. In 1991 it became the youngest building to be given Grade I listed building status in Britain, and in 2001 it won the Concrete Society award for mature structures.

ICE 200
POMPIDOU CENTRE
THE WORLD'S FIRST "INSIDE-OUT" BUILDING

LOCATION PARIS, FRANCE
CONSTRUCTION DATES 1971–77

MORE THAN FOUR decades after it opened to the public, the Pompidou Centre remains a touchstone for how engineering-led architecture can lead to inspiring, relevant and adaptable public buildings. Controversial from the start, its arresting yet functional form is still a powerful statement that public arts facilities should be open, engaging and democratic, not elitist and grandiose.

A team of Ove Arup, Richard Rogers & Renzo Piano unexpectedly won the 1971 French design competition for a new gallery, public library and museum in the Beauborg area of Paris. Their vision was striking for such a historical city as Paris. The Pompidou Centre would become an exemplar of "high-tech" building, where the engineering was expressed as part of the architecture with both disciplines co-equal throughout the design process.

If conventional wisdom was that galleries should be "palaces of art", the Piano/Rogers/Arup team's winning idea was the opposite. The design should leave the building's curators with spaces that could become whatever they needed. President Pompidou himself had expressed a desire for a building that "will be constantly evolving". The resulting scheme was both bold and yet simply logical: placing all the building services on the outside would make all the internal space infinitely flexible. Even the main supporting columns are set outside the facade line to provide a more graceful entry and allow the facade to be removed or reconfigured at will.

All functional elements of the building are arrayed on the outside and colour coded for legibility. The vertical circulation – escalators and lifts – are combined with the structure on the front face, with the pipes and ducts integrated into the rear facade. Large air trumpets adorn the piazza while ventilating the underground car park. The engineering team was initially led by Ted Happold then Povl Ahm, with Peter Rice and Lennart Grut for the superstructure and John Morrison for the infrastructure.

That such a design would scandalise the city's elites wasn't hard to predict – they variously decried it as an "oil rig" or an unwelcome spaceship that had landed in their neighbourhood. But Pompidou was a hit with the public from the day it opened, and since 1977 more than 180 million visitors have travelled up its externally tubed escalators to the art, books, films and music that continue to fill the space within. As a building it continues to inspire young people to wonder what else engineering might reimagine and achieve.

BLACKPOOL TOWER

BRITAIN'S ONLY SURVIVING AMUSEMENT TOWER

LOCATION BLACKPOOL, UK
CONSTRUCTION DATES 1891–94

BLACKPOOL TOWER OPENED to the public in May 1894. Perhaps unsurprisingly, since its design was inspired by the Eiffel Tower, it remains Blackpool's pre-eminent tourist attraction and the town's only Grade I-listed building. It is also one of the most famous buildings in Britain.

The tower, designed by engineer Richard Read and constructed by Heenan and Froude, is 158 metres tall and alone contains 2,493 tons of steel and 93 tons of cast iron. The base comprises 985 tons of steel and 259 tons of cast iron. The architects were James Maxwell and Charles Tuke of Lancashire. They oversaw the laying of the tower's foundation stone on 29 September 1891 but, sadly, neither of them lived to see it open three years later.

Blackpool Tower is the common name for Tower Buildings, an entertainment complex in a red-brick, three-storey block that houses a circus, amusement halls, a cafeteria, an aquarium, roof gardens and the famous ballroom, as well as the tower.

Maxwell and Tuke also designed the New Brighton Tower at Wallasey on Merseyside, which, at 173 metres, became the tallest building in Britain when it opened at the end of the 19th century. However, it was neglected during the First World War and the tower was dismantled in 1919 and sold for scrap.

EDINBURGH SEWAGE DISPOSAL SCHEME

CLEANING WATER IN THE SCOTTISH CAPITAL

LOCATION EDINBURGH AND LEITH, SCOTLAND, UK
CONSTRUCTION DATES 1971–76, 2001

HISTORICALLY, MUCH OF the sewage and storm water from the Edinburgh conurbation, with a population or around half a million, discharged untreated into the Firth of Forth, leaving the water and beaches badly polluted.

In 1966, feasibility studies were carried out for a new sewage-disposal scheme for the city. The decision was made to build Scotland's largest waste-water treatment works from reclaimed land at Seafield in Leith. Two new interceptor sewers connecting Edinburgh and its outskirts were also required to carry the city's waste water for treatment at the new works.

The eastern and western interceptor sewers, serving Midlothian, East Lothian and Edinburgh, were laid close to the coastline, constructed via a mixture of open-cut trenches and tunnels. Pumping stations were also built to pump waste water into the new sewers that fed directly to Seafield. In 2001, the Cramond Wastewater Improvement Scheme removed the last major untreated sewage discharge from the area into the River Forth.

The result of the work undertaken in the construction of these sewers and treatment works, as well as subsequent schemes over the past 40 years, has led to major improvement in water quality in the River Forth and its estuary. The public now have access to better bathing water at beaches that, in the past, they may have avoided visiting.

ICE 200
SYDNEY OPERA HOUSE
THE BUILDING THAT CHANGED THE IMAGE OF AN ENTIRE COUNTRY

LOCATION SYDNEY, AUSTRALIA
CONSTRUCTION DATES 1959–73

IF ASKED TO name a symbol of Australia, there is a fair chance that you would think of the Sydney Opera House. Not only is it an important venue for concerts and festivals and an amazing backdrop to the New Year's Eve firework display, but it is also a symbol for this modern, forward-thinking country. Completed in the early 1970s, this iconic building still looks modern and radical and continues to amaze the millions of tourists who flock to admire its unique and bold design every year.

Like so many iconic structures, it required the vision and drive of the sponsor, in this case the New South Wales premier Joseph Cahill and the genius of both the winning architect, Denmark's Jørn Utzon, and Anglo-Danish civil engineer, Ove Arup, to bring it to life.

One of the most significant challenges for the architects and engineers alike was how best to design the shells to make them as practical and economical to build as possible. A design that was based on a 'repetitive geometry', to maximise the reuse of material was critical. It took years to finalise and involved one of the first applications of computer-aided design.

The idea that the form of the shells could be derived from the surface of a sphere marked a turning point in the design of the building and represented a milestone in 20th-century architecture. The popular myth was that Utzon derived the solution while peeling an orange. Another major challenge was the design of the beams supporting the concourse, but Arup was instrumental in providing an elegant solution that removed the need for internal columns. The project was not without controversy, being finally completed 10 years later than planned and significantly over budget. Utzon's plans for the interior of the building never materialized and he never returned to Sydney to see his creation.

The Sydney Opera House was finally opened in 1973 by Queen Elizabeth II. In 2007, it was included on the UNESCO World Heritage List and was formally recognised as one of the most outstanding places on Earth. It has become a benchmark for iconic building design, being an architectural and engineering masterpiece. According to American architect Frank Gehry, it is "a building well ahead of its time, far ahead of available technology... A building that changed the image of an entire country."

ICE 200
EDEN PROJECT
THE LARGEST GREENHOUSE IN THE WORLD

LOCATION CORNWALL, UK
CONSTRUCTION DATES 2006–10

THE EDEN PROJECT is a unique redevelopment that has transformed a china clay pit in Cornwall into the largest greenhouse in the world. Conceived by Tim Smit and designed by architect Nicholas Grimshaw and engineers Anthony Hunt & Associates, it took two-and-a-half years to construct, opened as a visitor attraction in 2001 and won the Institution of Civil Engineers Merit Award 2002 for "an outstanding example of civil engineering".

Its immediate popularity had a lot to do with its impressive scale and bold design. Each of the project's spectacular biodomes comprises a series of four interconnected spherical caps of various sizes. The biggest of these, the Humid Tropics biodome, is 55 metres high, 100 metres wide and 200 metres long. It covers 15,590 square metres and is designed to maintain a temperature between 18 and 35 degrees Celsius. The air inside is kept moist by abundant water movement, including a waterfall. The smaller Warm Temperate biodome is 35 metres high, and is designed for temperatures maintained above 10 degrees Celsius in winter and between 15 and 25 degrees Celsius in summer.

The geodesic domes have a galvanised steel framework that supports a series of hexagonal panels. As glass panels would have been too heavy and too dangerous, a special air-filled panelling system was devised. This unique engineering structure connects us with each other and the living world, exploring how we can work towards a better future.

ICE 200
RESILIENT MATERIALS FOR LIFE PROJECT
PIONEERING BUILDINGS AS LIVING, SELF-HEALING STRUCTURES

LOCATION CARDIFF, BATH, BRADFORD, CAMBRIDGE, UK
DATES PRESENT DAY

RESILIENT MATERIALS FOR Life (RM4L) is a research project at Cardiff, Bath, Bradford and Cambridge universities, funded by the Engineering and Physical Sciences Research Council (EPSRC). The aim is to create construction materials that can adapt to their environment, develop immunity to harmful actions, self-diagnose the onset of deterioration and self-heal when damaged. This innovative approach uses biomimetic methods – those that imitate natural, biochemical processes – and has the potential to engender a step-change in the value placed on infrastructure materials, providing a much higher level of confidence and reliability in the performance of our infrastructure.

The project comprises four research themes: self-healing of cracks at multiple scales; self-healing of time-dependent and cyclic-loading damage; self-diagnosis and immunisation against physical damage; and self-diagnosis and healing of chemical damage. "This research will have a significant impact on the sustainability of our infrastructure," says Professor Bob Lark of Cardiff. Under the guidance of the project's industrial partners, the themes will address a diverse range of applications, including cast in-situ and precast concrete, repair systems, overlays and geotechnical systems.

The nature of the research is both varied and exciting, encompassing the fundamental physico-chemical actions of innovative healing systems. Over the next 200 years, civil engineering and the future built environment could be transformed by the outputs of this project.

ICE 200
TENSAR GEOGRIDS
THE INNOVATION THAT REVOLUTIONISED CIVIL ENGINEERING

LOCATION WORLDWIDE
DATES PATENTED 1978, INTRODUCED EARLY 1980s

THE 1970S HERALDED a revolution in the construction of retaining structures and roads as civil engineers adapted centuries-old methods of strengthening earth structures using new materials and analytical methods. One of the most significant such developments was Tensar's invention of polymeric geogrids. The main function of these stiff, mesh-like geometric grids – usually made from polymers such as polyethylene or polypropylene – is to reinforce soil slopes and retaining walls. Geogrids provide safe access over soft ground, reduce aggregate layer thickness in pavements and increase the bearing capacity of soft ground beneath roads and railways.

Geogrids were invented by Dr Brian Mercer, who originally patented the Netlon process of extruding molten plastic into grids – rather than weaving polymer fibres – in the 1950s. They proved popular in many industries, including civil engineering. Mercer saw the potential for the wider use of geogrids in civil engineering if he could make them stronger and more robust.

He began developing a way of delivering these improvements and eventually invented the "Tensar process" in 1978. This stretched the grid to align the polymer's long chain molecules in the ribs and through the junctions, increasing strength and durability.

Tensar geogrids were first trialled in 1980 to build a temporary retaining wall supporting a railway at Newmarket Silkstone Colliery in Yorkshire. Performance exceeded all expectations, with no discernible settlement in three years, despite the railway carrying up to 300 tonnes of waste every hour. Since then, Tensar geogrids have been used on thousands of projects globally to build earth-retaining structures with overall heights in excess of 60 metres and to support roads, railways and trafficked areas.

Geogrids continued to evolve, with a hexagonal grid, TriAx, launched in 2007. For roads, aggregate stabilised with TriAx delivers high-performing pavements that are considerably thinner, last longer and use fewer materials, which helps to drastically reduce the environmental impact.

Mercer – who was awarded the Royal Academy of Engineering's MacRobert Award for innovation in 1984 – was convinced Tensar would be revolutionary. In 2013, 15 years after his death, he was proved right when Tensar technology was named one of Britain's 100 history-changing discoveries of all times, alongside discoveries including Alan Turing's Universal Machine, penicillin and the splitting of the atom.

DE LA WARR PAVILION

A SEAFRONT ART DECO CLASSIC

LOCATION BEXHILL-ON-SEA, EAST SUSSEX, UK
CONSTRUCTION DATES 1935

IN THE 1930s, hoping to attract more visitors to this part of Sussex, the visionary Labour Mayor of Bexhill, Herbrand Sackville, 9th Earl De La Warr, launched a competition to design a seafront pavilion in the New International or Modernist style. It was to provide a new kind of entertainment and culture for all, to promote healthy mind and healthy body, with a large auditorium, restaurant, reading room, lounge, sun parlour and roof terrace. The winning design by Erich Mendelsohn and Serge Chermayeff was as pioneering in construction and design as it was in spirit. It was the first public building in the UK to use a welded steel frame (by structural engineer Felix Samuely) to support slender cantilevered concrete balconies.

Damage during the Second World War and a seaside location meant that the fabric of the building deteriorated, as funds to maintain it were limited. Fortunes changed in the 1980s when it was Grade I listed by English Heritage and a trust was set up to support it. It closed in 2003 for a major refurbishment project funded by Arts Council, Heritage Lottery and English Heritage amongst others, reopening in 2005 with two galleries, a café, a shop and an education centre with renewed access to the roof terrace. It now receives 400,000 visitors a year, bringing over £16 million to the local economy.

SALT'S MILL AND SALTAIRE

VICTORIAN PHILANTHROPY AT ITS FINEST

LOCATION SALTAIRE, WEST YORKSHIRE, UK
CONSTRUCTION DATES 1853–73

"SALTAIRE IS AN outstanding and well-preserved example of a mid-19th century industrial town," said UNESCO, when it awarded the town the status of World Heritage Site in 2001. "Its layout and architecture admirably reflect mid-19th century philanthropic paternalism, as well as the important role played by the textile industry in economic and social development."

Salt's Mill was the largest building in the world by floorspace in 1853. It was named after the industrialist Sir Titus Salt, a deeply religious man who was concerned with the well-being of those who worked in textile mills, who often lived in slum conditions and suffered from poor health. Salt commissioned architects Lockwood and Mawson and engineer William Fairbairn to build a mill three miles outside Bradford, next to the Leeds and Liverpool Canal. Fairbairn designed the iron structure, a tubular bridge over the Aire and all the machinery. When completed the mill turned out 18 miles of fine worsted Alpaca yarn each day on 1,200 looms attended to by 3,000 workers.

Over the next 20 years Salt built an Italian-style village named Saltaire to house the workers. Each house had fresh water, sanitation and gas supply, and the village had a church, hospital, school, park, public baths and wash houses. The mill closed in 1986 and has been successfully redeveloped as a shopping and recreation centre, creating work for over 1,000 people.

ICE 200

REPOSITIONING BELLE TOUT LIGHTHOUSE

THE MOVING OF A CLIFFTOP LANDMARK

LOCATION BEACHY HEAD, UK
PROJECT DATE 1999

BELLE TOUT LIGHTHOUSE was built by William Hallett and James Walker from Aberdeen granite on the cliffs near Beachy Head in 1832. It has since enjoyed a successful show-business career, appearing in the Bond film *The Living Daylights* and in the BBC's *The Lives and Loves of a She-Devil* and *Changing Rooms*, in which Laurence Llewelyn-Bowen made over its glass "round room".

But it has generally found itself in the wrong place at the wrong time. Originally, its 100-foot distance from the land's edge meant the cliffs obscured its beam for any vessels in close range; and even after the cliffs eroded over time, sea mists often made it difficult to spot. The lighthouse was decommissioned in 1902 and a new one was built at Beachy Head, this time at the bottom of the cliffs.

The lighthouse authority Trinity House sold off Belle Tout a year later and it has changed hands several times since. It was badly damaged during the Second World War, when the Canadian Army used the area for target practice. The local council took ownership of it in 1948 and decided to restore Belle Tout because of its historical significance. Building work

was carried out under lease to the Cullinan family in 1956 and the lighthouse was renovated. There have been various leaseholders since, including the BBC and private families. It is currently a bed and breakfast location.

Several cliff falls during 1998 left the Grade II listed building just 12 feet from the edge of the cliff. By 1999, this erosion was threatening its foundations and drastic steps had to be taken to stop it falling into the sea. In March of that year, Abbey Pynford engineers achieved the impressive feat of moving all 850 tons of it to its new foundations 17 metres (56 feet) away. Twenty-two hydraulic jacks were used to lift the building onto four steel-topped concrete beams. The jacks were then used to push the lighthouse along the beams, which had to be greased constantly to keep the building moving.

Belle Tout's new foundations were designed to allow for future moves; which is just as well as the cliff at Beachy Head continues to erode at a rate of 60 cm each year. Belle Tout will need to be moved again in the future.

SMART CITIES

TACKLING TOMORROW'S CIVIL ENGINEERING CHALLENGES

LOCATION WORLDWIDE

DATES 21st CENTURY

THE WORLD'S POPULATION is predicted to reach eight billion in 2023 and 10 billion in 2056, with nearly all of this growth likely to take place in developing countries. Currently three million people move to cities every week. If this trend continues there will be 2.5 billion more people living in cities by 2050, which will account for 70 per cent of the world's population. The challenge for civil engineers and planners is to plan for cities and citizens to continue to grow while providing and retaining pleasant and healthy spaces.

Traditionally cities have grown and thrived in places that were easy to defend, had access to fresh water and were convenient for trading. As they have evolved to diverse megacities, the infrastructure they require has increased in both scale and complexity. Cities need reliable energy grids, efficient transport systems, food networks, sewerage systems and telecommunications networks. Delivering any one of these systems represents a great triumph of engineering, but modern prosperous cities require us to do this in a complex social, political, economic and technical context.

For example, many of the world's cities are situated in coastal regions and are susceptible to sea-level rise. International targets for carbon reduction mean that urban infrastructure is expected to deliver extra capacity while reducing emissions. Increasing aspirations for social inclusion means that there is pressure to undertake accessibility upgrades to transport infrastructure. The digital revolution offers new opportunities for infrastructure optimisation and maintenance, but it is still unclear how the potential of this can be realised while retaining appropriate anonymity and safety measures.

One proposition is to build whole new cities from scratch, such as Songdo in South Korea or the planned Gujarat International Finance Tec-City (GIFT) in India. These new cities provide the opportunity to integrate critical infrastructure at the planning stage, building in novel ICT solutions. However, they have also been the subject of much criticism, particularly with respect to their ability to provide dynamic, engaged and prosperous communities.

It is clear then that adaptation will be the key for any city wishing to thrive in the 21st century and beyond. This will necessitate retrofitting ageing infrastructure that is straining under the pressures of urbanisation. The challenge faced by civil engineers is to make the best use of technology to integrate existing systems. For example, one step is to implement smart sensors to control traffic flow (smart motorways), dim street lights when there is no one around and identify issues such as water leaks.

It will also be a city's capacity for innovation that ensures its resilience and prosperity. Asia is leading the way in waste innovation by incorporating vacuum-powered waste-disposal systems in some new developments. The system removes waste using underground pipes and is particularly suitable for high-rise buildings, public spaces, hospitals, and hotel and office complexes. As well as reducing congestion and pollution from waste-removal vehicles, the system reduces overspilling bins and improves the environment.

With all this talk of the smart city, infrastructure upgrades and technological innovation, engineers must remember that cities are much more than nuts and bolts. Urban infrastructure ultimately exists to serve the needs of citizens and communities, and to enable them to prosper. While the 20th century saw engineers get to grips with the technical implications of environmental sustainability, the challenge of the 21st century will be on the more complex issue of social sustainability, social justice and inclusion.

ICE 200
BT TOWER, BIRMINGHAM
A LOFTY FEAT OF COMMUNICATION

LOCATION BIRMINGHAM, UK
CONSTRUCTION DATES 1963–66

AT 152 METRES (nearly 500 feet) in height, the BT Tower is the tallest structure in Birmingham. The Ministry of Public Building and Works designed it for the General Post Office (GPO), a precursor to British Telecom. Before the introduction of the fibre network, communication towers needed to be tall enough to receive microwave TV, radio and telephone signals unhindered.

The Birmingham tower was originally intended to be circular like the Post Office Tower in London, but construction delays on the latter led the Birmingham construction to adopt a square concrete design. It was conceived to be stable, with channels on each corner to help resist wind movement and keep a steady signal. The circular aerial gallery at the top of the tower houses the satellite dishes. These were raised up on a trolley running on two steel rails as far as the aerial gallery, and then hoisted into place using a system of steel cables and poles. The larger analogue dishes have been removed; no mean feat, as the last to go weighed 700 kg. Around 80 smaller dishes remain, sending signals to areas without fibre coverage.

Peregrine falcons have long nested on a ledge near the top of the tower. In 2010, the BBC and the Royal Society for the Protection of Birds installed a webcam there, which in 2015 filmed their first falcon chick.

ICE 200
POST OFFICE TOWER
A HIGH-POINT OF THE CAPITAL'S SKYLINE

LOCATION LONDON, UK
CONSTRUCTION DATES 1961–65

THIS ICONIC LONDON landmark, now known as the BT Tower, superseded Millbank Tower as the UK's tallest building for 15 years from its opening in October 1965. At 191 metres in height, including its aerial rigging, it supports the UK's telecommunications network – from transmission of microwave signals in the 1960s to modern-day television broadcasting.

The tower's structural engineer was SG Silham of the Ministry of Public Building and Works. It was constructed at a cost of £2.5 million by Peter Lind & Company. Built of glass-clad concrete, it was a feat of engineering design that had to withstand wind speeds of up to 95 mph without swaying more than 25 cm. The building's levels are accessed via two high-speed lifts that can reach the top of the tower in just 30 seconds. The foundations are sunk through 53 metres of London clay and formed of a 27 metres square concrete raft.

The tower was a popular social destination in the 1960s and 1970s, featuring a cocktail bar and rotating restaurant on the top floor that was managed by holiday camp operator Butlins. Public access closed in 1980 (the same year it lost its tallest building title to the NatWest Tower), although it was briefly reopened in October 2015 to 2,400 winners of a lottery to celebrate its 50th anniversary. Over the years, its title changed to reflect the changing name of its owner: known variously as the GPO Tower, the Post Office Tower, the Telecom Tower and, finally, the BT Tower.

UKCRIC

INSPIRED INFRASTRUCTURE FOR BETTER LIVING

———————

LOCATION UK
ESTABLISHED 2015

"IT HAS BEEN a tremendously interesting and rewarding few years getting UKCRIC off the ground," says Professor Lord Robert Mair, President of ICE. "The level of vulnerabilities of UK cities' infrastructure, combined with an uncertain future, demands a step-change in our collective approach to complex challenges through multi-disciplinary research."

It has been estimated that inadequate infrastructure costs the country £2 million a day. The existing research on this issue, however, is fragmented and under-resourced. The United Kingdom thus needs a coherent national research programme to help de-risk, prioritise and provide evidence for investment.

The UK Collaboratorium for Research in Infrastructure and Cities (UKCRIC) provides leadership and support for the development of a coordinated and coherent research community, looking at world-class national infrastructure and urban systems. UKCRIC's founding higher-education partners represent 14 of the UK's world-leading infrastructure, civil and construction engineering research groups. Collectively, they engage with government, industry and academia to drive innovation and value creation in the exploitation of services provided by national infrastructure.

UKCRIC's vision is to make the country's infrastructure and cities more sustainable, more adaptable and more resilient to extreme events such as flooding. It tries to understand how to provide services that are more affordable, accessible and usable to the whole population.

This is being achieved through several means. The first is by establishing a network of joined-up national infrastructure laboratories to carry out research on the basic science, technology and engineering that underpins the economic infrastructure sectors. The second is to create a multi-level modelling and simulation environment using high-performance computing environments. The third is to create a connected network of urban observatories that enable rapid trialling of engineering solutions at scale, providing data on current and proposed infrastructure assets to inform decisions based on evidence, analysis and innovation. The fourth is research into new business models, the social science of changing digitally enabled communities with different attitudes and behaviour, and resources and functional resilience in the face of extreme events. And the fifth is coordinating UKCRIC's portfolio of facilities and research programmes to cultivate coherence, effectiveness and efficiency in the use of resources and delivery of solutions.

ICE 200
BSI GROUP
SETTING NATIONAL STANDARDS FOR MORE THAN A CENTURY

LOCATION LONDON, UK
ESTABLISHED 1901

THE MOST SUCCESSFUL industry standards in the world, as published by the International Standards Organisation (ISO), are based on British business and engineering practice. These consensus standards originated in BSI, an organisation that is appointed by government as the national standards body and is responsible for the catalogue of around 37,000 British standards that support the UK economy.

BSI's roots lie at the turn of the 20th century, when foreign competition led senior UK engineers to seek a way for small British firms to compete against larger overseas enterprises. One approach, coined "standardisation", sought uniform national specifications for components. Two presidents of ICE, Sir John Wolfe Barry and Sir Douglas Fox, supported the establishment of the Engineering Standards Committee (ESC) in 1901. ESC remained part of ICE until 1918 by which time 78 British Standards were published for rolled-steel sections, rails, Portland cement, road-stone, electrical goods, locomotives, automotive and aircraft materials.

Both the International Electrotechnical Commission (IEC) and the International Standards Organisation (ISO) were founded in London (in 1906

and 1946, respectively). In 1918, the ESC became incorporated as the British Engineering Standards Association (BESA), acquiring a Royal Charter in 1929 and changing its name to the British Standards Institution (BSI) in 1931.

Representing the UK, BSI is a permanent member of the governance bodies of ISO and IEC, and the three European standards organisations, CEN, CENELEC and ETSI. BSI manages around 1,200 committees, covering subjects from robot ethics to quality management, big data to children's toys. BSI places particular emphasis on supporting trade and innovation and is working at the cutting edge of technologies such as the commercialisation of graphene and smart cities.

In the built environment, in addition to leading work on the Eurocodes, BSI has developed a suite of internationally recognised standards supporting building information modelling (BIM). These have been transformational for many companies and their clients, setting out a basis for digital collaboration during the design, construction and through-life stages of any built asset. Just as the ICE intended in 1901, these UK best practices in BIM are now recognised globally through ISO and have contributed directly to the quality and competitiveness of UK industry.

ICE 200
KING ABDULAZIZ UNIVERSITY SPORTS HALL

A LARGE, LIGHTWEIGHT ARENA BUILT FROM CABLE-NET TECHNOLOGY

LOCATION JEDDAH, SAUDI ARABIA
CONSTRUCTION DATE 1981

RESEMBLING A SAND dune, or a huge Bedouin tent, King Abdulaziz University Sports Hall is a multi-use hall designed to hold 5,000 spectators and to host sporting events and graduation ceremonies.

One of the main requirements for the design was to use as little material as possible, so a tensile (or stretched fabric) over a cable-net design was adopted. Architect Frei Otto, a pioneer of lightweight construction, devised cable-net technology with Rolf Gutbrod, using it to create the German Pavilion at the Expo '67 World Fair in Montreal. Otto collaborated closely with engineers Ove Arup and Ted Happold. Michael Dickson of BuroHappold led the Jeddah design team.

Eight steel tube masts support the sports hall's cable-net structure. The exterior of the building comprises a heavyweight polyester fabric coated with PVC; a light fabric tent hanging below the cable net forms the interior. The net was formed on the ground and took seven days to lift into place.

The space between the two fabrics and the gaps around the masts allow natural ventilation, avoiding the need for air conditioning, at least during cooler weather. The fabrics are light in colour to make the most of the natural light that enters and to blend the building with its surroundings. The design mixes tradition with modern technology, producing an environmentally sustainable building.

ICE 200
NINEWELLS HOSPITAL

ONE OF THE WORLD'S LARGEST TEACHING HOSPITALS

LOCATION DUNDEE, SCOTLAND, UK
CONSTRUCTION DATES 1965–74

NINEWELLS IS DUNDEE'S main hospital, internationally renowned for teaching clinical and surgical skills. It was the first one in Britain to carry out keyhole surgery and is a leading centre for cancer and diabetes research. When it opened in 1974 it was Scotland's largest, and one of the biggest teaching hospitals in Europe. It had 800 beds and extensive research facilities, with over 1,000 rooms in its laboratories block.

Unlike most hospitals of the day, which housed wards in multi-storey blocks, Ninewells comprised a group of low-level buildings for easy access. The innovative design, by architects Robert Matthew Johnson-Marshall and engineers Arup, involved 28,000 drawings and a large-scale model. Over £50,000 was spent on mock-ups so that certain key areas of the project, such as operating theatres, could be tested.

The hospital's position on the side of a hill allowed separate vehicle access for deliveries, ambulances and visitors. The sloping site, founded on rock, was prone to waterlogging during construction. Most of the buildings were made of concrete and many of the engineers involved had developed their skills on large hydroelectric power schemes. When it was completed in 1974, Ninewells received a special mention at the Concrete Society Awards.

The hospital was designed to cope with expansion: although new buildings have been added, the original buildings remain, demonstrating their durability, adaptability and sustainability.

DAVID KIRKALDY TESTING WORKS

A BREAKTHROUGH IN THE TESTING OF ENGINEERING MATERIALS

LOCATION LONDON, UK
ESTABLISHED 1866

EARLY ENGINEERS HAD little understanding of the critical properties of materials, so their constructions often failed, sometimes catastrophically. To ensure that structures were strong enough, they had to be made bigger and heavier, increasing project costs.

David Kirkaldy pioneered the development of accurate testing machines and standard test methods, allowing the strength of construction materials to be measured and compared. He designed the huge testing machine that still exists in working order at the Kirkaldy Testing Works.

Born in Dundee in 1820, educated at Edinburgh University and then apprenticed at Napier's Vulcan Foundry in Glasgow, Kirkaldy was soon promoted to Chief Draughtsman and Calculator for his expertise in collecting data on Napier ships and his skill as a designer. His exquisite coloured drawings of ocean liners were exhibited at the Paris Exhibition of 1855. Three years later, Napier started building high-pressure marine boilers and engines where the strength-to-weight ratio was crucial. Using a simple single-lever machine that could only test in tension, Kirkaldy spent three years experimenting on the metals that were used, and in 1861, to

great acclaim, he read his paper on the results to the Scottish Shipbuilders Association. Despite this, when the tests were completed, Napier declined to let Kirkaldy continue his work on materials, so he boldly resigned from the company.

By 1864, Kirkaldy had designed his own hydraulic testing machine and, having secured a patent, ordered it from Greenwood and Batley of Leeds. His machine was 15 metres long, operated horizontally and could exert a force of 4300kN. With this machine, he opened the world's first independent testing laboratory in January 1866 in Southwark, London. The celebrated civil engineer Joseph Cubitt quickly commissioned him to test the timber, cement, bricks, granite, wrought iron and cast iron for the new Blackfriars Bridge. Within weeks, steel samples were arriving from as far afield as Krupp of Essen, Germany. Kirkaldy also tested parts of James Eads' 1874 St Louis Bridge over the Mississippi, the links for Joseph Bazalgette's 1887 Hammersmith Bridge and samples recovered from the collapsed Tay Bridge.

Having founded the science of materials testing, he died in 1897, but the Kirkaldy Testing Works continued in business till the 1960s. The old Southwark Street building is now a museum that is open on the first Sunday of the month.

FULTON CENTER
TRANSFORMING NEW YORK'S TRANSPORT LINKS

LOCATION NEW YORK, USA
CONSTRUCTION DATES 2006–14

WHEN NEW YORK'S subways were built in the early 20th century by competing private companies, transfer between lines was not a high priority. Transfers remained inconvenient even when the lines were taken over by the Board of Transportation in 1940.

The Fulton Center is a transport centre connecting 11 subway lines and improving transfers between the subway and other public transport in New York. Collaborating with Grimshaw and James Carpenter Design Associates, Arup developed the centre's 8,500 sq ft feature "Sky Reflector-Net", a stunning domed atrium made of glass and steel featuring 952 uniquely shaped panels to reflect natural light. Contrasting with the modern Fulton Center, the project also involved the restoration of the historic Corbin Building, which called for more than 350 unique terracotta moulds. It is the first Metropolitan Transport Authority (MTA) subway station facility to be awarded LEED (Leadership in Energy and Environmental Design) certification in recognition of its environmentally sustainable construction.

Since opening in 2014, the Fulton Center has become one of the city's busiest interchanges, handling around 300,000 passengers on weekdays. Not only did it win the British Construction Award for Best International Project in 2015 but also – with more than 65,000 sq ft of new retail and commercial space – it is playing a major part in Lower Manhattan's economic recovery. "I'm really a little breathless about it," said Peter S Kalikow, past Chairman of the MTA. "It makes what was a mess into something beautiful."

SACRED HEART CATHEDRAL
AN ICONIC CATHEDRAL IN RURAL KENYA

LOCATION KERICHO, KENYA
CONSTRUCTION DATES 2012–15

DESIGNED BY JOHN McAslan + Partners and Triad Architects to hold 1,500 congregants, the Sacred Heart Cathedral is the second largest cathedral in Kenya. It is located close to the Rift Valley, 250 km west of Nairobi, and fuses historic ecclesiastical with East African references and enjoys magnificent views across the surrounding hills.

The cathedral's giant inclined roof and impressive interior (1,375 square metres) were engineered by Arup to create a naturally ventilated and acoustically moderating environment for all seasons. Care was taken to shape the cathedral's space and express its structure. The stone plinth, simply articulated concrete arch frames and timber-ribbed vaulting are all exposed in a strikingly crafted and honest manner. Credit is due to the local contractor Esteel Construction for achieving such perfect casting of the exposed concrete beams. The building's palette of materials respects the faith and frugality of this rural African context – the practice encouraged local skilled artisan trades and this work is embedded in the final project.

The cathedral sits in a highly seismic zone and complies with comprehensive seismic design standards. In an area with year-round rainfall, the landscaping – with terracing, drainage channels and soakaways – mitigates this problem. It has won numerous awards, including Civic Trust Awards and the Chicago Athenaeum International Architecture Award for 2017, and it was nominated for the 2018 RIBA International Award.

ICE 200
EASTBOURNE PIER
ONE OF THE FINEST PIERS OF THE REALM

LOCATION EASTBOURNE, EAST SUSSEX, UK
CONSTRUCTION DATES 1866–72

SEASIDE PIERS ARE about having fun. Of course, the concept of fun has changed greatly over the years. In the 1870s, when Eastbourne and Hastings piers opened, it was about promenading, catching a steamer, listening to a brass band or simply soaking up the sun in a deckchair. Even in the 1950s it was still possible to see a variety show, watch the death-defying antics of a diver or play bingo for small prizes in the amusement arcade. About the only constant down the years has been the fishing.

From Ryde Pier (1814) on the Isle of Wight onwards, around 100 piers were completed, of which just over half remain. The one in Eastbourne was designed by master pier builder Eugenius Birch (1818–84), the civil engineer responsible for 14 classic Victorian piers, including still-extant examples in Bournemouth, Hastings and Blackpool. It was opened by the Duke of Devonshire, whose family oversaw the transformation of the town into an elegant seaside resort. Like most piers it originally served as a landing stage, but soon started catering for leisure pursuits.

Eastbourne Pier is one of the south coast's finest and retains many of its original features, from the graceful lines of the seaward pavilion right down to the gargoyles with their lions' heads. It is a particularly graceful sight when viewed from Beachy Head. It has frequently been used by film makers and stood in for the Palace Pier for the 2010 remake of the iconic 1947 film *Brighton Rock*. Sadly, however, it was hit by a major fire in 2014, which destroyed the Funtasia amusement arcade (originally the ballroom). The pier was safely evacuated and the fire contained, though access to the pier head became temporarily impossible.

Eastbourne was the first winner of the coveted Pier of the Year in 1997, an award decided by the 900 members of the National Piers Society. That organisation was founded in 1979 to preserve and sustain interest in, and continued enjoyment of, these iconic – and uniquely British – coastal structures, with poet laureate Sir John Betjeman as its first honorary president. Even in these sophisticated days they continue to attract visitors of every age and class. Children in particular still enjoy the thrill of "walking over the waves". Long may they endure!

ICE 200
HYPED
EXPLORING THE HIGH-SPEED HYPERLOOP SYSTEM

LOCATION EDINBURGH, UK
CONSTRUCTION DATES 2015

HYPERLOOP IS A term coined by Elon Musk in 2013 to describe a new transport system that operates using a network of evacuated tubes with capsules travelling at nearly sonic speeds. The tubes provide a low-pressure environment, which – together with passive magnetic levitation and linear electric motor propulsion – reduces drag and allows the pods to efficiently achieve speeds of over 700 mph. Effectively, the system recreates the low-pressure environment found at an altitude of over 40,000 metres, while travelling near the ground. These speeds, along with a high level of integration with on-road autonomous vehicles, could create completely new opportunities for people to work and live, effectively turning entire countries into fully integrated economic regions.

Hyperloop combines many well-developed technologies into a completely new type of system. This presents challenges at a scale not encountered before. Human perception of acceleration puts very strict requirements on minimum curve radii at maximum speeds. The low-pressure environment requires life-support systems to be fitted into vehicles and robust safety procedures to be implemented. The relatively small size of pods and the need for high capacity mean that the latter can only be achieved by fully autonomous control of vehicle

movements. Although all those problems have successfully been resolved in various transportation systems before, the highly advanced specification of the Hyperloop puts them in a completely new perspective.

The University of Edinburgh Hyperloop Team "HypED" is a multidisciplinary collaboration uniting more than 50 students from across various departments of the University of Edinburgh and Heriot-Watt University. Within only 10 months, the team designed and built the UK's first Hyperloop prototype pod – named Poddy McPodface – thanks to a very fast iterative process enabled by leveraging digital methods of design, 3D printing and modern composite materials. The pod was then subjected to scrutiny at SpaceX testing facilities as part of Hyperloop Pod Competition II, in which 24 student teams took part.

Collectively speaking 25 languages, HypED is just one of many young and diverse teams from around the world that were created as a result of incentive competitions and open-source nature of the Hyperloop developments. The collaborative, competition-based effort to develop the Hyperloop technology demonstrates how innovative ways of sourcing ideas and talent can inspire future generations and help to tackle modern challenges.

DOWNLAND GRIDSHELL ROOF
WEAVING TOGETHER THE OLD AND THE NEW

LOCATION NEAR CHICHESTER, UK
CONSTRUCTION DATES 2001–02

THE DOWNLAND GRIDSHELL is a conservation centre and artefact store within the Weald and Downland Open Air Museum. The engineering design was by Buro Happold and, although it is a single, small building in a 40-acre museum, the innovative structure of its roof has led to the building attracting worldwide attention and being awarded numerous design awards.

A gridshell is a shell concentrated into strips – a structure with the shape and strength of a double-curvature shell, but made of a grid instead of a solid surface. The grid can be made of any kind of material – steel, aluminium, even cardboard tubes – but the Downland Gridshell is made of slender oak laths bent into shape. The two-way spanning structure, which provides a clear column-free interior space, is made from a series of long, straight pieces of wood that can be laid out flat and then manipulated into a complex doubly curved surface.

The construction method had previously been established in the Mannheim Garden Festival Gridshell, constructed in 1976 and designed by Frei Otto with Arup engineers. The Downland Gridshell was one of the first buildings to be designed in accordance with the new timber Eurocode and was the first timber gridshell in Britain. It was built with "green" oak, which is fresh, undried timber. Significant defects were cut out in an optimisation process of finger jointing. There are approximately 10,000 finger joints and – as green oak is difficult to join – care, skill and modern technology was needed to successfully produce the strips of oak, up to 50 metres long, that were needed for the structure. Through rotation of the nodes and the flexibility of the timber, the gridshell technique allowed a flat grid of simple components to be lowered into its finished shape.

The design and construction combine advanced engineering and analysis with traditional carpentry skills, an appropriate combination for a structure exhibited within a museum of great buildings of the past. Having won multiple awards – including the RIBA Regional Architecture Award 2002 and the British Construction Industry Award 2002 – the Downland Gridshell set a precedent for the design and construction of the roof of the Savill Building in Windsor Great Park, which applies the timber gridshell method on a larger scale.

BRITISH AIRWAYS i360

A SPACE-AGE LANDMARK OVERLOOKING BRIGHTON BEACH

LOCATION BRIGHTON, UK
CONSTRUCTION DATES 2014–16

WHEN THE WEST Pier closed in 1975, Brighton lost one of its great tourist attractions. The West Pier Trust was set up in 1978 with a view to restoring it and, in 1982, it became the first pier to be Grade I listed. A Heritage Lottery Fund Award was granted and the restoration was about to begin when, in 2003, the pier was destroyed in two arson attacks. The remaining cast-iron skeleton has since become a popular landmark.

Following the success of the London Eye, its architects – Marks Barfield – were approached by many towns wanting a wheel. In many cases, the Eye's design model wasn't viable due to the land and visitor numbers required. In Brighton's case, this led to the development of the i360, a vertical equivalent with a large circular viewing platform holding up to 200 guests and room for a visitor centre at the base.

The people of Brighton were consulted and it was one of the few major planning applications to receive support from the public, businesses, English Heritage and conservation groups. It even achieved unanimous cross-party support from the planning committee. Work was due to begin in 2008 but, due to a dip in the economy, it did not begin at the shore end of the pier until 2014 and the British Airways i360 opened on 4 August 2016.

The work was carried out by the team of companies responsible for the London Eye, including chief engineer John Roberts of Jacobs, which was responsible for engineering design and project management. The tower was built from cylindrical steel sections, nicknamed "tin cans". At 162 metres in height and just 3.9 metres in diameter, it is one of the slenderest towers in the world. Replica West Pier toll booths were constructed on either side as a ticket office and tea room.

The building is designed with sustainability in mind. The observation pod uses very little power, and as it descends it creates around half the energy required for it to be raised again. The West Pier Trust hopes that the success of the British Airways i360 will help it to raise funds towards eventually building a new pier. The project won the Judges' Special Award at the British Construction Industry Awards 2017.

ICE 200

CANARY WHARF REDEVELOPMENT

URBAN REGENERATION AT ITS GRANDEST

LOCATION ISLE OF DOGS, LONDON, UK
DATES 1988–

ONE OF THE largest urban regeneration projects in Europe, the redevelopment of the Isle of Dogs is an ongoing success story, transforming the once defunct docks into a financial and business hub and, more recently, a desirable residential area.

The engineering marvel that was the West India Dock system was constructed in the early 19th century by canal and dock engineer William Jessop on behalf of the West India Dock Company, by creating three parallel docks (one being the City Canal) that cut across the northern tip of the Isle of Dogs peninsula. They provided a safe, enclosed and modern way of unloading and storing goods, cutting the waiting time for ships to be unloaded from months to a handful of days.

In 1868, the docks were expanded by the L-shaped Millwall docks and a passage linking the two systems. The area also became a centre of associated industries and shipbuilding. Isambard Kingdom Brunel's *Great Eastern* was built by J Scott Russell & Co and launched at Millwall, with the site still partly visible today.

The shift to containerisation in the 1960s moved London's main port further out into the Thames Estuary at Tilbury in Essex. The Isle of Dogs and the surrounding area fell into decline, resulting in high unemployment and dereliction, and the docks officially closed in 1981. That same year, the Docklands Development Corporation was set up by Environment Secretary Michael Heseltine. It declared the area an Enterprise Zone, offering incentives to attract businesses and developers through public and private investment. Initial take up was slow (the first investor group, Olympia & York, went bankrupt in 1992) and there was opposition from locals, who feared the rising cost of housing due to gentrification.

However, construction began in 1988 and, two years later, the pyramid-topped One Canada Square was completed. At 244 metres it was Britain's tallest building (until overtaken by The Shard, 20 years later). By 2005, 24 large office buildings, from 10 to 50 storeys, were constructed, attracting the likes of HSBC, Citigroup, Credit Suisse and Reuters. A boom in residential skyscrapers has expanded the development zone further south.

New transport infrastructure was critical to linking the area to central London. The 1987 Docklands Light Railway, built by Mowlem, initially provided 15-minute shuttles to the City, but was later expanded to east and south London, connecting with Stratford International and City Airport. The airport, developed by Mowlem along the King George V Dock, offers short-haul flights to major UK cities and Europe's financial centres. The 1999 Jubilee Line underground extension links to Westminster, while the upcoming Elizabeth Line will link Canary Wharf to Heathrow. The submerged station built into West India dock – with its roof garden and translucent ceiling constructed from timber and air-filled pillows – resembles a moored spaceship.

Amid the glistening glass-and-steel business offices, shopping centres, bars, restaurants, public artworks and parks, the area's maritime past can still be glimpsed. The Sea Scouts practise manoeuvres in the docks on a Saturday morning. There is a row of early-19th-century warehouses that now houses apartments, restaurants and the Museum of London Docklands. You can often see the masts of a visiting tall ship reflected in the glass of surrounding office buildings, lending the area a unique character – one where the past meets the future.

ICE 200
EMIRATES STADIUM

ARSENAL FC'S 60,000-SEATER HOME

LOCATION LONDON, UK
CONSTRUCTION DATES 2004–06

ARSENAL FC HAVE long been one of England's biggest football clubs – only Manchester United and Liverpool can rival them in success, history or international fan base. However, as top-flight clubs converted to all-seater stadia in the 1990s, the capacity of Arsenal's historic home in Highbury, North London, had reduced from its historic peak of 73,000 to less than 38,000. With rivals inhabiting stadia with nearly double this capacity, Arsenal clearly needed a much bigger home ground.

The club wanted to remain in Islington, their home since moving from Woolwich in 1913, so a new site was uncovered on a nearby industrial estate. Designed by engineers Buro Happold & Arcadis and architects HOK Sport, and built by Sir Robert McAlpine, the stadium is an outstanding example of how a large project can be completed on time and within budget. The timing was crucial as failure to deliver would have resulted in the club having to play at Highbury for another season, which would have affected plans to redevelop the old stadium as housing. Work began in February 2004, and the stadium was completed in July 2006, ready for the start of the 2006/07 season.

McAlpine had to remove 25,000 cubic metres of contaminated soil and debris from the Ashburton Grove site before construction could begin. Considerably lighter than comparable stadia, the elegant steelwork structure was designed for ease of construction, saving time and cost. The 27,000 square metre roof is supported by four tubular triangular steel trusses. The two larger trusses each span 204 metres and weigh 720 tonnes, and the two smaller trusses span 100 metres. Highly efficient

structural design is at this project's heart, providing excellent views for all 60,000 spectators while keeping within challenging height constraints imposed by the local authority.

The sloping roof maximises sunlight and also helps reduce shadowing on the pitch, which can hamper television coverage. As the site is in a confined area, surrounded on two sides by railways, the stadium was designed as an oval to make the best use of the site and to maximise the distance from nearby housing. There are seating and hospitality boxes on four tiers, while smooth cladding underneath the upper tiers gives an uncluttered appearance and helps reflect sound, building atmosphere in the seating below. High-spec corporate entertainment boxes and meeting spaces in the building provide conference and meeting facilities to provide additional revenue streams on non-match days.

The redevelopment project also included a new access road, two bridges over the railway, an office building, a residential building and a new state-of-the-art waste and recycling centre to replace the old inefficient facility demolished to build the stadium. The Emirates Stadium project has also benefited the local community. Over 2,600 new jobs were created and £2.2 million worth of supply and construction contracts were awarded to local companies. The scheme also delivered 2,000 new homes, as well as new open spaces, which have improved the local area.

The stadium won the British Construction Industry Award for Major Projects 2007, the CIBSE Major Project of the Year 2007 and three London Planning Awards: two in 2006 and one in 2012.

TATE MODERN

AN ICONIC INDUSTRIAL BUILDING, BRILLIANTLY REPURPOSED

LOCATION LONDON, UK

CONSTRUCTION DATES 1947–63; CONVERTED 1995–2000

TATE MODERN IS an excellent example of the adaptive reuse of an industrial building, Bankside Power Station, designed by Sir Giles Gilbert Scott. The building was built in two stages between 1947 and 1963, enabling the existing power station to continue working while its replacement was built. It is a 200-metre steel-framed, brick-clad building with a central chimney standing 99 metres tall.

When the power station closed in 1981, the building was at risk of being demolished by developers until it was chosen as the home of the new Tate Modern in 1994. Herzog and de Meuron won the international competition to become the architects for the new gallery. Arup was engineering consultant and Carillion the contractor. The huge machinery was removed and the building stripped back to the original steel structure and brickwork. Construction was completed in January 2000, taking five years at a cost of £134 million. At 35 metres high and 152 metres long, the Turbine Hall became a dramatic entrance hall and the Boiler House evolved into the galleries.

It was described by *American Society of Civil Engineers* magazine as: "A unique and iconic structure that confirms London's place as one of the world's leading art capitals." The gallery received 5.25 million visitors in its first year, more than the three other Tate galleries combined. The conversion won the first British Construction Industry Prime Minister's Award in 2001.

JODRELL BANK OBSERVATORY

HOUSING THE WORLD'S THIRD-LARGEST STEERABLE RADIO TELESCOPE

LOCATION LOWER WITHINGTON, CHESHIRE, UK

CONSTRUCTION DATES 1945–57

THE JODRELL BANK Observatory was established in 1945 by the physicist and radio astronomer Sir Bernard Lovell. Part of the University of Manchester's School of Physics and Astronomy, it hosts a number of radio telescopes that detect radio waves emitted by distant planets, stars and galaxies.

Its centrepiece is the Lovell Telescope, one of the world's largest steerable radio telescopes and visible from miles around. Lovell, with Sheffield engineer Henry Charles Husband, designed it and 30 firms were engaged in its construction. Its most striking feature is its huge white paraboloid bowl, 250 ft in diameter, which can be aimed at any part of the sky to gather incoming radio waves. The bowl is formed of a continuously welded membrane of 7,100 steel sheets, 2 mm thick, supported on a steel frame. Radio waves are reflected to an aerial in the focus box at the centre of the bowl. The motor system, which turns the telescope, re-used part of the gun turret mechanisms from the battleships HMS *Revenge* and HMS *Royal Sovereign*, which were being broken up.

Within days of being operational, the telescope tracked the rocket carrying the Soviet Union's Sputnik 1, the world's first artificial satellite. This led to a role in ballistic missile early-warning systems during the 1960s. Today the observatory is an important hub for astronomical research and its Discovery Centre attracts many visitors.

ICE 200

MILLENNIUM DOME

THE WORLD'S LARGEST TENSILE DOME STRUCTURE

LOCATION LONDON, UK
CONSTRUCTION DATES 1997–98

RICHARD ROGERS' REMIT for the Millennium Dome was clear – to design and build a structure to celebrate the new millennium in an area already earmarked for regeneration.

A number of difficult challenges had to be faced: contaminated soil containing mercury and arsenic; a huge tar pit; and the problem of unexploded Second World War bombs. The Blackwall Tunnel also passes underneath the site and its ventilation shaft had to be incorporated into the structure (now visible as a circular hole in the Dome's canopy).

Rogers, a keen astronomer, was inspired by time, space and the symbolism of the calendar – which seemed appropriate for celebrating the new millennium in the land of Greenwich Mean Time, with the prime meridian passing slightly to the west of the building. The diameter of the Millennium Dome is 365 metres, its centre is 52 metres tall and it is supported by 12 masts. The canopy is made of 72 sections based on the lines of latitude and longitude, and there are 24 scalloped edges at its base.

Designed by the engineering consultancy BuroHappold, the Dome is the largest tensile dome structure in the world. Its PTFE-coated glass fibre fabric canopy is supported on a network of 72 km of steel cables suspended from the 100-metre-high masts. The advantage of this type of building is that it creates a large flexible space, ideal for an exhibition but also for reuse afterwards. Interestingly, the entire roof structure weighs less than the air within.

Construction began on 23 June 1997 and was completed a year later. Main contractors were Sir Robert McAlpine and John Laing Construction. Opinion was divided about the New Millennium Experience exhibition, which it initially hosted, but the Dome itself has stood the test of time. In 2005, it was remodelled and became the O2 Arena, a popular concert venue. Those with a head for "urban mountaineering" can even scale it via a specially constructed walkway.

It won the 2000 British Construction Industry Award (in the "major project" category) and a Royal Academy of Engineering MacRobert Award for Innovation, the first construction project to win this prize since the Severn Bridge.

ICE 200
LLOYD'S BUILDING
INSURANCE ENTERS THE HIGH-TECH AGE

LOCATION LONDON, UK
CONSTRUCTION DATES 1978–86

THE LLOYD'S BUILDING, completed in 1985, remains a powerful example of how high-tech architecture and engineering can produce buildings where form and function are deftly combined. Lloyd's of London insurance market had twice outgrown its existing homes in Leadenhall and its management was determined that a new building should have future growth, change and adaptability built-in. A design competition was won by the Richard Rogers Partnership and Ove Arup & Partners team that had just completed the striking Pompidou Centre in Paris with Renzo Piano.

The Lloyd's Building consists of three main towers and three service towers, arranged around a central 60-metre-high atrium. This produced galleries around a central atrium that allowed traders on multiple levels to participate in a single market; with building services located outside to allow continuous trading during maintenance or adaptation. The resulting design allows for the addition or removal of partitions or walls on any floor.

Due to the nature of Lloyd's business, the building and its cooling and ventilation system is designed for high occupancy rates. The building services strategy Arup developed was a fittingly high-tech concept, with tempered air puddling out beneath the desks – wafting up and cooling people, computers and light fittings – before exiting through the open concrete ceiling structure that also provided stabilising thermal mass. The air would then pass back down through the triple glazing to temper the solar energy coming through the glazing in summer and ensure zero heat loss in winter; before being sucked out through external manifolds into the exposed air ducts. This largely self-balancing system could even be remotely monitored and controlled if necessary.

The concrete structure intersperses the complicated pre-cast concrete connecting nodes and floor grillages with simpler in-situ cast columns and beams. The stainless-steel toilet blocks were completely made and fitted out in Asia before being shipped to site and slotted into the external service towers like shipping containers. This was the start of a practice known as "Design for Manufacture and Assembly" or DfMA.

Today, the Lloyd's building sits comfortably among a wide array of modern buildings in the City of London, becoming the youngest building ever to gain Grade I listing in 2011.

ICE 200
DITHERINGTON FLAX MILL
THE GRANDPARENT OF ALL SKYSCRAPERS

LOCATION SHREWSBURY, SHROPSHIRE, UK
CONSTRUCTION DATES 1796–97

IT'S ONLY AS tall as a latter-day five-storey building, but this Grade I-listed structure is very much the grandparent of the modern skyscraper. When it was constructed more than 220 years ago, the Ditherington Flax Mill was the first cast-iron-framed building in the world. In the intervening two centuries, it has undergone dramatic changes because of the industries that have used it.

The building was commissioned by Leeds-based flax merchant and manufacturer John Marshall, along with brothers Thomas and Benjamin Benyon. After experiencing a devastating fire in 1796 at their timber-floored spinning mill in Water Lane, Leeds, they purchased a seven-acre site in Ditherington, on the outskirts of Shrewsbury. This time, instead of timber, they made what was then a radical and fire-proof choice of building material – cast iron – hiring engineer/architect Charles Bage because of his understanding of iron's structural properties. The project cost only £17,000 – less than £2 million in today's money.

This part of Shropshire was not traditionally associated with the textile industry, but it proved a wise choice. Ditherington was not only on the

turnpike route from Shrewsbury to Whitchurch and Market Drayton, but it was also constructed next to the proposed route of the Shrewsbury Canal. Opening in January 1797, the canal allowed coal to be unloaded directly into the boiler house of the spinning mill.

The flax industry declined in the 1870s and the mill closed in 1886. It was bought in 1897 by William Jones (Maltsters) Ltd and converted into a maltings. This saw the addition of new buildings to the site, including the kiln, and the blocking up of the majority of flax-mill-phase windows – providing the required conditions for the germination of barley.

The Ditherington Flax Mill first became a listed building in 1953, because it displayed "technological innovation or virtuosity", as an exceptionally early survivor from the first generation of steam-powered textile mills. It is now deemed of national and international importance and, in 2005, the complex was taken over by Historic England, which, in partnership with Shropshire Council and the Friends of the Flaxmill Maltings, is leading a project team to secure the future of the spinning mill to bring it back into productive use.

DRUK PADMA KARPO SCHOOL

DELIVERING ECO-FRIENDLY SOLUTIONS TO A REMOTE LOCATION

LOCATION LADAKH, JAMMU AND KASHMIR, INDIA
DATES 1998–

AT AN ALTITUDE of 3,500 metres and accessible for just six months of the year, the Leh Valley in Ladakh, India is about as remote a location as it gets – a fact that only makes the construction of the award-winning Druk Padma Karpo School all the more impressive.

The people of Ladakh wanted a school that would help maintain their rich cultural traditions, based on Tibetan Buddhism, while equipping their children for life in the 21st century. To this end, the school has dormitories that enable pupils from remote areas to attend and, as a not-for-profit institution, it receives no direct public funding but relies on donations and sponsorship instead.

Ladakh is an area that boasts few resources and extreme temperatures. Designed by architects and engineers from Arup, the Druk Padma Karpo School is built of locally available material and uses a number of sustainable design elements to reduce its environmental impact, including ventilation and solar heating. The residential blocks face south and use heat-absorbing Trombe walls that capture and store solar heat, which is then released overnight providing comfortable dormitories.

Water is scarce in Ladakh and the school's gravity-feed water system pumps snow melt water to reservoirs at the top of the site for drinking and irrigation. The school is also in an earthquake zone and the buildings use timber frames to resist damage from ground motions. The school survived a devastating mudslide in 2010 and continues to develop.

NEW ENGINEERING CONTRACT

EASY-TO-UNDERSTAND CONTRACTS TO PROTECT ALL PARTIES

LOCATION LONDON, UK
ESTABLISHED 1993

"IT IS RIGHT to say that the NEC [New Engineering Contract] suite of contracts has been one of the central key enablers," said Ken Owen, Commercial Director for the CLM, the delivery partner for the Olympic Delivery Authority. "Such performance has resulted in over £600 million of public money being saved without missing one key schedule completion and handover date. NEC is not just a contract, it is a way of project managing a complete project like this."

All engineering projects require a number of contracts or agreements. ICE has published Conditions of Contract since 1945, with the seventh and final edition appearing in 2001. In 1986, ICE commissioned Martin Barnes to lead a team to draft an innovative contractual approach aimed at encouraging good project management and avoiding costly disputes. It was launched in 1993 and steadily grew in popularity. A fourth edition was published in 2017.

NEC is a suite of contracts suitable for managing a project from start to finish. There are versions applying to all the partners involved, from project managers and designers to sub-contractors and suppliers. The contracts are written in plain English with a straightforward structure that is easily understood. The NEC has been used on major projects worldwide such as Heathrow Terminal 5, Delhi Airport and the 2012 London Olympic Parks.

JEWEL CHANGI AIRPORT

MORE THAN A FLIGHT OF THE IMAGINATION

LOCATION SINGAPORE
CONSTRUCTION DATES 2014–

SINGAPORE CHANGI AIRPORT is the major civil airport for Singapore and one of the largest transport hubs in south east Asia. It handles 62 million passengers per annum, with four terminals, Terminal 4 opening in 2017, with a fifth due in the late 2020s. It has won the Skytrax World's Best Airport six times consecutively.

Currently under construction is Jewel Changi Airport (Jewel), scheduled to open in 2019. Jewel is a combination of nature, leisure, shopping and dining opportunities, hotel accommodation and airport facilities. It was conceived by architect Moshe Safdie, inspired by Singapore's reputation as a city in a garden. Safdie's design is intent on integrating nature into the urban landscape.

Jewel's distinctive glass and steel facade itself is an impressive feat of engineering design by BuroHappold. Made up of more than 9,000 pieces of specially manufactured glass, close to 18,000 pieces of steel beams and over 6,000 steel nodes, the installation of the facade is highly complex due in part to the sheer number of components, as well as the custom-made glass panels and steel nodes. The roof facade alone weighs 3,500 tonnes and spans an area 200 metres long and 150 metres wide. For visitors to enjoy a column-free environment without visual obstruction, a support system comprising a ring beam and 14 tree-like columns circling the edge of the roof was designed. These 12-metre tall columns prop up the entire roof facade, suspending the cantilevered roof 37 metres above ground.

Behind this huge glass facade, Jewel has three elements. The Forest Valley is a vast five-storey garden boasting the country's largest indoor-plant collection where visitors will be able to hike through in an air-conditioned environment. On the top level will be Canopy Park – a huge indoor play space featuring nets for bouncing and walking on; giant slides that double up as sculptures; and a hedge maze and a mirror maze. The Rain Vortex will be the world's tallest indoor waterfall, which will cascade down through the centre from a height of 40 metres.

Linked to Terminals 1, 2 and 3, Jewel is set to be a destination in its own right, and a place where inspirational engineering and architecture combine to create a new airport experience where Singapore meets the world – an insight perhaps into the future of airports.

A DIVERSE PORTFOLIO

NAME JACOBS
HEADQUARTERS DALLAS, TEXAS, USA
WEBSITE WWW.JACOBS.COM

CONVINCING A CLIENT that a "no-build" option may be the most effective solution to their challenge is not an approach traditionally associated with the world of engineering and construction (E&C). But Jacobs is much more than a traditional E&C provider.

"It's about doing the right thing for our clients, employees, communities and supply chains – which often means taking an unconventional approach and finding a better way," explains Donald Morrison, Jacobs Buildings and Infrastructure Europe Senior Vice President and General Manager. "We're looking to create the type of company and ethos that doesn't yet exist, and that will involve disrupting the usual way of doing things."

As a global technical professional services leader, Jacobs is a unique force across the sectors it serves, drawing on a 125-year heritage in the UK to deliver complex, sustainable projects and programmes focusing on critical issues such as access to clean air and safe water, civil and national security, and safeguarding mobility. The one-person engineering consultancy launched by Joe Jacobs in California in 1947 is now a company with 15,000 employees in Europe (including 10,000 in the UK), and a global staff of 77,000 in more than 40 countries.

With that growth comes incredible diversity of staff and solutions. Jacobs has played a lead role in programmes ranging from the Panama Canal expansion to the planned refurbishment of the Palace of Westminster, and Transport Scotland's Queensferry Crossing. Its experience and expertise is not confined to this planet; the company is NASA's largest non-OEM (original equipment manufacturer)

services provider, working on everything from design and build to launch and maintenance, including ongoing support for the Space Launch System and Orion deep-space exploration programme.

Jacobs' success across divergent projects is built on a diversity of skills, knowledge and experience. The company's UK Graduate Development Programme, now in its 25th year (Morrison was one of the first), continues to grow year on year and currently has more than 800 graduates completing the programme. At any one time Jacobs is also training more than 170 UK apprentices. Alongside entrants from traditional civil engineering backgrounds, Jacobs also recruits professionals as diverse as animators, data analysts, aquatic ecologists, hydrogeologists and economists.

SUCCESS THROUGH DIVERSITY

Morrison believes such diversity is essential for the future. "In our sector, there's too much inevitability about how people approach things, and that won't deliver the best results," he says. "If we've got a water engineering challenge, we're much more likely to come up with a number of different innovative solutions from a diverse room of people with different backgrounds and perspectives: a water engineer alongside a transport planner, a geographer or a digital specialist."

Last year's acquisition of the global professional services company CH2M – heralded by Jacobs as the "dawn of a new era, where we create a more connected, more sustainable world" – has broadened and deepened the company's capability. But Jacobs' heritage and pedigree – which date back to the 1800s and include firms like

Previous pages
Panama Canal
Expansion Programme
for the Panama Canal
Authority (left) and
Thames Tideway Tunnel
(right)

Opposite
Transport Scotland's
Queensferry Crossing

Below
Experiential
development
opportunities for a team
of Jacobs graduates

Allott and Lomax, Sir Alexander Gibb and Babtie – will continue to play a crucial role in that new era.

The company recently announced a joint venture with Saudi Aramco to deliver professional programme and construction management services for social infrastructure projects throughout the Middle East and North Africa. Jacobs' long history of working in the region can be traced back to founder Joe Jacobs, the Brooklyn-born son of Lebanese parents. "There was a strong affinity with the region," says Morrison, "and it was Joe Jacobs who first took the company into the Middle East market."

That recognition of heritage and pedigree, combined with a focus on disruptive innovation, could also enable Jacobs to reinforce the UK's position at the cutting edge of connectivity and sustainable development. "One of my aims is to encourage the belief that the UK is still a leading engineering nation, and we can play a crucial role in that," adds Morrison. "At Jacobs, we've got passionate people with diversity of perspective delivering incredible projects that have a really great impact. They are solving some of the most critical issues of our time, and focusing on doing the right thing and finding better ways for our communities, clients and supply chain."

ICONIC CROSSING

That passion, commitment and innovation has never been more evident than in Transport Scotland's £1.3 billion investment in Queensferry Crossing, the iconic project upgrading the vital link between Edinburgh and Fife. Jacobs was lead partner in the Jacobs Arup Joint Venture which set out to improve traffic flow, traffic safety, air quality and accessibility. The project saw the first implementation in Scotland of Intelligent Transport Systems (ITS), used to control variable speed limits and manage bus lanes.

Working closely with Transport Scotland and the contractor, the joint venture's strategy made best use of the existing bridge and infrastructure as well as new technology and thoughtful procurement processes. Combined, these initiatives resulted in an overall saving of more than £1 billion on the original construction estimate in 2009 of up to £2.3 billion. Engagement with the wider community has been a hallmark of the project, including constructing the Contact and Education Centre, which has already helped achieve outreach to more than 25,000 school pupils during construction. The joint venture delivered more than 1.9 million work-hours involving over 1,700 staff globally; 15,000 people worked on the site, and local firms were awarded sub-contracts worth more than £350 million.

The joint venture placed great emphasis on people development. For example, Jacobs Project Manager Jennifer Bullingham, who joined the company in 2005 and, after graduating as a civil engineer, became part of the Jacobs Arup team in 2012. "The experience I gained allowed me to fully appreciate all aspects of contract, quality, and health and safety compliance, as well as working collaboratively with the contractor, designer and Transport Scotland," says Bullingham, who achieved chartered civil engineer status in 2013. "I was seconded to Shanghai to monitor fabrication of the 122 steel deck segments for the crossing. On my return, I was appointed senior site engineer, monitoring the north approach viaduct assembly and launch works; the successful completion was a proud moment."

Safety has also been at the forefront of the project, as David Climie, Transport Scotland Project Director, explains: "The 'BeyondZero' approach from Jacobs has been used as the foundation for the overall safety strategy. The contractors took a lot of elements from BeyondZero, and the project ended up with an extremely good safety approach because of that."

PROTECTING THE THAMES

Like Bullingham, Fiona Keenaghan is part of Jacobs' staff-development programme, and is now in the fifth year of a civil engineering apprenticeship with the company. A member of Jacobs' major programmes team, and now working in high-speed rail, Keenaghan spent the last four and a half years in the engineering delivery team on the 25 km Thames Tideway Tunnel, one of the world's largest wastewater programmes, designed to alleviate chronic overflows of London's Victorian sewerage system. Once completed, it will be Europe's deepest continuous tunnel, intercepting the sewage that floods into the river and providing London with a system fit for the next 100 years.

More than 200 Jacobs staff work on the £4.2 billion programme, embedded alongside client Tideway. "Being at the forefront of one of Europe's largest infrastructure projects so early in my career is incredible," says Keenaghan, who was the Science, Technology, Engineering and Mathematics (STEM) Network Inspirational Apprentice of the Year in 2014. "When this project is finished I will be proud to say: 'I was part of that'. I doubt I would have got the opportunity to work on such an innovative project anywhere else."

A SUSTAINABLE TRANSFORMATION

While the Thames Tideway project will create an underground legacy, few projects have so dramatically transformed the city above ground as the London 2012 Olympic and Paralympic Games. CH2M (now Jacobs) played a key role, as one of three companies programme-managing the design and construction of venues and infrastructure.

The challenge was to transform a derelict area into a remarkable sporting venue, delivering sustainability and environmental excellence as well as accessibility, employment and skills development. The £6.7 billion programme required careful management of schedules, budgets and construction progress. The result was a programme completed a year ahead of the games, and £1 billion under budget. It delivered 30 sustainable venues subsequently relocated or redeveloped for enduring uses, with the rate of interest to the British government exceeding £14 billion.

During the process, more than 10,000 workers were involved on-site, and 1.4 million square metres of contaminated soil was excavated and cleaned. The development of the Olympic Park set new standards in recycling and reusing waste materials; it was also widely known as the safest and most sustainable Olympic Games in history.

POWER FOR THE PEOPLE

It's not only the scale and impact of projects that sets Jacobs apart: so too does its range of services. Jacobs provides engineering and environmental support – including development and planning, site surveys and project management – for Horizon Nuclear Power's proposed Wylfa Newydd nuclear power station in North Wales. Horizon plans to provide at least 5,400 megawatts of new power-station capacity through its sites at Anglesey and Oldbury, enough to power 10 million UK homes. The proposed development at Wylfa Newydd will require up to 9,000 workers during peak construction and create up to 850 permanent jobs during operation, the majority of which will be held by people living on Anglesey.

The project requires a rigorous planning application called a Development Consent Order (DCO) setting out the effects of the development to be submitted to the government's Planning Inspectorate. Jacobs has been working alongside Horizon to undertake a full environmental impact assessment for the project's construction, operation and decommissioning, covering wide-ranging effects on the environment and

people, including bat-roosts, the potential impact of flooding and the Welsh language. Jacobs' team of project managers, environmental specialists and engineers helped Horizon to draw out the mutual benefits for the local community and the project.

Jacobs also introduced "lean production" techniques from the manufacturing industry to ensure the efficient delivery of the DCO submission. Rob Bromley, the project manager who led Jacobs' environmental team for Wylfa Newydd, says: "Our team analysed all options meticulously at every stage, tackling the scale of the challenges with a depth of experience and breadth of expertise across all environmental disciplines, from marine ecology to landscape and visual, socio-economics to health impacts."

ON THE ROAD TO SUCCESS

Transport is another specialist sector for Jacobs, and, once again, the approach is about much more than designing roads and bridges. "We're working with clients globally to deliver innovative approaches to assessing route options, covering economic, social and environmental impact using cutting-edge tools and methods," says David Riley, Jacobs Executive Director of Operations. "The analysis goes beyond traditional appraisals to look at material impacts on biodiversity, journey quality, stress, social connectivity and distributional impacts. This provides a more robust evidence base for evaluating route options while also supporting long-term transformational growth."

Jacobs is playing a lead role in several major Highways England projects including the Regional Investment Programme, the Smart Motorways Programme and the Lower Thames Crossing. The company is developing solutions for improving the transport network north-west of Manchester, as part of the Manchester North-West Quadrant (MNWQ). Highways England's Strategic Road Network forms part of a key east–west connection linking Liverpool and Manchester to Leeds, Sheffield and the north-east of England; the MNWQ project aims to improve the capacity and reliability of road connections, while boosting the regional economy.

THE BIGGER PICTURE

One programme that showcases a commitment to incorporating new, disruptive technology is Jacobs' work to bring intelligent big data to the centre of infrastructure planning as urban populations grow. Working with O2 and AECOM, Jacobs is providing transport demand-related data and information for London using big data analysis technology.

"We're leveraging the power of new technology to help Transport for London (TfL) address the challenges of population growth facing the city," says Morrison. "Using big data is a significant step change; the insight gained will enable TfL to improve urban mobility and make better-informed investment decisions."

The team is fusing anonymised and aggregated mobile network data with a range of complementary data sets to extrapolate trends and provide TfL with a previously unattainable insight into journeys around their network. The work provides TfL with a far more robust matrix – as well as a solution with applicability in cities across the globe. "The project is another example of how we are bringing world-class digital solutions to our customers," adds Morrison.

From the diversity of skills and experience to the innovative approaches and adoption of new technology, Jacobs is building for the future. Its global expertise continues to focus on solving critical issues, matching a commitment to doing the right thing. And by instilling that confidence in all stakeholders – clients, staff and communities – Jacobs is delivering innovative solutions for a more connected, more sustainable world.

DESIGNS ON THE FUTURE

_____

NAME WSP
HEADQUARTERS MONTREAL, CANADA
WEBSITE WWW.WSP.COM

ENGINEERING HAS ALWAYS been about building for what lies ahead, creating lasting legacies either in the form of extraordinary buildings and resilient infrastructure that can stand for centuries, or by coming up with new ideas and paradigms that allow engineers to tackle a knowable but complex future. WSP is one firm that has embraced these challenges. With more than 500 offices in 40 different countries and origins that go back more than a century (the initials stand for William Sale Partnership, an earlier incarnation), WSP is an international professional services firm, focusing on the built environment. Its Future Ready programme and apprenticeship scheme illustrate two of the ways it is anticipating what is yet to come.

"At WSP we do the thinking around the project, the designing and advising," explains Emma Wyatt, UK Director of Marketing and Communication. "But we don't just do engineering. We employ over 40,000 people around the world, including more than 7,500 in the UK, and we are trusted advisers to governments on funding, project management and environmental impact.

"We can give an overview of a project, or we can explore different areas like sustainability relating to climate change, or how best to run a big project in terms of planning, design and stakeholder management, and all associated areas. We provide the full range of consultancy services, right from the earliest stages of a project through to commissioning. Our scope can range from full project management to specific technical expertise in fields such as structural, acoustics, facade, building services, fire, geotechnics and

security, to name a few. We are often brought in to audit other firms' work. We also have a design centre in India that allows us to work around the clock – we can take a brief in the evening and get it back from India by morning. It makes us a 24-hour product offering, which is very helpful when we are under pressure to meet tight deadlines."

READY AND WILLING

A core aspect to WSP's offering is its Future Ready programme, which anticipates developing trends in climate, society, technology and resources with a view to creating intelligent, sustainable and adaptable infrastructure and buildings. The firm believes that this creative thinking is at the heart of what differentiates WSP from its competitors, and has made it an integral part of its planning programme, impacting every area of its business.

WSP's Future Ready policy encourages its consultants to think about changing demographics and climate, asking them to build for an older population, or to think about ways to support the hotter, windier, wetter cities that will be created by climate change. It can involve a mind-boggling range of situations, such as the way road tunnel safety needs to be adapted for driverless, battery-powered cars, or whether solar panels can be built into the surface of new roads.

David Symons is a global leader of WSP's Future Ready programme. He explains that, while many engineering companies have foresight programmes, WSP is unique in taking that thought leadership out of small specialist teams and placing it across the entire company. "Our aim is that we

give our staff a clear and practical view of what the future will bring," says Symons. "It's a key part of setting us apart from the competition."

WSP ensures that Future Ready thinking is part of its strategy and design when advising all clients. This can cover many areas – from large infrastructure projects to single buildings; from international firms to boutique companies – but it always centres on the idea that things are built to last and therefore need to be adaptable. To take two examples, a skyscraper has never been dismantled yet the electrical systems have an anticipated life of 25 years; a railway line may take 25 years to build and be in use for a further 100. Given these long-term and sometimes conflicting time frames, Future Ready ensures that WSP's consultants will anticipate the changes that will inevitably result.

Since unveiling Future Ready, WSP has accumulated a bank of case studies both large and small. Among its bigger projects are the UK's HighSpeed2 and California's High-Speed Rail, for which WSP has been asked to consider how rail use will change over time. This can include anything from developing new materials for embankments that effectively combat the effects of climate change on coastal areas, to debating whether to use wider gauge rails in California to "anticipate the ever-growing size of the average American bottom" (in the latter instance, they decided against). At the other end of the scale, WSP has

worked with whisky distilleries in the Scottish Highlands to explore whether Scotland will still grow barley in 20 years, and whether there will be enough water in the Spey to power a distillery. If you enjoy a single malt 25 years from now, you may wish to raise a toast to WSP.

Symons explains that the solutions do not necessarily have to be expensive – some problems can be solved by simply using larger expansion joints – but they do require engineers to build in flexibility and to support clients' awareness of the issue. "This is a long-term programme and it's about working with clients and helping them understand this," says Symons. "We are also challenging our consultants to not simply follow the same code they used last time. It's about positioning our design to be at the heart of solving these big issues and that's a new role. We're giving our incredibly talented people the chance to create something compelling and exciting that will be around for 100 years."

With a global reach, WSP is able to draw on best practice from all over the world as it looks to tailor solutions for specific circumstances, whether that is infrastructure, buildings, demographics or the need for increased flexibility in retail, in each case adapting to changing technology or the way people access services. Symons is enthusiastic about the potential, seeing WSP's Future Ready work as being at the leading edge of intelligent engineering. "It is all about inspiration, ambition

Left
WSP has worked with
the Highways Agency on
improving the M25 and
the Dartford Crossing

and challenge," he says. "It's much less about business process and building management systems. We are trying to challenge and inspire our design teams and give them purpose, put them at the centre of the project and encourage them to use their brilliance to do things differently."

THE TALENT OF TOMORROW

For WSP, it's crucial that this style of thinking is built into the next generation of professionals, which is why it is incorporated into the skills agenda of WSP's apprenticeship programme. Once again, the belief in the value of apprenticeships demonstrates the way WSP is placing the future at the centre of its offerings. As Emily Mahoney, the company's UK Learning and Development Specialist, says: "We see the potential of young people and believe fresh perspectives bring great ideas and new energy. We know they are the future of the industry, so we want to attract, engage and retain the best professionals in our fields of expertise. They are the pipeline of talent and they will help us deliver our growth plans."

As Mahoney explains, WSP saw that there were renewed opportunities as well as a need for apprenticeships in light of a growing skills shortage following government changes and ever more costly university tuition fees. As a result, the company elected to increase its UK apprenticeship numbers from 40 to nearer 100. These apprentices will be given a permanent position, with all related benefits and a salary, enabling them to gain work experience while also training at college or university. They have access to a mentor, as well as a dedicated learning and development team, and somebody to provide pastoral care. Moreover, WSP offers apprenticeships from BTEC Level 3 to degree level, with a structured training scheme mapped to the UK Engineering Council UK-SPEC competencies.

Above all, WSP teaches apprentices how to think innovatively. "We want them to think outside the box and challenge current ideas," says Mahoney, explaining that the apprentices are trained in such a way that the Future Ready programme underpins everything they do so it becomes second nature. "We have an internal corporate training scheme that unites all the technical disciplines and teaches teamwork, project management and presentation skills. Each part of the business has a technical training scheme to bolster what they learn at college and university, some of which will cross over into different areas."

WSP offers apprenticeships in most technical areas and is also focussed on improving diversity in the industry, as well as the image of apprenticeships among people who may not recognise their value. In this, as with so much else, WSP is facing the future with the ambition, intelligence and confidence that have sustained centuries of transformative and pioneering British engineering.

BUILT TO LAST

NAME OPUS INTERNATIONAL CONSULTANTS (UK) LTD
HEADQUARTERS BRISTOL, UK
WEBSITE WWW.OPUSINTERNATIONAL.CO.UK

"ENGINEERING IS NOT just about steel, concrete and tarmacadam," says Huw Edwards, Managing Director of Opus International Consultants (UK) Ltd. "It's about creating the environment in which we live. It is rewarding because, when you look out of a window, everything you see has been engineered."

Opus International Consultants was acquired by WSP in November 2017 but has its roots in a company that was founded in New Zealand more than a century ago. It is a global infrastructure and services company that has operated in Britain for 30 years and offers fully integrated asset development and management services at all phases of a project's life cycle: from conception, planning, design, procurement, construction and commissioning through to operation, maintenance, rehabilitation and upgrading.

For Edwards, what sets the company apart is its holistic approach and an overarching desire to create things that will matter to future generations. This means integrating engineering, behavioural science and big data with an understanding of physical infrastructure and the natural environment. At the heart of this is the need to identify how people will interact with a piece of infrastructure and the dedication to refine the design accordingly. In Britain this means designing road and rail systems to drive economies; buildings for growing cities; and water systems to sustain people and industries.

One standout example of this attitude to project design is its extensive work on the £60 million final phase of the Noah's Ark Children's Hospital for Wales in Cardiff. There, Opus provided and supervised geotechnical, civil and structural design during the construction of the six-storey building. The overall design, which contributed towards the project winning Constructing Excellence in Wales Project of the Year, prioritised clinical efficiencies over traditional design and now provides a state-of-the-art healthcare facility for the children of South Wales.

Opus's technical expertise was critical in its work on the design and construction of stations to house the new, faster and larger Tamar-class lifeboat. One of the most challenging of these was RNLI Porthdinllaen in North Wales, where the building needed to both harmonise with the outstanding natural beauty of the surrounding area and provide a functioning lifeboat station.

To meet all these challenges Opus employs some 500 engineers, designers, planners, researchers and advisors in Britain alone. But the company is part of a global operation of 3,000 staff that represents what Edwards calls "connected expertise" – an agile resource pool to provide seamless global and local resources and expertise.

Opus, which had an annual global turnover of £250 million in 2016, won the coveted Company of the Year award from *New Civil Engineer* in 2016, where it was the only firm to feature in the top of all five categories. It also won the Staff Development and Training Award at the Women in Construction Awards. This was especially gratifying as Opus set up its own Women in Leadership group four years ago to facilitate engagement, networking, mentoring and information sharing.

It's clear that Edwards understands the vision for Opus's future. "It is about increasing our positive social impact while growing the business; so that when future generations look at what we did, they can say we did a great job."

TRACK RECORD

NAME AMEY
LOCATION OXFORD, UK
WEBSITE WWW.AMEY.CO.UK

"WHAT ATTRACTED ME to civil engineering," says Andy Milner, Chief Executive Officer of Amey, "was the harmony between people's ingenuity and the natural environment. We need to make sure we have effective, modern amenities that enable the UK to flourish while keeping people safe and healthy."

As a leading consultant supplying infrastructure support services both at home and internationally, Amey is engaged in a whole swath of engineering activities: from frontline services like waste management in the City of London to high-end civil engineering for Network Rail. With 19,000 employees and more than 320 contracts, Amey is one of the largest and most diverse engineering consultants and public service providers in the UK.

The company has evolved through numerous stages of development since it started life as a quarrying firm in 1921 under William Amey. One of the changes that distinguished it most from its rivals was the acquisition in 2006 of design-and-build consultancy Owen Williams, most famous for building highways like the M1. This added greatly to Amey's breadth of capability, adding a professional services capability to its traditional aggregates business.

"Our strength lies in our understanding of the whole asset-management process," says Milner, "and our ability to deliver a seamless, integrated service to our clients. Because we ensure that our solutions are developed and delivered with long-term maintenance and delivery in mind, we're able to maximise the whole-life value of infrastructure assets."

The company prides itself on creating safer, smarter and sustainable places to live, work

and travel. It does this by designing, building, maintaining, and investing in the UK's services and infrastructure across engineering, facilities management, utilities, transport, environmental services, defence and justice.

A CENTURY OF COLLABORATION

Amey has been engaged in projects that affect people's lives on a daily basis for almost 100 years. During the Second World War it was building vital RAF bases. Fast-forward to the present day and its major projects include a contract to manage and maintain two iconic river crossings in the east of Scotland. From June 2015, Amey has managed and maintained the Forth Road Bridge and the Queensferry Crossing (currently under construction), as well as the associated approach roads.

One crucial aspect of these was the repair to faulty steelwork that meant the Forth Road Bridge had to be closed from December 2015. Thanks to the company's collaborative approach, the bridge was reopened to 90 per cent of traffic ahead of schedule later that month, generating tremendous goodwill from stakeholders and members of the public.

Amey was engaged in another time-critical project when the Hammersmith flyover was closed in December 2011 after structural assessments identified serious defects in the post-tensioning system. In partnership with Transport for London, Amey devised a new system that could be retrofitted to the structure yet still work in conjunction with the existing system. It also meant that the flyover returned to full load capacity within five months: traffic was kept flowing while vital maintenance was carried out, allowing it to perform

as a key artery on the 2012 Olympic route network. Milner describes how this collaborative approach involves working in close partnership with network owners, engineering contractors and specialist service and technology providers to identify new solutions that deliver long-term value.

A good example is Amey's partnership with Network Rail on the Northern alliance, which involves replacing switchings and crossings on a 125 mph section of the East Coast Main Line (ECML) in very short time slots. Traditionally, speed restrictions are put in place to help the ballast to settle safely under normal rail traffic. In this case, the Northern alliance team used a combination of advanced engineering techniques to ensure that the ballast was compacted within a weekend of works, eliminating the settling period and enabling Amey to hand the line back to ECML on time.

This contributed to Amey winning Transport Supplier of the Year at the North of England Transport Awards 2017. The award recognises outstanding contributions made by a supplier of equipment and services to the rail, light rail, bus and roads sectors of a given region.

Amey is also particularly proud of winning the Institution of Civil Engineers' inaugural People's Choice Award in 2016, since this is decided by the very people who use a civil engineering project. The company's reopening of the Forth Road Bridge was chosen as the project of the year, ahead of the 11 other schemes shortlisted from across the country.

GROWING SUCCESS

Such an impressive performance has translated into strong financial success for the Amey. In its latest financial year the company made an operating profit before exceptional items of £102.1 million on total revenue of £2.2 billion. At the heart of these achievements are the 19,000 people that Amey employs. "People are at the heart of everything we do," says Milner. "Putting people first is one of our core values." The company is currently making an determined effort to meet its target of reducing harm and injuries at work to zero.

Amey has committed to hiring over 1,000 apprentices in four years, on contracts ranging from highways maintenance, business administration and arboriculture to design, transport planning, logistics and IT. In 2016 it was included in the National Apprenticeship Service's list of top 100 employers for the third year running. It also liaises with the armed services to bring ex-servicemen and women into the organisation.

As the company looks forward to its centenary in 2021, it intends to redouble its efforts towards meeting the ever-growing and increasingly complex infrastructure and engineering needs of societies in the UK and around the world. "We want to celebrate the successes of the past," says Milner, "but also to rebase what success looks like in the future. In particular that means taking on board the challenge and opportunities from the demands that citizens now have for infrastructure. They're so much higher than they were a hundred years ago."

ATOMIC MASS

NAME ATOMIC WEAPONS ESTABLISHMENT (AWE)
LOCATION ALDERMASTON, BERKSHIRE, UK
WEBSITE WWW.AWE.CO.UK

ATOMIC WEAPONS ESTABLISHMENT (AWE) is a manufacturing and technology company, staffed by around 5,500 scientists, engineers and technologists. Its role is to manufacture and maintain the UK's nuclear warheads, and it forms part of the UK's national nuclear security capability. It enables the Ministry of Defence to provide Britain's nuclear deterrent, Trident.

To support this, AWE has an extensive and unique programme of infrastructure projects. "It's a really exciting programme," says AWE's Director Infrastructure Project Delivery Alison Atkinson. "There are very few places in the UK where there is this amount of investment in such diverse infrastructure." Atkinson, a chartered civil engineer has worked at AWE since 2005, is the Director responsible for delivering all capital projects. "Our portfolio ranges from small, half-a-million-pound projects right up to unique, critical, first-of-a-kind new nuclear builds in excess of £1 billion."

These are projects that contribute to developing the UK's capability in nuclear builds. One of AWE's current projects is the Orion laser facility. It is used to research high-energy density phenomena, and can replicate conditions found at the centre of the sun. "Our research in Orion is performed in partnership with academia," says Atkinson. "We outreach to UK universities including Imperial College, Heriot-Watt and Manchester. It's a phenomenal partnership."

During Atkinson's time at AWE, she has seen it shift from a programme of maintenance of the existing weapon system to an output-focused organisation using its nuclear skills to support UK national security and prosperity, and transforming the way it does business. "We continue to challenge ourselves," she says. "The impact of modern technology has really caused us to think and embrace the developments we can, recognising the serious security responsibilities we have around our data and information. We constantly think about how we can reinvent the way we work. We recognise that, by working and thinking differently, great ideas are generated, with innovative solutions driving better business performance. So it's about puncturing traditional myths. We have a proud 60-year history in delivering extraordinary solutions for the UK's defence: in the next 60 years we must deliver again."

CIVIC ENGINEERING

NAME CIVIC ENGINEERS
HEADQUARTERS MANCHESTER, UK
WEBSITE WWW.CIVICENGINEERS.COM

ASK STEPHEN O'MALLEY, founding director of Civic Engineers, what projects he finds the most enticing and he will talk about those that bring innovative ideas to the urban environment. "We want to find those organisations, institutions or authorities that are prepared to break from convention, explore different ideas and recognise that there are better ways of doing things," he says.

Founded by O'Malley and co-director Julian Broster in 2009, the name of the company is no accident. Harking back to Britain's rich history of civil engineering, in particular the pioneering work of the Victorian municipal engineers, one of Civic Engineers' foremost principles is understanding how towns and cities function and how buildings, structures and public spaces work within them.

"I don't know what happened," says O'Malley, "but engineers and engineering as a profession started to become increasingly siloed. It started to lose that composite view of the world. And we'd like to bring some of that back. We like to think that the real value in engineering is when you consider these problems as a whole, not just through what might be a car movement exercise or a drainage exercise, but how it relates to the physical and social geography of a place."

Having expanded from its bases in Manchester and London to Leeds and, most recently, Glasgow, and grown to 80 staff, Civic Engineers encapsulates its vision in a simple statement: "To be at the forefront of engineering design, creating inspirational structures and places that have a positive impact on the environment and enable people to lead healthier and happier lives."

This ethos can be seen in such transformative projects as the regeneration of the Park Hill estate in Sheffield, the "Avenues" initiative in Glasgow city centre and public realm improvements in Goose Green, Altrincham (pictured, above). The last of these has led to 90 new jobs, 24 new businesses and £30-£40 million of private-sector investment. "The perception and experience of the town is quite different from what it was before," says O'Malley. For Civic Engineers it's not just about a building, public space or road system, it's about transforming a city, improving residents' quality of life and ensuring the long-term commercial viability of the community: sustainable engineering.

FLOW PROGRESS

NAME WESSEX WATER
LOCATION BATH, SOMERSET, UK
WEBSITE WWW.WESSEXWATER.CO.UK

"I'VE WORKED IN slums in Africa," says Drummond Modley, Programme Manager at Wessex Water, "and I know what it is to have no running water."

Unlike most of us, Modley doesn't take tap water – its quality, quantity and reliability of supply – for granted. He joined Wessex Water 20 years ago and is celebrating the launch of the Wessex Water supply grid, a £228 million scheme to improve drinking water supplies across the West Country. He has managed the project from its inception in 2010, and is passionate about its potential to transform the water market. "From a legacy point of view," he says, "it's one of the most important pieces of civil engineering since Brunel."

The Wessex Water supply grid is an infrastructure upgrade comprising 200 km of new pipeline, 24 pumping stations and 12 reservoirs, integrating areas of variable supply via "optimisation" software. "Its central monitoring and control fundamentally changes how a water company works," says Modley. "It's one of the first applications in the UK water industry."

The system can allow for times and areas of high water demand and even reverse the flow of water. But what does mechanisation mean for the firm's

2,290 staff? "It's not about having fewer staff, it's about working differently," says Modley. "Even with autopilot you need someone to fly the plane if it goes wrong. But automation brings huge benefits." In the past, if a plant failed on a Friday night it meant emergency measures, overtime and weekend working. Under the new system, software recognises the problem automatically and redirects flow, so customers stay connected.

Modley is hot on cooperating with other water utilities and committed to principles like sustainability. "It's our duty as engineers to encourage trust in local people," he says. "With an integrated grid, you use existing resources more effectively. We haven't had to build a single new source of water to meet future supply requirements." Britain's other suppliers are taking note. And while Modley sees pan-regional cooperation as the future in this country, he believes Wessex Water's innovations have global scope.

"Water supply has immense power to benefit societies," he says "One billion people live without running water and this technology has the power to help. In 50 to 100 years, who knows how many more might be served?"

ROCK STARS

NAME GEOTECHNICAL CONSULTING GROUP
HEADQUARTERS LONDON, UK
WEBSITE WWW.GCG.CO.UK

THE EXPERTS AT Geotechnical Consulting Group (GCG) provide high-end knowledge and experience. It's a resource they offer those seeking pioneering solutions to problems related to geology and soil and rock mechanics. GCG is a consultancy run by a group of leading engineers who pool their knowledge and experience of working with foundations, deep excavations, slopes, embankments and tunnels. As well as taking its expertise to projects around the world, GCG has been involved in iconic projects near its headquarters in London, including the construction of the Eurostar terminal at Waterloo, the Jubilee Line extension and Crossrail.

"The ethos of the company is bringing cutting-edge research to engineering problems," says Dr Chris Menkiti, one of 10 senior partners at GCG. "So we exist at the boundary between research and industry. We work with several leading universities and attempt to bring the new research into practice as soon as practicable." The company began in 1983 in South Kensington and is still there, maintaining strong links with nearby Imperial College as well as with other leading global universities. As such, it can call

on experts such as Professor Lord Mair, co-founder of GCG and one of the world's leading experts on geotechnology and underground space engineering.

GCG has also led on the development of compensation grouting: it was the first company in Europe to apply this method of injecting grouting between a tunnel and overlying structures and utilities to control or annul the settlement felt by such surface infrastructure. It is at the forefront of providing technical analysis of soil-structure interaction problems and applied a new variant of the observational method in the Dublin Port Tunnel. This combined detailed geological logging, special testing for ground characterisation, a trial excavation, finite element analysis and close monitoring to minimise costs.

"Contractors tell us the problems they have with a project," says Dr Menkiti, "and we come up with solutions. Because we're consultants we don't introduce these ideas directly; instead, we introduce them into the design and construction process, working with others. We work in projects where the potential impacts can be very serious, so it's very important we get things right."

SHAPING COMMUNITIES

NAME MACE
HEADQUARTERS LONDON, UK
WEBSITE WWW.MACEGROUP.COM

"WE'VE ALWAYS WANTED to challenge convention, to find a better way," says Mark Reynolds, CEO of Mace. "We constantly challenge ourselves to find a different solution to our infrastructure and property challenges." Mace is an international consultancy and construction company that employs 6,000 people, including 4,000 in the UK. It operates in more than 40 countries and has revenues of just under £2 billion.

Many of Mace's accomplishments are world-renowned. They include major projects such as the London Eye, the Shard and the London 2012 Olympics. "Our ethos is to work closely with clients," says Reynolds. "Making sure we work closely with the supply chain and trying to find non-adversarial and more collaborative ways of working. We try to make sure we've got the right concept and the right brief from the outset. It's not just about what you do, it's how you deliver it."

Mace's current projects include Dubai Expo 2020, which will host 250,000 visitors a day, and the UK's "smart motorways" programme, which uses new technology to reduce traffic congestion and improve journeys. Mace is also working on Battersea Power Station, transforming it into a mixed-use development, helping to create over 25,000 jobs.

Mace takes a similar approach to each of these diverse projects. "It's about understanding from the outset what the business case is and what the client's objectives are," says Reynolds. "Then you make sure you work through with the design team and the supply chain to create the best solutions."

Mace's involvement with the London 2012 Olympics and Paralympic Games goes right back to 2003, when it helped prepare the bid. It will continue until legacy projects are completed in 2025.

"We're the only organisation that's been entrusted to deliver the entire programme," says Reynolds. "We got involved in the master plan, and then we secured the role of the delivery partner. Now we are the project partner doing all the legacy transformation work, helping to deliver things like the East Bank – the new culture centre where the London College of Fashion, Sadler's Wells and the new V&A Museum is going. And for us, it's been a brilliant journey."

Mace takes a creative approach to each project and learns from each experience. "There were some fantastic innovations on the Shard," says Reynolds. "How we demolished the building, how we did top-down construction while building the cores, putting cranes on top of the cores. It was a jump-form structure, so we worked closely with the crane company and the concrete company to make sure the jump-form could enable the crane to work without any down-time. Then we pre-assembled the spire on top of the building. Again, that's working closely with the designers and supply chain."

Reynolds is playing a key role in ICE's Project 13, which is looking at new ways of delivering infrastructure. "It's a collaborative approach, focusing on the outcomes, rather than just a commercial transaction," he says. "It's taking a long-term view of things, in order to provide those services. By 2050 75 per cent of the world's population will live in cities. I think ICE does a really good job about how it sees the future and how it can create environments around smart infrastructure, connected cities, better environmental solutions. Social infrastructure as well: good quality homes, hospitals, schools. Ultimately ICE's approach chimes with Mace's ethos: a vision that is about shaping sustainable communities."

ENGINEERING CHANGE

————

NAME ENGINEERING DISCIPLINE, VOCATIONAL TRAINING COUNCIL
HEADQUARTERS HONG KONG
WEBSITE ENGINEERING.VTC.EDU.HK

IT'S NO SECRET these days that industry is increasingly seeking graduates of the STEM subjects, who are in short supply. That need is driving efforts to encourage more young people to pursue these studies at higher education. The Hong Kong Institute of Vocational Education (IVE), a member institute of the Vocational Training Council (VTC) in Hong Kong, offers an Engineering Discipline, with places for more than 14,000 full- and part-time students.

The Engineering Discipline is the largest of the seven academic disciplines run by the IVE and offers a wide spectrum of studies, including construction, electrical and electronic engineering, transportation, mechanical and building services engineering, and transportation. Yet its teachers say that many are still put off by the mistaken impression that these subjects are some of the most challenging in the curriculum.

VTC is working with local secondary schools to promote STEM subjects to the next generation. "There's a myth that students taking science subjects have to be exceptionally intelligent," says Dr Eric Liu, Deputy Executive Director at VTC. "Students now choose the subjects they can get the highest grades in

to secure a place at university, with many bypassing science and maths in favour of non-science subjects." To address this, the VTC has established VTC STEM Education Centres in three of the IVE campuses. The new centres provide a place for students, teachers and secondary school pupils to participate in workshops, collaborate on projects, meet professionals and take part in competitions. Technology-enhanced learning techniques, using tools such as virtual and augmented reality and other e-learning packages, contribute to the innovative educational atmosphere fostered by the centres.

Once enrolled, students discover the benefits of vocational and professional education and training (VPET) that places an emphasis on practical skills and industry-based projects. "Our school has close ties with industry," says Dr Liu, "and we leverage this to create strong career aspirations for our students. Internships are key, with each student from the Engineering Discipline pursuing at least a three-month placement. This helps them build an understanding of their chosen field, and many of those doing an internship are welcomed back by their employer on completing their studies."

VIVE LA RESOLUTION

NAME HKA
LOCATION LONDON, UK
WEBSITE WWW.HKA.COM

WHEN ANY MAJOR civil infrastructure project is undertaken – from roads, bridges and tunnels to airports, rail systems and power stations – there's a reasonable chance that something will go wrong at some point in its life cycle. That's where HKA comes in. "We specialise in investigating and resolving issues on projects," explains Mark Lench, Partner and Head of Marketing. "Our specialist advisers, consultants and experts determine why things have gone wrong, whether they relate to cost, time or technical matters. We work with clients to develop strategies that deliver the best commercial outcomes."

The firm, which traces its roots back to the '70s, took its current form after uniting six brands into one in 2017, demerging from Hill International. HKA now has offices in 21 countries, helping government agencies, investors, developers, owners, operators, contractors, and specialist manufacturers to anticipate issues, identify risks, or investigate and resolve problems when they come about. Many of the firm's staff hold both engineering and legal qualifications. HKA's knowledge and experience is funnelled into the company's CRUX research programme that offers

valuable insight into the true complexity of disputes that arise on major capital projects. Resolving disputes requires forensic analysis, providing the opportunity to examine the complex web of issues impacting the operations of project stakeholders. "At the beginning of any project, we offer advice on risks that the client might encounter," says Lench. "If disputes arise, we have the expertise to assist and help resolve them."

HKA has managed and resolved claims and disputes on projects spanning all seven continents, including the Panama Canal Expansion, the Marmaray Project, the Channel Tunnel and the Halley VI British Antarctic Research Station. Lench believes it is the only firm offering this service with this degree of specialisation and multi-disciplinary expertise. "Our knowledge and experience extends across the entire project life cycle," he says, "from risk advisory at the front end through to commercial, contractual, cost and planning consultancy and expert delay, quantum and technical expertise in support of dispute resolution, litigation and arbitration. That makes us the world's leading construction claims and dispute resolution firm."

FROM LOCAL
TO GLOBAL

NAME FLUOR LIMITED
UK HEADQUARTERS FARNBOROUGH, HAMPSHIRE
WEBSITE WWW.FLUOR.COM

BIG INFRASTRUCTURE projects require serious investment and robustly engineered solutions, something Fluor Corporation has offered clients for more than a century since its founding in California in 1912. Now headquartered in Irving, Texas but with a truly global reach, Fluor has bloomed from its beginnings in oil and gas refining to areas including mining, power, advanced manufacturing, heavy civil infrastructure, life sciences and more.

"Our diverse portfolio of industries allows us to operate as a one-stop shop," says Steven Grech, Fluor's Infrastructure Head of Business development for Europe, Africa and the Middle East. "We can provide everything from front-end engineering design (FEED) to delivery to maintaining a customer's asset, be it a mining facility or heavy civils like roads, rail, bridges – all with full system integration."

Grech is based in Farnborough, Hampshire, having last year returned from the US, where Fluor has delivered notable projects including replacement of the eastern section of the iconic San Francisco–Oakland Bay Bridge – the world's largest self-anchored suspension bridge and the largest public infrastructure project in California's history – and Denver's Eagle P3, a $2 billion transit project connecting the airport to the city centre and suburban areas.

Fluor has operated in the UK for more than 60 years, with marquee projects such as the 10-year National Roads Telecommunications Service (NRTS) programme for Highways England (HE). "It was a big step forward for HE to have a systems-integrated programme delivered and maintained under public/private partnership [PPP]," says Grech. "We engineered, installed, operated and maintained all the telecommunication cables and motorway signage to provide motorists with advance-warning information, cameras and telecoms throughout the UK motorway network for the last nine years."

The feedback from HE was overwhelmingly positive and the service (where Fluor achieved 3 million safe working hours without a lost-time accident) was referred back as an example of best practice in system integration for a heavy civil infrastructure programme and associated financing. That bodes well for Fluor's bids on a number of projects around Europe.

Wherever it operates, Fluor seeks partnerships with local contractors to source specialist knowledge and the best possible workforce and skillsets. "Key to every successful penetration into a market is identification of local resources," says Grech. "Before we bid on any job we analyse the market and identify key partners that we can work with successfully."

This helps not only in the construction phase but in the legacy a project leaves behind. "We seek to ensure the footprint we leave is the most environmentally ethical engineering solution possible," he says. "But it isn't just about materials: these projects have significant impacts on local economies, increasing GDP and improving the local workforce for the future." Testament to its efforts in this area, Fluor is the only North American construction and engineering company listed on the Dow Jones Sustainability Index.

With a busy order book from both traditional markets (North America, Europe, Australia) and rapidly developing ones such as India and South America, Fluor's future looks bright. With more than 60,000 personnel and growing across 70 countries, the firm's ability to engineer solutions from concept to delivery provides attractive options for even the most ambitious of infrastructure enterprises.

A WINNING PARTNERSHIP

NAME EDF ENERGY
LOCATION LONDON, UK
WEBSITE WWW.EDFENERGY.COM

IN SLEEPY SOMERSET, Europe's biggest construction project is taking shape. The construction of Hinkley Point C for EDF Energy will deliver two new nuclear reactors, providing low-carbon electricity for around six million homes. These are the UK's first new nuclear power stations in a generation, but they are directly benefiting from a decade of major infrastructure projects.

"As part of our supply chain we are working with five of Britain's biggest contractors," explains David Speight, Head of Construction. "That's a huge amount of shared knowledge and expertise. We have people here with experience of High Speed 1, Crossrail, Heathrow, the Olympics – all the big heavy civil engineering and infrastructure projects that the UK has delivered in the past 15 years. We are benefiting from all that accumulated experience."

The £6 billion programme of civil engineering work has been broken into three packages. A joint venture between Kier and BAM Nuttall is delivering an £800 million programme of work involving site preparation and excavation. BYLOR, a joint venture between Bouygues and Laing O'Rourke, is delivering £4 billion of work on the main structures. And Balfour Beatty

is constructing the primary cooling-intake tunnels, at about £500 million. "With them, we have the expertise to deliver these megaprojects," says Speight. "The joint ventures work together. It's five companies with a shared aim, shared welfare, shared offices and shared lockers."

Around 25,000 jobs will be created over the lifetime of the project, which will be completed by 2026, with the first reactor coming into operation in 2025 and the second arriving the following year. "A thousand apprenticeships will have been created on this project," says Speight. "A big project like this is a great chance to develop apprentices: 250 apprentices have worked on the project so far, with well over 3,000 people working out on site."

Those apprentices will take their skills with them wherever they go. "When completed, these will be two of the most powerful nuclear power stations ever constructed in this country, and also the safest and the cleanest," says Speight. "We want to set new standards, so the men and women who move on to Crossrail 2 and HS2 and other big jobs take with them new standards of delivery and safety."

GOOD SENSE

—————

NAME SIXENSE LIMITED
HEADQUARTERS MAIDSTONE AND LONDON, UK
WEBSITE WWW.SIXENSE-GROUP.COM

"YOUR SIXTH SENSE is all about intuition," says Christophe Bourlart, General Manager at Sixense UK. "It gives you a first glimpse of understanding what the sensors don't always provide. That's why we describe ourselves as 'your sixth sense for risk mitigation', in this world of increasingly complex projects with more and more data to process and analyse in ever shorter timescales." It's a fitting analogy for a company that effectively digitises this notion of intuition, using hi-tech equipment to detect, measure and model structural, geotechnical and environmental behaviour.

Sixense, previously known in the UK as Soldata, was born in 1994 out of the monitoring requirements on the Jubilee Line Extension of the Underground. While it was created to monitor geotechnical risks, it soon added to its portfolio the management of the impact on the environment, such as vibration, noise and dust. Recently, Soldata joined the Sixense worldwide group and it now delivers tailored solutions for the infrastructure's entire life duration from a wide range of expertise, employing around 600 experienced technicians and engineers across 20 countries, including 60 in the UK alone. The firm, which

has a global turnover of €70 million, has played a crucial role in many major UK projects, including tube station upgrades at King's Cross, Tottenham Court Road, Bond Street, Paddington, and London Bridge, and work at Heathrow Airport, The Shard, Thameslink and Crossrail. Sixense was responsible for a third of the monitoring work at Crossrail, demonstrating the benefits of satellite monitoring of tunnelling, and winning a commendation in 2015 for its standards of workplace health. The firm is now working on the Thames Tideway Tunnel. Its environmental division has been appointed as noise, vibration and air-quality specialists to provide comprehensive consultancy and monitoring services for the six main worksites of the project's eastern section.

Sixense provides an integrated approach, assessing elements such as sustainability and resilience over the full cycle of a project, something increasingly required by asset managers. It uses technology and expertise to understand, analyse, anticipate and optimise each clients' investments. "Sixense collects and transforms data into useful information," says Bourlart, "so decisions can be taken by our customers in real time and all along the asset's life cycle."

CITY SLICKERS

NAME CHUN WO CONSTRUCTION HOLDINGS COMPANY. LTD
HEADQUARTERS KOWLOON, HONG KONG, CHINA
WEBSITE WWW.CHUNWO.COM

HONG KONG MIGHT be one of the world's most exhilarating cities, but its stacked-up environment poses huge development and construction challenges. Undertaking recent infrastructure projects on the island, Chun Wo Construction Holdings Company Ltd has had to use both innovation and pragmatism to deal with the challenges thrown up by working so close to the population.

One example of this was the construction of Whampoa station on the city's Mass Transit Railway system, which opened in October 2016 on the Kwun Tong Line Extension. Located in a congested residential and shopping area, the station had to be constructed in the face of heavy live traffic on the roads above it, all the while supporting and maintaining existing city utilities on the site. Key to getting the job done was reducing the noise the construction created, allowing work to continue through the night.

"A noise enclosure of structural steel and acoustic material was erected at the entrance of tunnel," says Assistant General Manager Eric Wu. "The noise level due to the construction plant inside tunnel could be reduced to an acceptable level, and tunnelling works could be operated 24 hours a day." Another major project that posed logistical hurdles was the upgrading works at Stonecutters Island Sewage Treatment Works – specifically in the effluent tunnel and disinfection facilities. The upgrades helped to tackle water pollution caused by the urban development around Victoria Harbour, requiring divers to work underwater with almost zero visibility to divert the live effluent water flow from existing box culverts to the new effluent tunnel.

Safety was paramount, as project manager Desmond Chung explains. "It required moving three concrete panels from the wall of an existing live effluent water open chamber. Diamond wire saw was used. Steel brackets were installed on both side walls of the chamber to prevent the concrete panels from toppling over and causing injury to the divers. After cutting the two vertical sides, the panel was then held by a crane before cutting the bottom side. Divers and workers had to evacuate and stay in the platform above water during all cutting work." These were extreme conditions, but Chun Wo dealt with them without hassle – something that characterises the firm's reputation in Hong Kong and beyond.

RAISING THE LEVEL

NAME UK BIM ALLIANCE
LOCATION LONDON, UK
WEBSITE WWW.UKBIMALLIANCE.ORG

JOHN EYNON HAS no doubt about the potential of digital information and the adoption of building information modelling (BIM) to revolutionise the construction and engineering industry.

"It's about transformation," says Eynon. "For the first time in decades we have a perfect storm of elements coming together – the need for change, the will to change, the technology to make it happen, and the understanding to put everything in place. We have the opportunity to make that transformation stick, to change the industry for the better, forever."

As Engagement Lead of the UK BIM Alliance, Eynon is a passionate advocate for the benefits that BIM can deliver. So too is the UK government which, in its 2011 Construction Strategy, set out its minimum requirement for "fully collaborative 3D BIM (with all project and asset information, documentation and data being electronic)" – known as Level 2 BIM – on all centrally procured public projects from April 2016.

With the government-funded BIM Task Group moving its focus to developing standards and definitions for BIM Level 3 (due to be adopted industry-wide in 2020), the UK BIM Alliance was launched in 2016. The idea is to create an umbrella organisation pulling together everyone across the sector, with the aim of making Level 2 "business as usual". "We've got a number of firms doing exemplary stuff and pushing the boundary of Level 2 BIM," explains Pam Bhandal, Communications Lead. "But there's still a large chunk of the industry who have yet to get their heads round it."

The UK BIM Alliance is keen for more organisations – particularly the Tier 2, 3 and 4 companies and SMEs – to become more involved in the alliance, whether by joining the network, signing up to the newsletter, becoming a patron or starting a project.

"We've been talking about industry change and transformation for many, many years," says Eynon. "While BIM isn't the answer for all issues that our industry faces, it is a powerful catalyst for disruptive change. It can have a positive impact on time, cost and quality metrics, as well as safety, the environment, diversity and inclusion, the skills gap, flexible working, and issues we haven't even recognised yet."

ON COURSE FOR SUCCESS

NAME QUEEN'S UNIVERSITY BELFAST
LOCATION BELFAST, UK
WEBSITE WWW.QUB.AC.UK

FOR ENGINEERING STUDENTS at Queen's University Belfast, gaining an education is as much about the real-world application of knowledge and skills as it is lecture-room learning. The university's Faculty of Engineering and Physical Sciences strives to ensure students have a practical understanding of engineering principles, while also focusing on two further fundamental tenets – inspiring the science, technology, engineering and mathematics (STEM) scholars of tomorrow, and collaborating internationally to create a global outlook.

The faculty comprises six schools, and caters for over 5,000 undergraduates, 600 master's students and 600 postgraduate researchers. The education it delivers is based on three key themes: students *acquire* knowledge on issues such as sustainability, security and health that will enable them to change the world; they *apply* that knowledge through project-based learning and internships; and they *augment* their learning by engaging with industry.

"As a faculty we span a range of sectors – from traditional engineering disciplines to diverse topics such as carbon dating and astrophysics – which impact on lives today and will shape our future," says Professor Mark Price, Pro-Vice-Chancellor for Engineering and Physical Sciences. "We work where industry and research meet, providing the platform for our academics to spin out research into commercial opportunities and engage with industry on cutting-edge research with real-world impact."

In recent years, these projects have included working with the coachbuilder Wrightbus on producing the cleanest hybrid bus technology to power Thomas Heatherwick's London Routemaster; and the pioneering work of the faculty's Institute of Electronics, Communications and Information Technology in developing more secure digital futures in a connected world. One initiative that highlights the faculty's ethos is The Big Bridge Build. This year-long project to create the world's largest Meccano structure was the brainchild of the faculty's civil engineers. Some 11,000 pieces of Meccano were used to construct a 100-ft bridge spanning Belfast's Clarendon Dock, designed and built by faculty students and local school children as part of Queen's programme to encourage more youngsters into careers in STEM. Engineering companies AECOM and McLaughlin & Harvey supported the project, which was officially opened by Meccano's Meccanoid G15KS buildable and programmable robot, and secured a place in *Guinness World Records*.

Queen's University Belfast is a Russell Group institution that is in the top one per cent of global universities, and is ranked by *Times Higher Education* as being in the top 25 most international universities.

Recently, the university affirmed its global outlook by taking the lead in a major collaboration with some of China's top engineering institutions. Queen's will head up a team of six Russell Group universities who will work with nine project partners in China to form the UK–China University Consortium on Engineering Education and Research. This will develop closer engagement and co-operation on postgraduate, higher education and engineering research between the UK and China. It will also have a particular focus on energy and intelligent manufacturing in support of both countries' manufacturing ambitions.

"We've made many great friends in China," says Professor Price, who is leading the partnership for Queen's. "By working together, we're now achieving great things in research and education. We all have outstanding teams and we look forward to becoming even stronger by developing a more co-ordinated and synergised approach to research and teaching. Together, we can tackle the major challenges facing the world and make a difference for everyone. There are exciting times ahead!"

A FLEXIBLE APPROACH

NAME UNIVERSITY OF MANCHESTER
LOCATION MANCHESTER, UK
WEBSITE WWW.SE.MANCHESTER.AC.UK

PROFESSOR MARTIN SCHRÖDER casts his eye over the vast, nascent building site near the heart of the University of Manchester's city-centre campus. Workers in hard hats beaver away on the site of the Manchester Engineering Campus Development (MECD), which currently consists of foundations and a vast hole where the basement will sit. The university recently awarded a £287 million contract for the project and, in 2021, the finished building will welcome the university's engineering disciplines and associated research institutes under one roof.

The development is central to the university's "Campus Masterplan", a ten-year project to create world-class facilities and consolidate the majority of the university's estate onto one main campus. The intention is to create a more compact and coherent infrastructure that reduces the institution's carbon footprint and costs.

MECD will house a broad range of expertise and disciplines, spanning electrical and electronic engineering; mechanical, aerospace and civil engineering; materials; and chemical engineering and analytical sciences – together with the BP International Centre for Advanced Materials and the Dalton Nuclear Institute. It will produce a unique focal point where groundbreaking research sits alongside innovative teaching and new opportunities for learning.

As Vice President and Dean of the Faculty of Science and Engineering, Professor Schröder takes enormous pride in the design and development of this project. A key aspect he wants to see featured in the building is that of flexibility.

"A problem with some offices and laboratories is that they can be fixed spaces defined by bricks and mortar with built-in benching," he explains. "Over time, they can become unfit for purpose

since it is difficult to change configurations in line with the evolution of research and teaching. Eventually working spaces become either too big or too small or are the wrong shape and no longer provide appropriate accommodation for new teams and activities. Sometimes new equipment does not easily fit into the space that is available because the technology has advanced. Therefore, a priority for the design of this building is flexibility in terms of work space. There is some common provision in all of the laboratories, but the infrastructure allows the introduction and removal of services as required."

ENGINEERING CHANGE AND INNOVATION

The development will bring together the university's engineering strengths. Scientists and engineers will work side-by-side, collaborating on projects, but specialisms will not be sacrificed for adaptability.

"There will be bespoke laboratories specifically designed for research in areas such as high-voltage electricity," says Professor Schröder. "And the basement is designed to transmit the very lowest levels of vibration possible, so it can house sensitive microscopes with which to examine materials at the highest possible resolution. Critically important are also the teaching areas that will provide us with versatile and modern facilities, enhancing and maximising the student experience."

The plan is for MECD to host a wide range of flexible, high-specification laboratories and lecture spaces for up to 7,000 students and 1,300 staff. It will incorporate blended learning facilities, workshops and a "maker space" where students will see their engineering creations come to life. This is a building designed to evolve along with the research and teaching that takes place within. Teaching must continue to meet the needs of current and future generations of engineers; a commitment which sits at the heart of the university's efforts to help students along the path from scientific theory to employable engineering practice.

"The biggest revolution will be in teaching," says Professor Schröder. "We need to continue to implement the most innovative methods to deliver teaching to future generations of students. To a certain extent, what and how we teach is predicated on the space in the buildings we have. Once you have a new building that is more efficient and flexible, it becomes easier to innovate, and to introduce exciting changes to our curriculum and the way we deliver it."

FORWARD THINKING

It has been nearly 200 years since the Manchester Mechanics' Institute (MMI) opened its doors. Located in the city where the Industrial Revolution began and the textiles industry was born, the MMI was created to equip Manchester with knowledge of the latest technology and infrastructure. It was here that the study of civil engineering began, pioneered by the likes of William Fairbairn, Richard Roberts and Eaton Hodgkinson.

Two centuries on, multi-disciplinary engineering continues to innovate, providing solutions and technologies for diverse sectors from energy and aerospace to composites and materials, and from environmental policy and robotics to the nuclear industry and transport. It's why the University of Manchester has made it a priority to invest in engineering.

Just across the road from MECD, another building is taking shape. The £235 million Henry Royce Institute is the UK's national centre for research and innovation in advanced materials. Nearby, a significant number of the university's engineering graduates go on to further study at the Alliance Manchester Business School; another building in the midst of an ambitious transformation to provide facilities which match the school's international reputation for excellence.

Next door sits the National Graphene Institute where Professors Sir Andre Geim and Sir Kostya Novoselov continue their Nobel Prize-winning research on graphene. Lightweight, flexible, conductive and many times stronger than steel, graphene is the building block of the future, with potential applications as diverse as desalination of seawater and advanced manufacturing.

"Collaboration and interdisciplinarity are what we do," says Professor Schröder. "Our engineers progress into all different walks of life, from construction and business, to finance and research. By investing in their skills, we are preparing engineers for the many opportunities available to them after university, so they may contribute to society, the economy and the common good."

As he surveys the local architecture, it's clear Professor Schröder is confident that bringing together research, teaching and learning from across the university's large engineering community and co-locating it with the institution's impressive South Campus will lead to a host of exciting new opportunities.

Progress occurs not by accident but by the diligent application of scientific enquiry, in environments that support new ideas, innovation and social responsibility. That is the pledge that MECD, its associated schools and institutes, and the keen scientific minds within, seek to fulfil.

HANDS-ON EDUCATION

NAME KINGSTON UNIVERSITY
LOCATION KINGSTON, SURREY, UK
WEBSITE WWW.KINGSTON.AC.UK

ENSURING THAT STUDENTS "belong", gain a broad knowledge through hands-on experience and become employment-ready is a top priority at Kingston University's Faculty of Science, Engineering and Computing. "We have many first-generation university students and one of the challenges is inspiring them with confidence," says faculty dean Professor Mike Sutcliffe. "We have a strong track record of developing individuals irrespective of their background. There's no doubt about their ability – but they may not have been told before that they can succeed."

To this end, mentoring the yearly intake of around 100 or so undergraduates is vital. Recent graduates are invited to talk to new students about the importance of perseverance – especially when things gets tough. "They know what the course involves," says Professor Sutcliffe, "so they can be honest about how they overcame challenges during the course and grew in confidence. We get new students engaged from the start, to help them feel they belong. Teamwork is imperative, too, rather than them getting lost in a large year group."

Based in south west London, Kingston has a long history of teaching civil engineering. In 1942, the university's predecessor, Kingston Technical College, introduced a full-time diploma enabling servicemen returning from the war to obtain academic qualifications. It also laid the foundations for today's School of Engineering degrees.

The focus is still firmly on engineering graduates gaining a broad knowledge through hands-on experience of real-world problems underpinned by a theoretical understanding of their subject. Employers are directly involved in shaping the curriculum to ensure that it remains relevant. As students finish their final year, they are assessed on their project work by a panel of experts from top industry firms.

Apprenticeships are a crucial part of – and help to strengthen – a curriculum that is taught by professionally qualified academic staff. A number of Kingston students were involved in the development of Heathrow Terminal 5 and also the new Wembley Stadium. Professor Sutcliffe describes this active involvement as invaluable experience that benefits both students and employers. "They make tangible contributions and increase their chance of a good job at the end," he says. "It's like an extended interview."

Kingston ensures that students cover a broad range of subjects, including geotechnics and water engineering, demonstrating its emphasis on obtaining practical experience. For a project on a brownfield site, for example, the undergraduates will examine ground conditions first. Then they will use their findings to determine the "skeleton" of the construction suitable for the site and the best materials to produce it.

"Everything they do has to be commercially viable and practical – and follow green targets," says Professor Sutcliffe. "It's about looking at available resources nearby to minimise the impact on the environment while ensuring that the construction is serviceable and user-friendly. There's no point in a building getting cold in winter and hot in summer."

This innovative approach is also reflected in the structure of its courses. Kingston is developing a Master of Engineering degree, which incorporates a year in industry in a four-year course – the first of its kind in the discipline.

Just as every new building requires solid foundations, so too does the next generation of engineers need a solid practical and academic base. Whatever their background, those graduating from Kingston are assured of a future career that is grounded in success.

COASTAL ENGINEERING

NAME UNIVERSITY OF PLYMOUTH
LOCATION PLYMOUTH, UK
WEBSITE WWW.PLYMOUTH.AC.UK

THE SOUTH WEST of England is famous for its rugged coastline and holiday beaches, but in recent years it has become a hotspot for research and development in marine renewable energy. The University of Plymouth is at the forefront of this development, building on its established reputation in coastal engineering – a specialism within its teaching of civil engineering.

The university's recently launched School of Engineering is home to the Coastal, Ocean and Sediment Transport (COAST) Laboratory. The main facility comprises a unique 35 metre by 16 metre Ocean Wave Basin whose depth is adjustable up to 3 metre by virtue of a moving floor. There are also a smaller and shallower coastal basin, and two wave channels. A specialist technical team supports and manages all experimentation carried out in the facilities.

This state-of-the-art teaching and research facility proves popular with commercial organisations in the assessment of their new marine engineering technologies. The university has been working with developers and research groups from the UK, Europe and across the world. The Plymouth team believe their expertise and laboratory facilities offer the perfect development pathway for wave energy technologies in conjunction with the two nearby field test facilities.

"The aim is to get developers to come to the South West with their prototype design for a wave energy device, which they can evaluate at laboratory scale in COAST," says Professor Deborah Greaves, Head of the School of Engineering. "They can then proceed to carry out subsequent testing, at larger scale in a sheltered field environment at Fabtest in Falmouth Bay, before taking prototype devices to the Wave Hub test site off the North Cornwall coast."

Going forward, there are plans to build a new home for the School of Engineering on campus. "This will provide flexible teaching laboratories and project spaces, linked to adjacent specialist research facilities," says Professor Greaves. "Students will be supported not only by our academics but also by dedicated laboratory instructors and specialist technical teams. This will enable us to identify and build upon synergies in our teaching and research in engineering and across other disciplines. There's always been a strong demand for our engineering graduates, but we see clear opportunities for developing new, exciting degree programmes focused on regional and national needs."

The MSc in Marine Renewable Energy was developed with this philosophy in mind. Students can combine studies of engineering with economics, law and environmental science. "As engineers we are already well down the road of interdisciplinary collaboration, working across engineering and the natural sciences, as well as medicine, arts and the human sciences," says Professor Greaves. The new MSc in Advanced Engineering Design similarly brings together both mechanical and civil engineering across a range of subjects including design practice, modern design tools and advanced technologies.

"We've also worked hard to forge strong links with industry," concludes Professor Greaves. "Our strengths in Coastal Engineering and now Marine Renewable Energy reflect our coastal location and heritage. When employers are looking for graduates with coastal expertise Plymouth is one of the first places they come to. Our plan for the future is to create an environment in which we nurture and inspire the next generation of outstanding engineers that our industries will need in the 21st century."

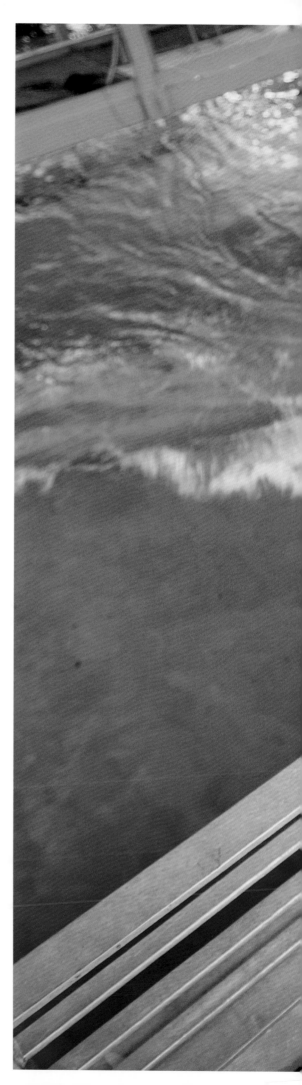

HIGH-SPEED TRAINING

NAME THE NATIONAL COLLEGE FOR HIGH SPEED RAIL
LOCATION BIRMINGHAM AND DONCASTER, UK
WEBSITE WWW.NCHSR.AC.UK

"DEMAND FOR HIGH-SPEED rail professionals is going to go through the roof," says Clair Mowbray, Chief Executive of the National College for High Speed Rail. "We don't currently have a great deal of high-speed rail expertise in this country, and HS2 is going to need 25,000 people working on the project at its peak of construction and delivery."

That's why the college was created, says Mowbray. "We're trying to fill the gaps in UK engineering skills to deliver the next generation of professionals and leaders that the industry desperately needs." The National College for High Speed Rail, which opened in September 2017, is the largest of five national colleges set up by the government to train students in learning world-class skills for the benefit of Britain's emerging growth industries. The 45 staff at its purpose-built campuses in Doncaster and Birmingham provide specialist workshops, digital learning and classroom teaching for the benefit of a growing tranche of learners (set to recruit more than 1,000 learners annually).

The college is working closely with HS2 as it prepares for construction of the new high-speed route, which will run from London to Birmingham and then fork to the north-west (to Manchester) and north-east (to Leeds). Possible future rail projects to complement HS2 are already under consideration, with Northern Powerhouse Rail being a potential future project that will better connect populations living east–west across northern England.

"Birmingham is already seen as the heart of that network," says Mowbray. "HS2 Ltd's headquarters are based here and a fair amount of the project's supply chain is also headquartered in the city. Doncaster offers an exceptionally rich rail heritage, with lots of national and international rail and engineering companies. Both our campuses are rooted in regions that are heavily steeped in the past and future of rail."

Although the college has a definitive title, it has a wide-ranging remit. "We are looking to appeal to a diverse range of people who will be required to do work at different levels of high-speed rail and rail infrastructure more generally," says Mowbray. "The college will serve the needs of both the rail industry and engineering sectors at large as their technology changes and as new, associated industries develop."

A QUALIFIED SUCCESS

NAME NOCN GROUP
LOCATION SHEFFIELD, SOUTH YORKSHIRE, UK
WEBSITE WWW.NOCN.ORG.UK

WITH THE INTRODUCTION of new technical-based T Levels and the continuing development of Trailblazer Apprenticeships, it is clear that vocational training and qualifications in the construction and civil engineering arenas are currently undergoing something of a revolution. Firmly in the vanguard of these changes is the NOCN Group, one of the UK's biggest Ofqual-regulated Awarding Organisations (AOs) in the construction sector.

"Most of the bigger construction companies, contractors, project management and design firms are on board with the changes to apprenticeships, and the introduction of Trailblazers – including the demand for T-Levels and Level 4 and Level 5 apprenticeships," explains Graham Hasting-Evans, Managing Director of the NOCN Group. "We have Laing O'Rourke and Van Elle on our board as major employers, and close links with major companies such as Balfour Beatty. The Trailblazer Apprenticeships are increasingly in demand, not only for civil engineering qualifications but across other engineering disciplines including mechanical and electrical engineering, as well as areas such as building services, maintenance and steel fixing."

Having built a strong reputation as a charitable organisation focused on general skills training, over the past decade NOCN Group has concentrated on specific sectors including construction and engineering. Its acquisition of Cskills from the Construction Industry Training Board (CITB) in 2017 – and with it the transfer of some 4,000 apprentices – took place just as the industry was highly vulnerable to potential skills gaps.

NOCN Group is now the UK's leading end-point assessment organisation (EPAO) for construction apprenticeships, and is a key driver towards achieving the government's targeted three million apprenticeship starts by 2020. However, there is still work to be done. Over the next five years the industry will see an increasing skills gap at the "technician" levels.

"The government's current plans for T-Levels and the fragmented nature of the Trailblazer Apprenticeship Standards won't address this gap," says Hasting-Evans. "We need to develop a clear career pathway for technicians in civil engineering and infrastructure, and push the government to adapt its T-Level and Apprenticeship Standards to match our requirements."

IN THE LOOP

NAME UNIVERSITY OF EDINBURGH
SCHOOL OF ENGINEERING
LOCATION EDINBURGH, SCOTLAND, UK
WEBSITE WWW.ENG.ED.AC.UK

WHEN ENGINEER AND scientist Elon Musk launched his Hyperloop competition, the University of Edinburgh's School of Engineering students rose to the challenge. The task was to help develop futuristic passenger "pods" that travel at 750mph: daunting for experts, let alone beginners. But the Edinburgh team, HYPED, succeeded in being the only British entrant to reach the final rounds.

This achievement demonstrated how the School of Engineering's values of teamwork and broadening outlook, help to create successful innovators. "HYPED is a great example of students seizing the opportunity to widen their horizons and apply their problem-solving skills to a potential game changer," says Professor Hugh McCann, Head of the School of Engineering. "We don't just focus on teaching engineering theory but also on design, and how to find new ways of tackling tasks." Putting creative design at the heart of civil engineering degrees earned the school the prestigious Excellence in Structural Engineering Education Award.

Today's Edinburgh engineering talent is proud to follow in the footsteps of high-achieving alumni, including eminent civil engineer and locomotive builder Robert Stephenson, inventor of the Stirling engine Robert Stirling, Dorothy Buchanan, the first woman member of ICE, and Mary Fergusson, ICE's first female Fellow.

The school is active in seeking gender equality and diversity. Professor Jin Ooi, Head of the Civil Engineering discipline, is delighted to report that 38 per cent of the current civil engineering intake is female, the aim being to reach 50 per cent in the future. The school is partnering with programmes such as "Primary Engineer", which encourages children from a young age from all backgrounds to be inspired into engineering. "There's a false perception that engineering is all hard hats and oily rags," says Professor Ooi. "Today it's increasingly about digital hi-tech and is a creative and stimulating career."

2018 marks 150 years since Queen Victoria conferred the first Regius Chair of Engineering in Britain upon Edinburgh University, an honour that continues to inspire students and staff to aim high. The impact of the school's activity demonstrates its continued commitment to excellence. The school has always looked to the future, as well as encouraging its students to do so. In addition to core courses in the principal disciplines of engineering, the school is set to launch a new MSc aimed at mid-career professionals seeking to acquire skills in leading major programmes, with people aspects to the fore.

"Engineering careers are increasingly complex," says Professor Gordon Masterton, Chair of Future Infrastructure, "with a growing demand for the multi-disciplinary skills required to handle major programmes that affect people's quality of life. Our aim is to teach students not only to design successful engineering solutions but also to acquire the leadership and political skills required to improve society."

The school's impact was recognised in 2015, when its spin-off company Artemis Intelligent Power was presented with the Royal Academy of Engineering MacRobert Award, for innovative digital displacement hydraulics that improve engine efficiency and reduce carbon emissions. The school's BRE Centre of Fire Safety Engineering has established structural fire engineering as a mainstream skill, highly relevant and in demand today for safeguarding citizens – just two examples of how engineering at Edinburgh still leads the way, 150 years on.

ENLIGHTENED ENGINEERS

NAME UNIVERSITY OF ADELAIDE
LOCATION ADELAIDE, SOUTH AUSTRALIA
WEBSITE WWW.ECMS.ADELAIDE.EDU.AU

IT WAS UNIVERSITY of Adelaide lecturer, Sir William Henry Bragg, who first solved the mystery of how crystals are structured. His pioneering work won the Nobel Prize for Physics in 1915 and the technique called X-ray crystallography is still used more than 100 years later. Passionate about education, Bragg also played a role in founding the university's renowned engineering faculty, part of which is now housed at the Braggs Building (pictured, right), named after Sir William and his son Sir William Lawrence Bragg. Today, undergraduates and staff are committed to upholding his values, as well as those of Sir Robert Chapman, the department's first chair.

"Adelaide was one of the early leaders in cutting-edge science, driven by the need to build South Australia," says Professor Martin Lambert, Head of Civil, Environmental and Mining Engineering. "A lot of the best engineering developments came from scientific breakthroughs. Bragg and Chapman had the farsightedness to realise there was a practical application of mechanics to society and infrastructure – a vision we follow to this day."

Following Bragg's early example, the university is now committed to developing new ways of looking inside structures to solve modern problems. In the water industry, for example, leaks and blockages are an expensive hazard. But detecting them – or the likely risk – can be a serious challenge. "Pipes deteriorate at different rates and you don't want to dig up a good one," says Professor Lambert. "Researchers and students have developed mathematical techniques using pressure waves to detect the size and location of defects. Our system lets them determine what needs replacing, rather than spending billions getting rid of ageing pipelines indiscriminately."

Innovative solutions like these attest to the success of the teaching approach at Adelaide. For the students who come to study here from all over the world, the emphasis is on understanding all areas of civil engineering. There are no barriers between disciplines; engineering students are encouraged to embrace new academic fields such as artificial intelligence to tackle real world issues.

It is a fitting tribute to visionaries like Bragg. As Professor Lambert points out, it takes all types of leaders to create the future, from researchers to staff to students. As he knows, real vision does not necessarily require genius – but it does take courage, determination and insight.

FORGING AHEAD

NAME UNIVERSITY AT BUFFALO
LOCATION BUFFALO, NEW YORK, USA
WEBSITE ENGINEERING.BUFFALO.EDU/CIVIL-STRUCTURAL-ENVIRONMENTAL

IT MIGHT BE a stretch to describe engineers as superheroes, but when Professor Joseph Atkinson maintains that communities in every continent rely on engineers to build and maintain their integrity, he's not resorting to hyperbole. "Civil and environmental engineers work at the interface between society and the environment," says Professor Atkinson, Chair of the Department of Civil, Structural and Environmental Engineering at the University at Buffalo (UB). "They develop and maintain infrastructure essential to the safety and prosperity of communities throughout the world."

His department's mission is to provide engineering students with the requisite tools and training to address the changing needs and challenges facing society. This year the department is ranked fifth among engineering schools in the US and 12th worldwide in the Academic Ranking of World Universities (also known as the Shanghai Ranking).

For Professor Atkinson, challenges associated with maintaining societal wellbeing comprise the built environment, transportation infrastructure, water supply and wastewater treatment. The department provides a comprehensive curriculum covering the basic elements of civil and environmental engineering, with both civil and environmental degree paths at undergraduate and graduate levels. From these central building blocks, students can specialise in a variety of areas, including structures and earthquake engineering, transportational systems engineering and geomechanics and geotechnical engineering.

Hands-on experience is also encouraged. Shortly after the Mexico City earthquakes in 2017, a team of UB faculty members, students and alumni visited the area to survey the damage. Multi-hazards research is also conducted at the affiliated Multidisciplinary Center for Earthquake Engineering Research (MCEER) and advance bridge engineering at the Institute of Bridge Engineering.

The department is constantly at the forefront of new ways of learning. Its new Environmental and Water Resources Engineering MS degree, for example, pairs students with academic, governmental and private sector partners to conduct actionable research. "Our programmes provide pathways for students choosing to work in consulting or agency work," says Professor Atkinson, "or to develop their research skills to pursue an academic role."

BUILDING A REVOLUTION

NAME ULSTER UNIVERSITY'S BELFAST SCHOOL OF
ARCHITECTURE AND THE BUILT ENVIRONMENT
LOCATION BELFAST AND JORDANSTOWN, UK
WEBSITE WWW.ULSTER.AC.UK/BUILTENVIRONMENT

"WE'RE CAUSING A revolution from below," says Professor Philip Griffiths, Head of Ulster University's Belfast School of Architecture and the Built Environment. "Traditionally, our sector has produced graduates to do their own particular job in a silo. But today our students are overthrowing old ways of working. We need a more holistic approach. Our aim is to provide a built environment that is safe, environmentally neutral, while considering its economic, cultural and social impact."

The performance gap (the disparity between the energy use predicted in a building's design stage and its actual energy use), along with cost overruns and recent tragedies (most notably the fire at Grenfell Tower in west London) have brought this need for change sharply into focus. Professor Griffiths believes a lack of communication and cooperation between experts has contributed to problems. "Traditionally, we've had a segregated industry," he says. "Building information modelling (BIM) is changing that, and there is a need for the social context to be more fully explored and understood by designers and engineers."

Professor Griffiths' Belfast-based institution meets such challenges head-on. "Our students learn to create spaces that are safe for human habitation, considering the environmental, economic, cultural and social impact," he says. "In the past, it was about building something, getting the money and moving on to the next job. But, at Ulster, we deliver research-formed education, ensuring that our graduates are aware of new developments and challenge traditional thinking and process. They are working to deliver high-quality, economically viable products that are environmentally sound and exceed the client's expectations. We talk about the 'New Built Environment'. It's not about the old siloed ways of doing things, it's about sitting round a table to get the best outcomes."

Ulster University's unique Fire Safety Engineering, Research and Technology Centre (FireSERT) can replicate the effects of a fire in a two-storey building in its laboratory. Its new degree Safety Engineering & Disaster Management is about designing engineering solutions with safety at the forefront. The MSc Fire Safety Engineering programme is recognised internationally for the quality of its graduates. The university's Studies Allied to Built Environment Research centre (SABER), meanwhile, explores aspects such as pavement construction and construction management.

The school brings together disciplines from architecture, real estate and planning to civil engineering, renewable energy and sustainable technologies. It is the largest school in its field in the whole of Ireland, with around 1,400 undergraduates, postgraduates and research students. Moreover, the school has been ranked in the top six for built environment research since 1992 in UK assessments, fifth by the *Sunday Times* for building, and third for real estate.

Industry links and work placements, both home and abroad, are integral to achieving these accolades, enabling the school to stay ahead of the curve. "Students return from these placements invigorated and with a sense of purpose," says Professor Griffiths. "These real-world experiences give students an edge when they enter the workplace. We're providing a professional education for a professional career."

By keeping a finger on the pulse of academic and professional progress, Ulster's Belfast School of Architecture and the Built Environment thoughtfully navigates rapid changes in the industry. Its graduates lead the way, meeting new challenges – and perhaps even revolutionising their sector.

REAL-WORLD LEARNING

NAME UNIVERSITY OF CALGARY
LOCATION CALGARY, CANADA
WEBSITE WWW.SCHULICH.UCALGARY.CA

CIVIL ENGINEERING STUDENTS who embarked on their higher education 50 years ago would scarcely recognise the field today. While the core skills remain – gaining a deeper knowledge of building and structure – today's civil engineering students can also look forward to some fascinating applications of this knowledge.

Three of the faculty members at the University of Calgary's Schulich School of Engineering illustrate this point perfectly. Dr Nigel Shrive – a long-time expert in civil engineering – has spent his career applying structural engineering principles to biological structures. He is perhaps best known for his work on the healing of knee ligaments after injuries. Similarly, Dr Andrew Tay, a Canada Research Chair in Wastewater Engineering, has developed more than 30 treatment processes to achieve cleaner water. The work of Dr Lina Kattan – a recognised expert in intelligent transportation systems – includes understanding and anticipating the impact driverless cars will have on traffic stability and traffic control. Her research is resulting in a body of knowledge that will ultimately save lives, increase road safety and ease traffic congestion.

What these lines of research all have in common is their real-world impact, something the school achieves thanks to the interdisciplinary nature of its work. "There are some interesting opportunities to solve problems, where the solution lies in the intersection of traditional and modern areas of civil engineering," says Schulich School of Engineering Dean Bill Rosehart. "We make sure that an interdisciplinary focus is always at the heart of what we do, from undergraduate right through to research programs. Faculty members from different fields get together on a regular basis, and that can lead to interesting research collaborations."

Civil engineering is a foundational programme at the University of Calgary, one that was established when the university was founded over 50 years ago. Leaving its academic achievements aside, the university also places a significant emphasis on student success – helping them find jobs in an exciting and diverse range of careers, including within biomedical and environmental fields.

"We encourage our students to get an integrated experience at university," says Rosehart. "They're not here to only learn knowledge, they're here to develop as a person and as a thinking, positive contributor to the world."

BREAKING NEW GROUND

NAME CURTIN UNIVERSITY
LOCATION PERTH, AUSTRALIA
WEBSITE WWW.CURTIN.EDU.AU

"WITH CURTIN UNIVERSITY celebrating its 50th anniversary," says Associate Professor Andrew Whyte, Head of the civil engineering department, "we've broadened our global footprint. We have a well established campus in Malaysia, and new campuses in Dubai and Singapore: all part of our international identity."

Associate Professor Whyte's department benefits greatly from its expert international senior faculty. Civil engineering has been a core focus of Curtin University ever since it was founded in 1966. The university's enduring slogan – "Make tomorrow better" – remains reflected in its civil engineering courses, across both undergraduate and postgraduate degree programmes.

Curtin's civil engineering department was ranked above world-class standard in the Australian government's 2015 assessment of Excellence in Research for Australia (ERA). Whyte points out that its home campus location continues to present rich possibilities. "Western Australia is an enormous region, with a very big catchment," he says, "and it's a very exciting part of the world. It might not have the architectural heritage of Europe, but its new build engineering creates super scope for success and opportunities."

At Curtin, the civil engineering programmes actively embrace innovation, as well as traditional research areas. "We've focused on diversifying disciplines," says Whyte. "One of our main focuses is geotechnological. There is huge demand for road and pavement maintenance in Australia. Our material scientists investigate the long history of using waste materials within a new structural context; and we also study water conservation and sustainable systems. We're at the cutting edge with our blast-impact centre, besides our approach to nanotechnology. Civil engineering has traditionally been about big projects. Now we can also delve right into the nanoscale of structural engineering."

Undergraduates and PhD students have access to Curtin's state-of-the-art research facilities, which have been upgraded with funds of over $5 million. These include a 500-tonne-capacity heavy-testing rig nicknamed "Big Blue" ("It can bend or break anything on a huge scale," says Whyte). The school's gravitas stems both from its fresh vision and recognised heritage; as Associate Professor Whyte says, "Our higher degree students become experts in their field." There is a blueprint here for a brilliant future.

SETTING THE STANDARD

NAME GHANA INSTITUTION OF ENGINEERING
HEADQUARTERS ACCRA, GHANA
WEBSITE GHIE.ORG.GH

ENSURING A HIGH-QUALITY and well-regulated engineering industry is indispensable to the transformation of any economy, particularly for a fast-growing emerging market such as Ghana. The Ghana Institution of Engineering (GhIE) has embarked on a mission to ensure that the profession can play its part in meeting these goals.

"We are trying to achieve a very well-regulated industry," says Carlien Bou-Chedid, President of the GhIE. "We have a situation where no one is legally bound to use any particular code or standard, so anyone coming to work in Ghana can more or less do what they like."

In 2015, a new law that passed the regulatory role to a new engineering council became operational. Since then the institution has focused on helping to draft the legislation that will make registration mandatory. At the heart of this is a set of definitions of four classes of professionals: craftsmen, technicians, technologists and engineers. Bou-Chedid and her colleagues are working on the definitions and regulations that she says are necessary to build up a comprehensive picture of the industry. "I don't know of any other country

that has as comprehensive a system," she says. "Other countries have built this up piecemeal, but we have the opportunity to do this together all as one."

The rewards will be huge in terms of the benefits to Ghana as a whole and to the individual users of engineering schemes such as oil, energy, mining and road building projects. The registration system, which will roll out over the coming years, will ensure not only that all people and firms working on projects in an engineering capacity are registered, but also that all the bodies involved in a project can be traced and held accountable. This will help address the current problem that should a project go wrong, it is often hard to identify the people and organisations to hold to account. A good example of this is the construction of new roads, which have not always achieved the lifespan originally promised.

The GhIE celebrates its 50th anniversary this year, just as the Institution of Civil Engineers marks its 200th birthday. It will hold a year-long celebration to mark this milestone with a series of lectures and events. "We hope to gather some oral histories from our older engineers," says Bou-Chedid, "to capture the history of engineering in Ghana and inspire the generations of engineers to come."

APPENDICES

ICE PRESIDENTS

Thomas Telford
March 1820 – September 1834

James Walker
January 1835 – January 1845

Sir John Rennie
January 1845 – January 1848

Joshua Field
January 1848 – December 1849

William Cubitt
December 1849 – December 1851

James Meadows Rendel
December 1851 – December 1853

James Simpson
December 1853 – December 1855

Robert Stephenson
December 1855 – December 1857

Joseph Locke
December 1857 – December 1859

George Parker Bidder
December 1859 – December 1861

John Hawkshaw
December 1861 – December 1863

John Robinson McClean CB
December 1863 – December 1865

John Fowler KCMG
December 1865 – December 1867

Charles Hutton Gregory KCMG
December 1867 – December 1869

Charles Blacker Vignoles
December 1869 – December 1871

Thomas Hawksley
December 1871 – December 1873

Thomas Elliott Harrison
December 1873 – December 1875

George Robert Stephenson
December 1875 – December 1877

John Frederic La Trobe Bateman
December 1877 – December 1879

William Henry Barlow
December 1879 – December 1880

James Abernethy
December 1880 – December 1881

Sir William George Armstrong CB
December 1881 – December 1882

James William Brunlees
December 1882 – December 1883

Sir Joseph William Bazalgette CB
December 1883 – December 1884

Sir Frederick Joseph Bramwell
December 1884 – May 1886

Edward Woods
May 1886 – June 1887

George Barclay Bruce
June 1887 – May 1889

Sir John Coode KCMG
May 1889 – May 1891

George Berkley
May 1891 – May 1892

Harrison Hayter
May 1892 – May 1893

Alfred Giles
May 1893 – May 1894

Sir Robert Rawlinson KCB
May 1894 – May 1895

Sir Benjamin Baker KCMG
May 1895 – June 1896

John Wolfe-Barry CB
June 1896 – April 1898

William Henry Preece CB
April 1898 – November 1899

Sir Douglas Fox
November 1899 – November 1900

James Mansergh
November 1900 – November 1901

Charles Hawksley
November 1901 – November 1902

John Clarke Hawkshaw
November 1902 – November 1903

Sir William Henry White KCB
November 1903 – November 1904

Sir Guilford Lindsey Molesworth KCIE
November 1904 – November 1905

Sir Alexander Richardson Binnie
November 1905 – November 1906

Sir Alexander Blackie William Kennedy
November 1906 – November 1907

Sir William Matthews KCMG
November 1907 – November 1908

James Charles Inglis
November 1908 – November 1910

Alexander Siemens
November 1910 – November 1911

William Cawthorne Unwin
November 1911 – November 1912

Robert Elliott-Cooper
November 1912 – November 1913

Anthony George Lyster
November 1913 – November 1914

Benjamin Hall Blyth
November 1914 – November 1915

Alexander Ross
November 1915 – November 1916

Sir Maurice Fitzmaurice CMG
November 1916 – November 1917

Harry Edward Jones
November 1917 – November 1918

Sir John Audley Frederick Aspinall
November 1918 – November 1919

Sir John Purser Griffith
November 1919 – November 1920

John Alexander Brodie
November 1920 – November 1921

William Barton Worthington
November 1921 – November 1922

William Henry Maw
November 1922 – November 1923

Sir Charles Langbridge Morgan CBE
November 1923 – November 1924

Basil Mott CB
November 1924 – November 1925

Sir William Henry Ellis GBE
November 1925 – November 1926

Frederick Palmer
November 1926 – November 1927

Ernest Frederic Crosbie Trench CBE
November 1927 – November 1928

Sir Brodie Haldane Henderson KCMG, CB
November 1928 – November 1929

William Wylie Grierson CBE
November 1929 – November 1930

Sir George William Humphreys KBE
November 1930 – November 1931

Sir Cyril Reginald Sutton Kirkpatrick
November 1931 – November 1932

Sir Murdoch MacDonald KCMG, CB
November 1932 – November 1933

Sir Henry Percy Maybury GBE, KCMG, CB
November 1933 – November 1934

Sir Richard Augustine Studdert Redmayne KCB
November 1934 – November 1935

John Duncan Watson
November 1935 – November 1936

Brigadier-General Sir Alexander Gibb GBE, CB
November 1936 – November 1937

Sydney Brian Donkin
November 1937 – November 1938

William James Eames Binnie
November 1938 – November 1939

Sir Clement Daniel Maggs Hindley KCIE
November 1939 – November 1940

Sir Leopold Halliday Savile KCB
November 1940 – November 1941

Charles Edward Inglis
November 1941 – November 1942

Sir John Edward Thornycroft KBE
November 1942 – November 1943

David Anderson
November 1943 – November 1944

Francis Ernest Wentworth-Shields
November 1944 – November 1945

Sir Thomas Pierson Frank
November 1945 – November 1946

Sir William Thompson Halcrow
November 1946 – November 1947

Sir Roger Gaskell Hetherington
CB, OBE
November 1947 – November 1948

Sir Jonathan Roberts Davidson CMG
November 1948 – November 1949

Vernon Alec Murray Robertson
CBE, MC
November 1949 – November 1950

William Henry Glanville CBE
November 1950 – November 1951

Allan Stephen Quartermaine CBE, MC
November 1951 – November 1952

Henry Francis Cronin CBE, MC
November 1952 – November 1953

Wilfrid Philip Shepherd-Barron
November 1953 – November 1954

David Mowat Watson
November 1954 – November 1955

William Kelly Wallace CBE
November 1955 – November 1956

Harold John Frederick Gourley
November 1956 – January 1957

Sir Frederick Arthur Whitaker KCB
January 1957 – November 1958

Alfred John Sutton Pippard MBE
November 1958 – November 1959

Arthur Clifford Hartley CBE
November 1959 – February 1960

Sir Herbert John Baptista Manzoni CBE
February 1960 – November 1961

Sir George Matthew McNaughton CB
November 1961 – November 1962

Reginald William Mountain
November 1962 – November 1963

Harold John Boyer Harding
November 1963 – November 1964

Sir Robert Meredydd Wynne-Edwards
CBE, DSO, MC
November 1964 – November 1965

James Arthur Banks CVO, OBE
November 1965 – November 1966

Ralph Freeman CVO, CBE
November 1966 – November 1967

Hubert Shirley-Smith CBE
November 1967 – November 1968

John Holmes Jellett OBE
November 1968 – November 1969

Angus Anderson Fulton CBE
November 1969 – November 1970

Thomas Angus Lyall Paton CMG
November 1970 – November 1971

George Ambler Wilson CBE
November 1971 – November 1972

Roger Le Geyt Hetherington OBE
November 1972 – November 1973

Sir Kirby Laing
November 1973 – November 1974

Sir William Gordon Harris KBE, CB
November 1974 – November 1975

Sir Norman AF Rowntree
November 1975 – November 1976

John Walter Baxter CBE
November 1976 – November 1977

Alan Muir Wood
November 1977 – November 1978

Reginald Charles Coates
November 1978 – November 1979

William George Nicholson Geddes CBE
November 1979 – November 1980

Peter Arthur Cox
November 1980 – November 1981

Ian McDonald Campbell CVO
November 1981 – November 1982

John Vernon Bartlett CBE
November 1982 – November 1983

James Anthony Gaffney
November 1983 – November 1984

John Anthony Derrington
November 1984 – November 1985

Donald Arthur David Reeve CBE
November 1985 – November 1986

David Gwilym Morris Roberts
November 1986 – November 1987

H William A Francis CBE
November 1987 – November 1988

Alastair Craig Paterson CBE
November 1988 – November 1989

Peter Frank Stott CBE
November 1989 – November 1990

Roy Thomas Severn
November 1990 – November 1991

Robin Lee Wilson CBE
November 1991 – November 1992

Michael Norman Tizard Cottell OBE
November 1992 – November 1993

Stuart Norman Mustow
November 1993 – November 1994

Edmund Cadbury Hambly
November 1994 – March 1995

Tony Melville Ridley CBE
March 1995 – November 1996

David Green
November 1996 – November 1997

Sir Alan Cockshaw
November 1997 – November 1998

Roger Norman Sainsbury
November 1998 – November 1999

George Fleming
November 1999 – November 2000

Joseph A Dwyer
November 2000 – November 2001

Mark Whitby
November 2001 – November 2002

Adrian Long
November 2002 – November 2003

Douglas Oakervee OBE
November 2003 – November 2004

Colin John Clinton
November 2004 – November 2005

Gordon Grier Thomson Masterton
November 2005 – November 2006

Quentin John Leiper
November 2006 – November 2007

David Orr
November 2007 – November 2008

Jean Venables OBE
November 2008 – November 2009

Paul William Jowitt
November 2009 – November 2010

Peter George Hansford
November 2010 – November 2011

Richard James Coackley
November 2011 – November 2012

Barry Goldsmith Clarke
November 2012 – November 2013

Geoffrey Howard French
November 2013 – November 2014

David John Balmforth
November 2014 – November 2015

Sir John Armitt CBE
November 2015 – November 2016

Professor Tim Broyd
November 2016 – November 2017

Lord Robert Mair CBE
November 2017 – November 2018

ICE TIMELINE

1818
Eight young engineers, average age 25, meet in Kendal's Coffee House on Fleet Street on 2 January and plan to set up formal society for persons studying civil engineering

1820
The institution moves to its first rented rooms at 15 Buckingham Street, near what is now Charing Cross station. Thomas Telford, the greatest engineer of his day, became ICE's first President on 21 March

1825
Stockton to Darlington railway opened

1826
Menai Bridge opened. Thomas Telford's A5 road completed

1828
Royal Charter granted by King George IV on 3 June

1830
Liverpool and Manchester Railway opened

1833
ICE moves to its own premises at 1 Cannon Row, close to Parliament Square

1837
ICE moves to Great George Street, initially occupying numbers 24–26

1843
Thames Tunnel opened

1849
High Level Bridge opened across the River Tyne

1850
Britannia Bridge opened

1855
Robert Stephenson, father of railways, starts a two-year stint as President of ICE

1863
Metropolitan Railway opened

1864
Clifton Suspension Bridge opened

1866
Bazalgette's London Sewers completed

1867
Student membership added, giving engineering students access to ICE

1876
Swing Bridge opened across the River Tyne

1883
Joseph Bazalgette, engineer of London sewerage system, becomes ICE President

1884
First regional student association opens in Glasgow, followed by one in Birmingham (1886) and Leeds (1894)

1890
Forth Bridge opened

1894
Manchester Ship Canal opened

1895
Benjamin Baker, engineer behind the London underground, Forth Railway Bridge and the Aswan Dam, becomes ICE President

1896
ICE is, by now, an international institution: one fifth of members are based overseas, including 500 in India, 300 in Australia and 200 in South America

1897
ICE introduces its first professional examinations

1913
ICE moves to current headquarters at One Great George Street, one of London's first steel-framed buildings, designed by Glasgow architect James Miller

1925
First female civil engineering student, Helen Grimshaw

1927
First official overseas ICE association opened in Argentina.
First female ICE Member Dorothy (Dot) Buchanan is admitted. She works as a bridge engineer on Sydney Harbour Bridge

1928
Tyne Bridge opened

1936
Sir Alexander Gibb, a fourth-generation civil engineer behind harbour constructions during the First World War and numerous hydro-electric schemes, becomes ICE President

1946
Sir William Halcrow, who helped to design the harbours to support the D-Day landing, made ICE President.
Heathrow Airport opened for civil aviation

1952
Regional ICE office opens in Hong Kong, followed the next year by one in West Africa

1958
Preston Bypass became the UK's first stretch of motorway

1964
Forth Road Bridge opened

1966
Severn Bridge opened.
One of its engineers, bridge expert Sir Ralph Freeman, is made ICE President

1973
Sydney Opera House opened.
The first Bosphorus Bridge opened

1974
Sir William Harris, a former Admiralty civil engineer who helped build the UK motorway network, becomes ICE President

1977
Tunnelling expert Sir Alan Muir Wood, becomes ICE President

1984
Thames Barrier opened

1986
New Delhi's Lotus Temple opened.
M25 motorway opened

1994
Channel Tunnel opened

2000
Blyth Wind Farm opened

2001
Gateshead Millennium Bridge opened

2003
Douglas Oakervee, the engineer behind Hong Kong Airport, HS2 and Crossrail, is elected ICE President

2008
Sutong Bridge opened.
ICE elects its first female President Jean Venables

2012
Queen Elizabeth Olympic Park opened

2013
London Array Wind Farm opened

2016
Teesside Wind Farm opened.
Gotthard Base Tunnel completed

2017
Queensferry Bridge opened.
Professor Lord Mair from the Centre for Smart Infrastructure and Construction is elected ICE President

2018
Northern Spire bridge opened across the River Wear.
Crossrail (the Elizabeth line) to be opened.
ICE now has 90,000 members in more than 150 countries

ICE 2025 VISION

ICE has, and will continue to, transform the lives of millions of people across the globe through the work its members, and those associated with it, do. The vision of the Institution in the 21st century is to continue to transform lives by helping to build a sustainable world.

It will do this by having a vibrant community of passionate people, from an ever-increasing range of backgrounds and experiences, who are working together to look at the global challenges and solve them with innovative, sustainable solutions. The community and the individuals within it will be trusted by society for the quality of their work and the manner in which they do it and that will lead to the Institution being the leader of the global infrastructure debate.

All of this is building upon the past 200 years and seeks to enable the next 200 years of success, impact and delivery of social value. It is an ambitious and bold vision, but when achieved will have shaped the world.

SPECIALIST KNOWLEDGE SOCIETIES

As well as having one of the world's largest civil engineering libraries, and a growing online catalogue of journals, videos and books, the Institution of Civil Engineers works closely with specialist learned societies across the spectrum of engineering. It has very close links with a number of societies that share the same objective; to share knowledge to improve the way society lives and make people aware of the good engineers do across the globe.

BRITISH DAM SOCIETY

The British Dam Society (BDS) exists to advance the education of the public and the profession in technical subjects relating to planning, design, construction, maintenance, operation, safety, environmental and social issues. It is open to anyone wanting to share experience or knowledge of all aspects of dams and reservoirs. BDS outputs include nationwide knowledge meetings and events, a biennial conference, the *Dams and Reservoirs* journal, and various awards and competitions.

BRITISH GEOTECHNICAL ASSOCIATION

The British Geotechnical Association (BGA) is the principal association for geotechnical engineers in the United Kingdom. Starting out as the British Geotechnical Society in 1949 – a then unincorporated association – it became the British Geotechnical Association by statutes adopted in June 2000. BGA organises regular technical discussion meetings about a range of topics relevant to ground engineering. Regular events include the Rankine Lecture, the Touring Lecture (which travels around the UK regions), the Geotechnique Lecture and the Geotechnical Engineering Lecture. BGA works closely with other learned societies and holds regular joint meetings and events with the Engineering Group of the Geological Society, the British Tunnelling Society, the International Geosynthetics Society and the Offshore Engineering Society.

BRITISH HYDROLOGICAL SOCIETY

The British Hydrological Society (BHS) was formed in 1983 in response to a clear need for a new, broad-based national society for the advancement of hydrology. The BHS aims to promote all aspects of hydrology – the scientific study and practical implications of the movement, distribution and quality of freshwater in the environment. The society caters for everyone interested in the inter-disciplinary subject of hydrology. It aims to encourage good practice and scholarship in scientific and applied aspects of hydrology and to foster the involvement of members in national and international activities. Activities include meetings and networking facilities to benefit professionals at all levels.

BRITISH TUNNELLING SOCIETY

Formed in 1971 to provide a forum for meetings and discussion on tunnel-related matters, the British Tunnelling Society (BTS) publishes industry guidelines and codes of practice, and conducts training courses to advance the education of tunnelling professionals. It also actively supports the recruitment of young people to the industry, acknowledges excellence in tunnelling, and sponsors and supports industry conferences. Finally, it advises government and the general public on the tunnelling industry. The BTS has a current membership of 868 individual members and 83 corporate members, making it one of the most vibrant gatherings of professional tunnellers in the world.

CEDA UK

The Central Dredging Association (CEDA) aims to be the independent forum for all stakeholders involved in dredging and the wider associated industries in Europe, Africa and the Middle East. The UK section regularly organises technical evening programmes and site visits. These are excellent opportunities to meet peers, exchange knowledge and get the latest information in an informal and friendly atmosphere. The UK section of CEDA plays an active role in the development of relevant UK legislation.

HAZARDS FORUM

The purpose of the Hazards Forum is to contribute to the ongoing challenge of mitigating and reducing hazards and disasters, both man-made and natural. Founded in 1989 by the four principal engineering institutions (Institution of Civil Engineers, Institution of Mechanical Engineers, Institution of Chemical Engineers and Institution of Engineering and Technology), it now also incorporates members from other engineering bodies, the public sector, the charity sector and industry. The Hazards Forum brings together engineers and other specialists to promote inter-disciplinary sharing and the adoption of good practice in hazard and risk management.

INGENIEURS ET SCIENTIFIQUES DE FRANCE: BRITISH SECTION

The British Section of IESF, a French "learned society" with branches worldwide, is dedicated to linking Anglo-French engineering and science. It welcomes members from a wide range of disciplines and professions, and provides an annual programme of technical evening meetings and social events.

IRRIGATION AND WATER FORUM

The Irrigation and Water Forum (IWF) aims to promote British expertise in the science and art of irrigation, drainage and flood control. The IWF is very active both nationally and internationally and acts as the British section of the International Commission on Irrigation and Drainage (ICID). ICID was established in 1950 as a scientific, technical and voluntary not-for-profit international non-governmental organisation (NGO) with headquarters in New Delhi, India.

OFFSHORE ENGINEERING SOCIETY

The Offshore Engineering Society (OES) acts to promote interest and scholarship in both the scientific and applied aspects of offshore engineering. OES provides networking opportunities for offshore engineers of all disciplines and the dissemination of technical information of offshore engineering through a programme of lectures and other events.

PIANC UK

The International Navigation Association (PIANC) provides access to worldwide trends and challenges in port and waterway development and management. Members of the UK section, including representatives from government, the private sector and individuals, work together with other nations to address a broad range of issues for the advancement of waterborne transportation.

RAILWAY CIVIL ENGINEERS ASSOCIATION

The Railway Civil Engineers Association (RCEA) was founded in 1921 and exists to support the exchange of knowledge and experience between railway civil engineers and to encourage continuing professional development. It promotes the benefits that railway civil engineers bring to our world via a fast, comfortable, safe and sustainable means of transport. As well as a nationwide programme of knowledge and networking events, RCEA works closely with other engineering disciplines through the Railway Engineering Forum and Young Railway Professionals to develop coherent strategies to ensure the future of the UK rail network and to foster training and development of engineers at all levels.

SOCIETY FOR EARTHQUAKE AND CIVIL ENGINEERING DYNAMICS

The Society for Earthquake and Civil Engineering Dynamics (SECED) promotes the study and practice of earthquakes and their related civil engineering implications, including blast, impact and other vibration problems. It is the main forum in the UK for students, academics and practitioners with a keen interest in earthquakes, blast and other dynamic effects to keep abreast of rapid developments in the field. SECED organises regular evening meetings, as well as periodical conferences and courses. SECED is the British branch of the International Association and the European Association of Earthquake Engineering.

TRANSPORT PLANNING SOCIETY

The Transport Planning Society (TPS) exists to facilitate, develop and promote best practice in transport planning and to provide a focus for dialogue between all those engaged in it, whatever their background, interest or other professional affiliation. As well as being influential in setting the transport agenda at a national, regional and local level, TPS provides a structured training programme, assessments and qualifications for the profession that are aimed at supporting the career progression of transport planners.

WIND ENGINEERING SOCIETY

The Wind Engineering Society (WES) exists to promote the advancement and application of knowledge in all aspects of wind engineering. Wind engineering is a wide-ranging, multidisciplinary subject concerned with the effects of wind on the natural and built environment. WES organises regular technical meetings and acts as a representative body for wind engineering in the UK. It is also the national delegate to the International and European Associations for Wind Engineering.

ICE ACKNOWLEDGEMENTS

CONTRIBUTORS

Carol Morgan
Gordon Masterton
Michael Chrimes
Barry Clarke
Richard Adam
Robert McWilliam

Nisarg Acharya
Hussam Uddin Ahmad
Gordon Airey
Lawrance Ajuyah
Sarah Allen
Elira Alushi
Ian Anderson
Richard Anderson
Silvana Andrade
John Andrew
Ewan Angus
Helen Apps
Richard Armstrong
Roderick Baird
Emily Bamber
Anousheh Barbezieux
Henry Bardsley
Melanie Barker
Barry Barton
Peter Bazalgette
Catherine Beardsley
Hannah Besford
Polly Blythe
Ian Boocock
Laura Boyce
Chris Broadbent
Peter Broughton
David Brown
Phil Brown
John Burland
Mark Calvert
Tristram Carfrae
Mervyn Carter
Vicki Chapman
Natalia Chudoba
Rachel Clark
Clive Cockerton
Paul Codd
Kath Coldwell
Ellie Cosgrave
Peter Cross-Rudkin
Stephen Curtis
Bob Daimond
Robert Davies
Roger Davies
Andrew Dawson

David De Haan
Claire Delgal
Ayanangshu Dey
Rebecca Di Corpo
Moira Doherty
Philip Donald
Hamish Douglas
Yuli Doulala-Rigby
Colin Eddie
Graham Edmond
Julia Elton
Gavin English
John Evans
Graeme Falla
Paul Farnell
Cassie Farrar
Bill Fawcett
Tony Fawcett
Shelagh Fleming
Ian Flower
Debra Francis
Lucy Fraser
Ria Gaffney
Alvaro Garcia
Jodie Garner-Jones
Sushma Gaur
Julian Glover
Neil Glover
Rachel Glynn
David Greenfield
Antony Greenwood
Alan Haley
Alexander Hamilton
William Hamilton
Richard Harris
Edward Haynes
Robert Heffernan
Jennifer Henderson
Tim Hill
E J S Hiscocks
Ken Ho
Duncan Holden
Lee Seng Hoor
Taylor Hughes
Elodie Huiban
David Hunter
Alan Hutchison
Ruth Hutchison
Ernest Irwin
Rachel Irwin
Li Ivan
John Ives
Matthew Jarron
Robert Jeans

John Jeffrey
Ian Jenkinson
Charles Jenson
Trevor Jessop
Erica Jones
Stephen Jones
George Kalathil
Jordan Kenny
Mark Knight
Bhavani Krishna
Angelina Lambourn
Stephen Lawrence
Dean Lenton
Raymond HM Leung
Sally Ann Lycett
Ben McAlinden
Christine McAllister
Chris MacDonald
Hugh MacGillivray
Sean Macintosh
Paul Maliphant
Grzegorz Marecki
Michail Mavrommatis
David Meigh
Malith Mendis
John Metcalfe
Grahame Millar
Hui Min
Allan Morgan
Natasha Morgan
Christine Morley
Jenny Munday
Emer Murnaghan
Eulid Ng
Martin Nixon
Dermot O'Dwyer
Amber Olah
David Orr
Liz Paddon
Leslie Pakianathan
James Parry
Charlotte Pascoe
Kendall Paul
Rachel Pether
Rabinder Phull
Ricardo Pittella
Anna Plodowski
William Powles
Jon Prichard
Sandra Purves
Gemma Rathbone
Rebecca Reeves
Jessica Roberts
Frank Robinson

Phil Robinson
Chris Rogers
Leanne Rogers
Keith Rose
Annette Ruehlmann
Shelley Ann Russell
Sach Sandhu
Yogesh Sawdadkar
Ligia Schuurman
Isobel Scott
Lawrence Shackman
Nadia Sheikh
Conor Sheridan
Ben Sherriff
Hannah Shroot
Jane Simpson
Josie Sinden
James Sloan
Lily Smalley
Ben Smith
Sam Smith
William Smith
Stavro Sofios
Tom Sommerfelt
Max Soubain
Scott Steedman
Douglas Strachan
Carly Tait
Chris Talbot
Y G Tan
Elton Cheong-Nam Tang
J Michael Taylor
Sue Threader
Robert Torday
Malcolm Tucker
Andrew Turton
Sandor Vaci
Brendan Van Rooyen
Simon Venn
John Vignoles
Anna Vrede
Chris Waite
Lucy Warren-Meeks
Rob Wassell
Ken Watson
Ian Weir
Richard Wheeldon
Anthony Wills
Tracy Williamson
Barrie Willis
Camilla Wrey
Michael Wright
Nowshard Yehiya
Danielle Young

PHOTOGRAPHY

AECOM
Alamy
Ian Anderson
Apache Corporation
Arup
Babcock
Balfour Beatty
Cath Bowen/Sydney Metro
British Airways i360/Kevin Meredith
British Construction Industry Award
David Brown
BuroHappold
Canary Wharf Group
Christopher Hill Photographic
Chun Wo Construction Holdings
Company Limited
Civil Engineering and Development
Department, Hong Kong SAR
Government
ConocoPhillips
Crossrail
Peter Devlin
Drainage Services Department, the
  Government of the Hong Kong
Eden Project
Esler Crawford Photography
James Ewing
Bill Fawcett
Flickr @robwassell
Friends of Jubilee Pool
Fritzology Photography
Gamuda/ SMART Stormwater
Management and Road Tunnel
Getlink/Channel Tunnel
Getty
Sir Alexander Gibb/Enplan Group
  Consortium
Graeme Peacock Photography
Gujarat International Finance
  Tec-City (GIFT)
Harland and Wolff Heavy
  Industries Ltd
David Head
Historic England Archive
Hufton and Crow for Herzog
Reece Hugill/Canal & River Trust
HYPED
Ian Flower/Engineers for Overseas
Development
ICE Archive
David Iliff
iStock
iStock©Euan Brownlie

Jacobs
Chris James
Jewel Changi Airport
  Development
John Laing and Son Ltd
Julius Berger Nigeria PLC
Kalgoorlie Consolidated Gold
  Mines (KCGM)
Ken Watson
London Array
Manchester Airport
Mecanoo
David Meigh
Meridian Energy (NZ) Ltd
Mike Brookes-Roper
Nick Millson
Jeffrey Milstein
NASA
NI Water
Northern Lighthouse Board/
  Kimberley Fahlen
Olympic Delivery Authority
David Orr
Panama Canal Authority
Roland Reinardy
RNLI/Nathan Williams
Rodoula Gregoriou
Sam Lane Photography
Schulich School of Engineering
Severn Trent Water
Shell UK Limited/Allseas
Siemens Collection, Shannon
  Scheme Postcards
Siemens Gamesa Renewable
  Energy
Skyedge
Eric Soltan/BuroHappold
Southern Water
Edmund Sumner
Tay Road Bridge Joint Board
Tayside Medical History Museum,
University of Dundee Museum
  Services/NHS Tayside
Tensar International Ltd
Thames Water
Tideway
Tony Gee and Partners
University of Calgary
Unsplash
Paul K Veron
Volker Stevin/High Camera Ltd
John Wilkie
www.neildenham.co.uk
www.venturer-cars.com

CREDITS

Artifice Press Limited
298 Regents Park Road
London N3 2SZ
United Kingdom

+44 (0)020 8371 4000
office@artificeonline.com
www.artificeonline.com
www.sjhgroup.com

Chief Executive
Richard Freed
richard.freed@stjamess.org

Publishing Director
Anna Danby
anna@artificeonline.com

Managing Director
Stephen van der Merwe
stephen.vdm@stjamess.org

Sales Director
Richard Golbourne
r.golbourne@stjamess.org

Communications Director
Ben Duffy
ben.duffy@stjamess.org

Head of Editorial
Stephen Mitchell
stephen.mitchell@stjamess.org

Senior Designer
Aniela Gil
aniela.gil@stjamess.org

Deputy Editor
John Lewis
john.lewis@stjamess.org

Designer
Michelle Kliem
michelle.kliem@stjamess.org

PHOTOGRAPHY

AECOM: Thames Water.

ArcelorMittal: Tidal Flood Defences
on the River Arun at Littlehampton.
Photo courtesy of Volker Stevin/High
Camera Ltd.

Green Port Hull: Siemens Gamesa
Renewable Energy.

Jacobs: The Panama Canal Authority;
Tideway; Graeme Peacock Photography;
Olympic Delivery Authority; NASA.

University of Calgary: Fritzology
Photography; Schulich School of
Engineering.

University of Manchester: Mecanoo.

WSP: David Iliff.

Other images are the copyright
of individual organisations.

ABOUT THE SJH GROUP

The SJH Group is a world-leading creative media group that delivers bespoke solutions for a global client base and has offices in London, Manchester, LA and New York City. Comprising five unique publishing companies – St James's House, Artifice Press, Black Dog Press, SJH Publishing and HCB – the SJH Group embodies a diverse selection of industry-leading publishers with a wide range of expertise. From engineering to autobiographies, luxury lifestyle to global business, each imprint within the group shares a core ethos of quality and professionalism.

Today's high-end publishing companies frequently serve as strategic partners for organisations that understand the power of well-connected publishers to communicate key messages for awareness, education and diversity. To this end, the group's strategists provide companies, governments and campaigning bodies around the world with publishing, business and marketing expertise for entertaining, informing and engaging some of their most important audiences.

As a recognised global publisher with top-tier clients and impeccable industry relationships, the SJH Group's publications provide partners with a once-in-a-lifetime chance to create a tangible product that tells their story, defines their DNA and clearly differentiates them in the marketplace. In a media landscape that is saturated with digital, broadcast and disposable print formats, the group's books command attention and respect from readers and provide a timeless resource for decades to come.

ST JAMES'S HOUSE provides brands, governments and campaigning organisations with business and marketing expertise for communicating key messages to target audiences. The company's strategists start by finding out what makes a brand tick, where it is coming from and where it wants to go, and then create a campaign to help it achieve these goals. With in-house expertise in bought, earned and owned media, St James's House can create a holistic brand experience that is imaginative, practical and tailored to a specific audience. The fact that it specialises in publishing, advertising, social media, editorial, film and photography, as well as print and online media, means that the company can really inject the thrill factor into any tailor-made message.

ARTIFICE PRESS produces high-quality books on the subjects of engineering, architecture, urbanism and design. Artifice works with an international selection of independent studios, larger firms, scholars and institutions within a start-to-finish collaborative module to produce books that transcend disciplinary constraints to address many of 21st century society's most topical concerns, including: urbanism and the landscape, environmental and ecological concerns, and science, education and technology.

BLACK DOG PRESS produces an extensive range of illustrated books that respond to and showcase developments in contemporary art and culture. Black Dog Press is committed to delivering robust critical content, imaginative design and high production values in every title. All books are produced in collaboration with international artists and organisations, and the company works with long-standing distributors to supply its titles to bookshops, galleries and organisations worldwide.

SJH PUBLISHING is the best-selling retail publishing division of the SJH Group, specialising in compelling autobiographies, memoirs and other non-fiction publications. Working with some of the world's leading authors, ghostwriters, editors, illustrators and graphic designers, SJH Publishing produces engaging and entertaining titles. Thanks to the company's broad network of media contacts, it is also ideally positioned to manage the publicity of its titles, and regularly secures coverage in major newspapers and broadcast media.

HCB was established in 1980 to help those involved in the transport and storage of dangerous goods keep up to date with changing regulations. It has grown to become essential reading in the industry, covering regulatory developments and bringing its readers news of products and services that aim to make their operations safer and more efficient. The monthly magazine reports on the transport of all kinds of dangerous goods, but particularly liquid chemicals, liquefied gases, explosives and radioactive materials.